Workbook/Laboratory Manual to a

Грамматика в контексте

Russian Grammar in Literary Contexts

Benjamin Rifkin
University of Wisconsin, Madison

The McGraw-Hill Companies, Inc.
New York St. Louis San Francisco Auckland Bogotá Caracas
Lisbon London Madrid Mexico City Milan Montreal New Delhi
San Juan Singapore Sydney Tokyo Toronto

This is an  book.

McGraw-Hill

A Division of The McGraw-Hill Companies

Workbook / Laboratory Manual to accompany
Грамматика в контексте
Russian Grammar in Literary Contexts

5 6 7 8 9 0 QSR QSR 0 9 8 7 6 5 4

ISBN: 0-07-052834-9

This book was typeset in Excelsior on a Macintosh by Chris de Heer Design.
The editors were Thalia Dorwick, Gregory Trauth and Melissa Frazier.
The production supervisor was Michelle Lyon.
Semline was the printer and binder.

Grateful acknowledgment is made for use of the following:

Readings   **Page 15** from *Idut belye sneg* by Evgenii Evtushenko (Moscow:
Khudozhestvenniya literatura)

Realia   **Page 136, 254** © *Moskva* 68, supplement to *Argumenty i fakty* 40 (721)

Contents

---

*Unless stated otherwise, all Listening Tasks are based on the immediately preceding Lexicon.

Introduction

Each unit of the *Workbook/Laboratory Manual* (*WLM*) consists of:

- one or more "thematic lexicons" (such as "health and illness")
- "listening tasks" (correlated to the *Audiocassette Program*)
- additional exercises and activities (correlated to the grammar topics of the given unit in the textbook)
- a Russian-English glossary containing the unit vocabulary from the textbook as well as the additional vocabulary of the thematic lexicons and the "lexicon discussions" (see below) in this *WLM*. (All vocabulary items drawn from the thematic lexicons and the lexicon discussions are marked with the symbol #.)

Units 2–4, 11, 14–16, and 19–20 include "lexical discussions" that focus on problematic expressions, such as verbs of learning and teaching, verbs of asking and answering, verbs of memory and perception, *to try, to use,* and so forth. Units 7, 9, and 10 feature grammar supplements explaining the usage of **мно́го/мно́гие, не́сколько/не́которые, немно́го/немно́гие** (Unit 7), directional adverbs (Unit 9), and locational adverbs (Unit 10).

The sequencing of materials in each unit may vary slightly according to whether or not the unit's listening task is based on the thematic lexicon. For example, in Units 1–16 and 19–24, the thematic lexicons precede the listening tasks so that students may first learn the new vocabulary before they listen for it. In contrast, the listening tasks in Units 17–18 and Unit 25 are based completely on material presented in the corresponding textbook units and are presented before the thematic lexicons.

Most exercises and activities can be completed directly in this *WLM;* however, some require a separate sheet of paper. Such exercises and activities are indicated by a notepad icon.

Each unit of the *Audiocassette Program* (*AP*) consist of:

- a "listening text" (correlated to the "listening tasks" in the *WLM*)
- phonetics and intonation practice (correlated to exercises in the *WLM*)
- poetry (correlated to texts in the textbook)

All taped material is indicated in the *WLM* with a cassette icon. Units are separated by an audible tone (beep) to facilitate recognition of unit boundaries during cueing.

To the Instructor

The *WLM* and *AP* have been designed to help your students meet the following goals:

- improve and demonstrate their mastery of Russian grammar and syntax
- increase their vocabulary, in a number of topics, for receptive use in listening and reading as well as for productive use in speaking and writing
- improve their understanding of translation problems that occur in a number of high frequency topics in which English has one word or expression for several different words or expressions in Russian
- improve their awareness and control of the most basic intonation patterns

- improve their control of pronunciation of some of the most challenging sounds in the Russian sound system
- improve their understanding of Russian literary culture by means of listening to classic poetry of the 19th and 20th centuries

Coordinating the Exercises in the *WLM* with those in the Main Text

To help your students improve their mastery of the targeted grammatical and syntactical structures, I recommend that you first assign and go over the oral and written exercises in the textbook before assigning the corresponding exercises in the *WLM*. You may wish to provide your students with the corresponding parts of the textbook answer key (found in the *Instructor's Manual*) and have them correct their own work or, to stimulate their grammatical and syntactical awareness, the work of their peers. The exercises in the main text are generally quite short and, more often than not, the answers to these exercises can be inferred directly from the grammar explanations. In contrast, the exercises in the *WLM* tend to be more challenging and longer than those in the textbook. Each unit of the *WLM* has one or more translation exercises designed for a summative evaluation of the students' mastery of the unit's grammatical and syntactical structures. These exercises should be among the very last to be assigned. The activities in the *WLM*, which can be done at home or in class, are designed to elicit paragraph-length discourse that requires mastery of the unit's grammatical and syntactical structures. As such, they should be assigned ideally only after your students have successfully completed most of the exercises in the *WLM*. An answer key to the exercises in the *WLM* can be found in the *Instructor's Manual*.

It is not necessary to assign exercises in the *WLM* in sequence. If you choose to alter the sequence of topics in the textbook, you should, of course, be sure to make corresponding changes to the sequence of assignments in the *WLM*. I recommend that you assign the grammar supplements in Units 7, 9, and 10 of the *WLM* as soon as possible after beginning the corresponding textbook units, as that will provide students with the greatest number of opportunities to practice using the structures presented in these supplements.

Using the Thematic Lexicons and the Lexical Discussions

Each unit of the *WLM* has a "thematic lexicon" designed to help students increase their vocabulary for both receptive and productive use. The thematic lexicons, which in most cases provide the basis for the listening tasks, present expressions useful for communicating about particular topics. As such, they differ from the vocabulary presented in the textbook, which was selected on the basis of its relevance to the given grammatical and syntactical structures. The thematic lexicon of any unit may be presented together with the grammar and syntax of any other unit. To facilitate selective assignment of vocabulary items, the symbol # is used in the *WLM* glossaries to indicate vocabulary that appears in the thematic lexicons.

Scripts for additional listening and reading texts, along with attendant activities, can be found in the *Instructor's Manual*. Like the listening tasks in the *WLM*, these, too, are based largely on the vocabulary of the thematic lexicons and may be used for work in class, homework, or on tests. The *Instructor's Manual* also contains numerous role play and information gap activities, also based on the thematic lexicons.

The "lexical discussions," found in many of the units of the *WLM*, are designed to help students improve their mastery of challenging English-Russian translation problems. These discussions may be assigned in conjunction with work on any unit of the textbook and even any other unit of the *WLM*. Though designed primarily for classroom use, these exercises can be completed as homework.

Using the Phonetics and Intonation Exercises

The program in phonetics and intonation has been designed to provide your students with targeted practice in the reduction of unstressed vowels and intonation. Found in the first ten units of the

WLM, I recommend that these exercises be completed as early as possible—especially in the fall after a summer away from Russian-language study—so that your students will have maximum opportunity to practice and review these crucial systems. Like the thematic lexicons, the phonetics and intonation section of any unit can be assigned with material from any other unit in the *WLM* or textbook. After your students have completed the first ten units of phonetics and intonation, you may wish to encourage students to review units that treat their individual areas of weakness.

The phonetics and intonation exercises may be done in class or as homework. Each unit has at least one phonetics or intonation "self-quiz," in which your students can verify their mastery of the targeted system. Should you choose to conduct phonetics and intonation practice in class, I strongly recommend telling your students that they are not expected to achieve native pronunciation. I do, however, suggest that you require your students—at least those who are native speakers of English—to achieve flawless pronunciation of Russian sounds that are similar or identical to sounds in English. In contrast, you should probably allow your students considerable leeway in the pronunciation of Russian sounds that are markedly different from the closest sounds in English.

I suggest the following approach to presenting and practicing the phonetics and intonation sections: Model the sounds (or play the tape) and demonstrate proper position of the tongue and lips for the correct articulation of the targeted sound. Next, have your students listen to examples of the targeted sound and discriminate between good pronunciation (i.e. typical of normative Russian pronunciation) and poor pronunciation (i.e. not typical of normative pronunciation, though perhaps not necessarily typical of North American pronunciation). Only then, have your students repeat the sounds themselves. Your students can assess their pronunciation by recording their speech and listening to it, along with an accepted model of pronunciation; this approach may, in fact, help your students to develop their own pronunciation "monitors." I strongly recommend targeted presentation and practice of phonetics and intonation. However, when your students make pronunciation errors during activities dedicated to grammar, syntax, or fluency, such errors should probably not be corrected immediately unless they disrupt communication.

Using the Recorded Poetry

Listening to poetry helps students improve their understanding of Russian literary culture at the same time as it helps them improve their pronunciation. The *AP* contains a recitation of every poem in the textbook and in the *WLM*. You may wish to ask your students to memorize some or all of the poetry or to have students listen to the poetry and then recite it, using a copy of the text. The recordings of the poems may be played in class (perhaps for line-by-line repetition) or assigned as homework. Recitation of poetry is an old favorite of Russian pedagogy, and I believe that it can offer students great opportunities for improving their Russian. As with other sections of the *WLM*, the poetry in one unit can be assigned with material from any other unit. In fact, the texts—whether prose or poetry—in one unit often provide examples of grammar or syntax that are covered in other units. To facilitate flexibility in assigning literature, the textbook includes an index of the literary texts (pp. 397–398).

Benjamin Rifkin
University of Wisconsin, Madison

Acknowledgments

I would like to thank the following individuals who have made contributions to this *Workbook/Laboratory Manual:* Melissa Frazier, whose creative insights enhanced the development of this *Manual;* Elena Shchepina, who painstakingly proofread the manuscript and whose native-language acumen brought about many fine stylistic changes; Liudmila Longan Vergunova, who offered many creative suggestions for improving the *Manual;* Michelle Lyon and Kamila Storr for their careful attention to editorial detail; Gregory Trauth, for his support and encouragement; and Thalia Dorwick, publisher, without whom *Грамматика в контексте* would not have been.

Glossary Abbreviations

M	multidirectional verb of motion
P	perfective verb of motion
U	unidirectional verb of motion
I	first conjugation
II	second conjugation
	(e.g., **ходить** [M-II] multidirectional verb of motion, second conjugation)
м.	masculine
pl.	plural
ж.	feminine
кому́?	impersonal construction, see Unit 11, Textbook
род.	genitive
см.	see
(-ся)	reflexive ending may be added to this verb
*	irregular conjugation, see Unit 2, Textbook
!	imperative form
#	item from the given unit's lexicon *only*

To the Student: Learning Strategies That Work!

As you work with **Грамматика в контексте** you might want to consider trying new language-learning strategies to help you achieve success in your Russian-language studies more efficiently. There are three different types of strategies students can use when they are studying a foreign language. Most students find that some of the strategies of each type work well for them, so I encourage you to try all the strategies at least once to see which ones work for you. Successful students report that they use many of these strategies, while students who report great difficulties in mastering a foreign language generally tend to use few, if any, of these strategies.

1. Practice, Practice, Practice: Cognitive Strategies

Research has shown that the more often students "practice" using a piece of information (a grammatical concept, vocabulary), the more likely they are to recall that information on a test. Furthermore, research has shown that students who "practice" using information in several different ways (reading it, writing it, saying or singing it, listening to it) are more likely to recall that information than students who practice in only one way. Flashcards are one tool that can help you practice using information in different ways, because you must write them out; then you can practice reading and saying or singing the information recorded on them. If you tape-record yourself reading flashcards out loud, you will have the opportunity to listen to the information on flashcards, too.

Some students think that flashcards are not worth the time it takes to write them out, but I have discovered that most students (including those who resist making and using flashcards) ultimately find them a very useful tool to help them memorize. Before you begin to use the book I *strongly encourage* you to buy blank index cards (either 3.5 x 5 or 4 x 6) in at least three different colors, one color for verb conjugations, one color for noun declensions, one color for example sentences, and other colors for concepts and ideas that you want to select for special attention. You might want to buy a hole-puncher (for the index cards) and steel rings to keep the cards organized into sets. If you buy these items at the beginning of your course, you will be ready to make flashcards on the very first day and will be off to the best possible start.

I also *strongly encourage* you not to write answers to the exercises in this book, even when the exercises have blanks for you to fill in. Instead, write out the answers on a separate sheet of paper, so that you can use the exercises in the book to test yourself (and use your previous work as a key if you wish).

Throughout the book you'll find plenty of Russian sayings and proverbs that illustrate the grammar discussed in each unit. Try to memorize these sayings and proverbs: They'll help you remember the grammar and make your speech more colorful.

Here are a few "cognitive strategies" for practicing concepts and details of Russian grammar that will help you succeed:

- Make flashcards for each verb prototype (conjugation pattern) and every irregular verb presented in the textbook. On each flashcard, put the English infinitive (*to buy, to say, to hold, to watch,* and so on) on one side, and the Russian conjugation, imperative- and past-tense forms on the other. Use a different color index card for verbs (different from the color used for other parts of speech). Write out the conjugations in one color (for example, in black), and put the stress marks in the Russian forms in another color (for example, in red). Practice the conjugation by repeating all the forms out loud while reading the Russian side of the card and then test yourself by looking only at the English side. Review these flashcards for fifteen to twenty minutes a day, several days a week. Add to these cards throughout your Russian-language study and shuffle them frequently.

- Make out flashcards for all the declension patterns using a different color index card than that used for the conjugation patterns. Put the Russian nominative case singular and plural forms on one side of the card, making sure to mark the stress in each word, and the English meaning on the other side. Shuffle the cards frequently and review them for fifteen minutes a day, several days a week.
- Write out flashcards in a different color with entire sentences that illustrate important points of grammar and try to memorize them.
- Try to practice conjugation or declension patterns by setting them to the melody or rhythm of a favorite song, and "sing" them out loud again and again to the melody or rhythm that you've selected. (You might even try "singing" in the shower!) Use funny tunes, such as the theme music from *The Addams Family* or *Star Wars,* children's songs, such as "Old MacDonald," or some of your favorite songs. Instrumental music (without lyrics) tends to work very well for this kind of practice because you play the music and sing along "karaoke style."
- Repeat conjugation and declension patterns out loud over and over again, make a tape of yourself saying them and listen to the tape, and then write them out several times (on flashcards or in columns and rows on paper). Notice the rhyming patterns in the conjugations and declensions and emphasize the rhymes from one verb or noun to the next as you repeat them, listen to your tape, and write them out. The more you practice saying the conjugation and declension patterns out loud, listening to them, and writing them out, the better you will be at remembering them when you're speaking Russian (or taking a test).
- Pick out sentences from the textbook that illustrate different grammatical rules or vocabulary and write them out on flashcards. Try memorizing the sentences by writing them out in full, then writing out just every other word, then writing out just every third word. Then try writing out the first syllable of every word. Finally, write out the first letter of every word. Can you put those letters together to form a single word in English or Russian? Try memorizing that word as a "trick" to remember the whole sentence it represents.
- Sometimes words might seem very similar to one another except for the stress pattern or a spelling variation. For example, you may have a hard time remembering the stress patterns in the verbs платить (*to pay:* плачу́, пла́тишь, пла́тят) and пла́кать (*to cry:* пла́чу, пла́чешь, пла́чут). Try coming up with reasons for the stress pattern that relate to the meanings of the verbs you find challenging. For example, the verb *to pay* (платить) can be used to say that you are paying someone else or someone else is paying you (the emotional value varies), so the stress on that verb shifts, while the verb *to cry* (пла́кать) always means that someone is crying (the emotional value is constantly negative), so the stress on that verb never shifts. Try associating other reasons with the stress patterns for each verb you find difficult to remember.
- Make a list of words and expressions you want to memorize. Imagine a place, a song, a food, or a scent that you can associate with each word and expression. As you practice these words and expressions, continue to visualize or imagine the sensations you have associated with them.
- Reorganize your flashcards according to different principles: grammar and vocabulary for a particular unit, grammar and vocabulary related to a particular topic, grammar and vocabulary that caused difficulty on a recent test, feminine nouns, verbs ending in -овать, imperatives, and so forth. Reorganize your flashcards regularly, and review them fifteen minutes a day, several days a week.
- Before the midterm, select two points covered so far in the semester that you find challenging and find all your notes and flashcards that refer to them. Review these notes and flashcards carefully and write out new notes and flashcards on the same points. Practice them for fifteen minutes a day, several days a week.

- Write out flashcards with dramatic or funny sentences. Act out the meaning of the sentences as you practice saying them and/or imagine engaging in the movements described in the sentences.

2. Check In on Your Feelings about Learning Russian: Affective Strategies

If you feel good about your Russian-language studies, you are more likely to succeed. In order to have positive feelings about the task ahead, you need to "check-in" with yourself about how you feel about what you've done so far and what lies ahead. Think also about eating, sleeping, and exercise habits and how they might relate to your language studies.

- Do you find a particular grammatical concept challenging? Ask your classmates if they also find this topic a difficult one. For some students, challenging or difficult topics evoke anxiety or frustration that can reduce their ability to achieve success. Come up with two or three ideas you can use to lower your anxiety or frustration when you're working to improve your understanding of verb aspect, for example. Share your ideas with classmates. Consider short study sessions with regular breaks for relaxation, "rewards" for studying for a designated period of time, memorizing sample sentences that are humorous so you can laugh while you study, listening to relaxing music after your study session, checking how you're feeling as you study, and taking a moment or two to relax if you feel tense. Would some of these suggestions work well for you? What other ideas can you come up with?
- For a few days, keep track of what you ate in the three hours before (and during) your last three study sessions for Russian. Did each study session go well? Try varying what you eat to see if it has an effect on how well you pay attention to what you're studying. Some people find meals and snacks rich in protein (e.g. beans and rice, cheese, milk, yogurt, fish, chicken, or meat) help increase alertness, while meals and snacks rich in carbohydrates (e.g. potatoes and pasta) tend to decrease alertness. (One exception to the protein/carbohydrate rule: Both turkey and peanut butter tend to make people a little drowsy!) Sugary foods tend to increase alertness in the short run, but make people drowsy later (in what some people call a "sugar crash"). What foods help you to be the most productive student of Russian you can be?
- Keep a diary monitoring how much sleep you get on the night before Russian quizzes or tests. Do you do better on your quizzes or tests with a certain number of hours of sleep? If that's the case, plan your study sessions so you can get the sleep you need to do well!
- At what time of day do you usually study for Russian class? Are you most alert at this time of day? Try changing the time of day when you do your Russian homework. If you study at a different time than usual, try to determine if it is easier or more difficult to assimilate new material at that time.
- Do you get regular exercise? Students who exercise regularly often report increased concentration when working on their Russian. Keep a diary recording when you exercise and note whether study sessions later that day are more or less productive than study sessions before exercise or study sessions on days when you do not exercise.
- Talk with your classmates and try to come up with as many different places as possible on your campus where you can study. Where can you review your flashcards? Can you review them while riding a bus or in a car (as a passenger), while sitting at a table at a favorite cafe or campus hangout? Do you like to study in places where there is "white noise" in the background or in places that are absolutely quiet?
- If you're feeling that your Russian-language studies aren't going well, try to focus on something you've done for Russian class that has gone well. Visualize how you felt when you first realized that you successfully completed that task or assignment and concentrate on how you can feel that way again.

3. Monitor Your Learning Process: Metacognitive Strategies

Studying a foreign language is a challenging and complicated task. Successful learners "manage" their studying by establishing short-term goals (for example, memorizing a particular list of vocabulary items) for each study session, scheduling study sessions and assignments for "alert and productive" times of the day (or night), and monitoring the success of their study plans.

- Come up with two different strategies for memorizing grammar and vocabulary that work well for you. Using these two strategies, try to memorize new grammar and vocabulary. Record the time when you start work on memorizing these words and the time when you feel you have finished memorizing them. Then compare notes with your classmates: How long did it take you to memorize the information? Which strategies would you like to try next, based on what you've heard from your classmates. (Remember, some learners will have more success with certain strategies than with others! Not everyone will find a particular strategy to be the most effective one.)
- Make a list of three of the most effective study strategies you have used in studying Russian (or any other foreign language) and bring the list to class. Be prepared to explain your study strategies to your classmates and be prepared to listen to their favorite study strategies. Of the study strategies you hear about in class, pick a new strategy to try during the next week and determine in advance how you'll evaluate it (good results on a homework assignment? high score on a quiz?) if it works well for you.
- Before any Russian test, test yourself. Draw up your own test consisting of items drawn from the examples in the textbook, take the test, and check your answers against the examples in the textbook. Then determine what areas, if any, you need to review before you take your instructor's test.
- Look through the next unit you're assigned to work on before you start the first homework assignment in that unit. As you look through the unit, think about the parts that seem easiest and those that seem hardest. Look at the syllabus of assignments and determine which assignments are likely to require the most time and attention, and which are likely to be the easiest. Try to begin working on the most challenging topics or assignments a day or two before they are actually assigned to give yourself more time to assimilate the new information. Plan ahead!

Use these strategies and think of new ones that will work best for you. Share your strategies with your classmates and instructor(s) and try using the strategies they recommend. If you conscientiously apply these and other strategies in your Russian-language studies, you will increase the likelihood of your ultimate success.

Good luck!
Benjamin Rifkin
Madison, Wisconsin

UNIT1

Lexicon: Verbs of Learning and Teaching

Russian has several different verbs of learning and teaching that do not correspond neatly to the English verbs.

Учи́ться [где?]
To be a student at a particular institution

> Она́ у́чится в Йе́льском университе́те.
> *She is a student at Yale University.*

Учи́ться/на– [де́лать что?]
To learn to do something

> Он у́чится игра́ть на гита́ре.
> *He is learning to play the guitar.*

> Где вы научи́лись так хорошо́ говори́ть по-ру́сски?
> *Where did you learn to speak Russian so well?*

Учи́ть [что?]
To study a particular subject

> Зи́на у́чит англи́йский язы́к в э́том семе́стре.
> *Zina is studying English this semester.*

Изуча́ть [что?]
To major or specialize in something

> Я изуча́ю матема́тику, а Та́ня изуча́ет фи́зику.
> *I am majoring in math, and Tania is majoring in physics.*

Слу́шать курс [по чему́?]
To study or take a course for a semester or year

> Я слу́шаю три ку́рса по исто́рии в э́том семе́стре.
> *I'm taking three courses in history this semester.*

Занима́ться [где? чем?]
To do homework (for a couple of hours or in the evening)

> Оля сейча́с занима́ется хи́мией в библиоте́ке.
> *Olia's now doing her chemistry homework in the library.*

Гото́виться/при– [к чему́?]
To prepare for something such as a test

> Я гото́влюсь к контро́льной по биоло́гии.
> *I'm studying for a biology test.*

Учи́ть/вы́– [что?]

To memorize something (e.g., vocabulary words, a song, a part for a play, a poem)

Оле́г у́чит но́вые слова́.

Oleg is memorizing the new words.

Я вы́учу э́то стихотворе́ние на за́втра.

I'll memorize this poem for tomorrow.

Упражне́ние 1.1   Fill in the blanks with the Russian equivalent of the English word or phrase in parentheses. Check grammatical context to make sure you have chosen the correct verb of learning and teaching.

— В э́том семе́стре я (*study*) _____[1] филосо́фию Ренесса́нса.

— А я ду́мала, что ты (*study/major in*) _____[2] исто́рию!

— Да, но профе́ссор, кото́рая (*teaches*) _____[3] англи́йскую исто́рию, уе́хала в А́нглию на семе́стр, и поэ́тому я (*am taking*) _____[4] курс по филосо́фии.

— Что ты де́лаешь сего́дня ве́чером? Хо́чешь пойти́ в кино́?

— О́чень хочу́, но не могу́. Ве́чером я бу́ду (*study/do homework*) _____[5] в библиоте́ке. За́втра у меня́ контро́льная по матема́тике и я должна́ (*study/prepare for*) _____[6] к ней.

— Ты молоде́ц! Как ты мо́жешь (*study/memorize*) _____[7] все э́ти фо́рмулы и пра́вила?

— Не зна́ю, но мне не о́чень тру́дно.

Listening Tasks

The listening text for this unit consists of three dialogues between two people on courses and majors.

PRE-LISTENING TASK

List twenty subjects offered at your school. Do you know the Russian equivalent for these subjects?

LISTENING TASK

Listen to the text and then answer questions 1 through 3 in English and 4 through 8 in Russian.

1. In dialogue 1, where do the two speakers go to school?
2. In dialogue 2, what are the two students' majors?
3. In dialogue 3, what courses are the students taking this semester?
4. In dialogue 1, how does the first speaker ask if the second speaker is a student or not?
5. In dialogue 1, how does the speaker express the notion, *really*?
6. In dialogue 2, what conveys the notion of *majoring* in a subject ?
7. In dialogue 2, how is the term *Russian studies* conveyed?
8. In dialogue 3, what verb expresses *taking a course*?

DICTATION

Replay the tape and, as you listen, write out the dialogues in full.

PERFORMANCE

Practice reciting the dialogues.

POST-LISTENING TASK

Using the dialogues as models, work with a classmate to create and perform your own dialogues in which you discuss whether or not you are students, where you go to school, what you are majoring in, and what courses you are taking this semester.

CULTURAL PROBLEM

How can you tell that the speakers in dialogue 3 are probably not enrolled in a Russian educational institution?

Phonetics and Intonation

Native speakers of English use intonation patterns to establish whether a group of words form a statement or a question. In a certain sense, intonation provides the *punctuation* of the spoken language. Intonation also provides the emotional coloring of the words spoken.

ORAL EXERCISE

How many different ways can you say the words *she loved him* by altering your intonation? How about the words *he was late*?

Russian has five basic intonation patterns that determine the meaning of statements and questions. Some intonation patterns may seem similar to patterns in English, while others may seem very different from English patterns used to convey the same meanings.

Introduction to the Five Basic Intonation Patterns

Listen to the sentences on the tape. Each sentence is correlated with an intonation pattern. The boldfaced words are the center of the given pattern.

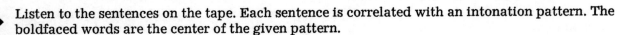

(Intonation pattern 1) Ната́ша уже́ пошла́ на рабо́ту.   (*neutral*)
(Intonation pattern 2) **Когда́** она́ пошла́ на рабо́ту?
(Intonation pattern 3) Ната́ша уже́ пошла́ на **рабо́ту**?
(Intonation pattern 4) А **Со́ня**?
(Intonation pattern 5) **Со́ня то́же пошла́ на рабо́ту!**

(Intonation pattern 1) Та́ня и Бо́ря рабо́тают над докла́дом.   (*neutral*)
(Intonation pattern 2) Над **каки́м** докла́дом они́ рабо́тают?
(Intonation pattern 3) Та́ня и Бо́ря ещё **рабо́тают** над докла́дом?
(Intonation pattern 4) А **Ве́ра**?
(Intonation pattern 5) **Каки́е интере́сные докла́ды!**

ANALYSIS

What kinds of statements or questions are used to illustrate each of the five intonation patterns?

Note: Each intonation pattern has a variety of uses. The sentences here are designed to provide an introduction to the concept of intonation, rather than a broad sampling of all the possible uses of each intonation pattern. The intonation patterns will be further explored in later units.

SELF-QUIZ

Read the following sentences and try to say them using the same intonation patterns as those used in the preceding sentences. Write in the number corresponding to the intonation pattern. After you say each sentence, listen to the correct intonation on the tape to see if you were right. The boldfaced words are the center of the given intonational pattern.

a. _____ **Ви́тя** гото́вит обе́д.   (*neutral*)

б. _____ **Что** он гото́вит на обе́д?

в. _____ **Ви́тя** гото́вит обе́д?

г. _____ **А Ма́ша?**

д. _____ **Како́й вку́сный обе́д!**

Exercises and Activities

Упражне́ние 1.2   Read the paragraph and list all the words for each part of speech: noun, pronoun, adjective, verb, adverb, conjunction, preposition, and interjection. Then answer the questions that follow.

Ella briskly opened the front door and picked up the *Wall Street Journal:* it was lying on the very cold staircase. She brought the cold newspaper into the kitchen, put it on the big table, and poured herself a cup of hot coffee. She drank her coffee slowly as she read the morning's business news. Her husband was still sleeping even though they had planned to get up early. She marveled at how sound a sleeper he was, but realized that he'd have to get up soon anyway, since her partners were expecting both of them at 9:30 downtown.

1. Which nouns are masculine? Which are feminine? Which have no gender? Is gender as important a grammatical category in English as it is in Russian?   2. Which pronouns are masculine, which are feminine, and which are neuter?   3. Do English adjectives have typical endings?   4. How do English verbs agree with their subjects?   5. Do prepositions affect the choice of pronouns in English, as shown in the text?

Упражне́ние 1.3   Fill in the blanks with the correct word in parentheses.

1.   We saw (they/their/them) _____ yesterday at the museum.

2.   (They/Their/Them) _____ were showing some Russian tourists

     around town.

3.   (They/Their/Them) _____ invited (we/our/us) _____

     to join (they/their/them) _____.

4. Betty said (she/her/her) _____ would go with (they/their/them)

_____ because (she/her/her) _____ would

enjoy a chance to practice (she/her/her) _____ Russian.

5. On the whole, the Russians were really glad that (they/their/them) _____

ran into (we/our/us) _____.

Was this exercise challenging for you or was it relatively easy to choose the correct word? Given the sequence of words for *they* (they/their/them) and *he* (he/his/him), can you explain why the sequence of words for *she* (she/her/her) repeats the pronouns *her*? What are the differences in meaning between these words? Which options represent the nominative case in English? Which options represent the accusative case in English? And which options can be linked to the genitive case in Russian to mean possession?

Упражнéние 1.4 Identify the gender of the nouns (masculine = **М**, feminine = **Ж**, neuter = **С**). The nouns in the left-hand column are singular, and the nouns in the right-hand column are plural. Form the singular of the plural nouns and then specify their gender.

1. инженéр _____ 6. дóчери _____

2. медсестрá _____ 7. профессорá _____

3. письмó _____ 8. занятия _____

4. бáбушка _____ 9. америкáнцы _____

5. пáпа _____ 10. óкна _____

Упражнéние 1.5 Determine whether the stem (оснóва) of the word is твёрдая (*hard*) or мягкая (*soft*) and mark them **Т** or **М**.

1. инженéр _____ 6. дóчери _____

2. медсестрá _____ 7. профессорá _____

3. письмó _____ 8. занятия _____

4. бáбушка _____ 9. америкáнцы _____

5. пáпа _____ 10. óкна _____

Упражнéние 1.6 Identify the part of speech of each underlined word, then...

- Identify the gender of the underlined nouns and note whether their stems are hard or soft.
- Identify the subjects with which the underlined verbs agree.
- Identify the nouns to which the underlined pronouns refer.
- Identify the nouns which the underlined adjectives modify.
- Identify the verbs, adjectives, or other adverbs which the underlined adverbs modify.
- Identify the prepositional phrases which the underlined prepositions govern.
- Find all the conjunctions in the text.

Элла быстро[1] открыла дверь,[2] спустилась вниз и вытащила газéту «Рýсские[3] вéдомости» из почтóвого ящика: онá поднялáсь к себé домóй и принеслá холóдную газéту[4] в кýхню, положила её[5] на большóй[6] стол и налилá себé чáшку[7] горячего[8] кóфе. Когдá онá[9] читáла ýтренние[10] нóвости из[11]мира бизнеса, онá мéдленно[12] пилá кóфе. Её[13] муж всё ещё спал, хотя они[14] собирáлись вставáть рáно.[15] Онá былá удивленá, как он крéпко[16] спит, но подýмала, что <u>емý</u>[17] всё равнó скóро придётся встáть, потомý что её партнёры ожидáют <u>их</u>[18] обóих в половúне десятого <u>в</u>[19] цéнтре.

Упражнéние 1.7 Identify the case and the gender or number (singular or plural) of each underlined word or phrase. Use the declension charts in the Appendix for help in identifying the endings. English translations are provided to help make this exercise easier.

1. Свéта чáсто хóдит в больнúцу № 15 со <u>своéй млáдшей сестрóй Úрой</u>.
   Sveta often goes to hospital no. 15 with her younger sister, Ira.

   Case: _____   Gender/Number: _____

2. Там онú помогáют <u>больны́м</u>.
   They help the patients there.

   Case: _____   Gender/Number: _____

3. Больнúца № 15 довóльно большáя: в ней óчень мнóго <u>больны́х</u>.
   Hospital no. 15 is very large: it has a lot of patients.

   Case: _____   Gender/Number: _____

4. Когдá онú хóдят по коридóрам с больны́ми, онú расскáзывают о <u>послéдних извéстиях</u>.
   When they walk through the corridors with the patients, they talk about the latest news.

   Case: _____   Gender/Number: _____

5. <u>Свéта и Úра</u> рáды помогáть больны́м.
   Sveta and Ira are glad to help the patients.

   Case: _____   Gender/Number: _____

Упражнéние 1.8 Circle the subject of each sentence and draw an arrow to the verb with which the subject agrees. Then identify the pronoun that matches the subject (first, second, or third person, singular or plural). Next, identify the tense and aspect of the verb.

Образéц: Светлáна Ильúнична поговорúт об э́том с Николáевым зáвтра.
         Svetlana Il'inichna will talk about this with Nikolaev tomorrow.

Pronoun: third person singular (**онá**)   Verb: future tense, perfective

1. Вúтя рабóтает в нóвом инститýте.

   Pronoun: _____   Verb: _____

2. Приходúли Вéра и Тóля.

   Pronoun: _____   Verb: _____

3. Óля зáвтра покáжет нам сво}ю нóвую машúну.

   Pronoun: _____   Verb: _____

4. Зáвтра я бýду весь день занимáться в библиотéке.

   Pronoun: _____   Verb: _____

5. Николáй Ивáнович преподаёт в Лингвистúческом университéте.

   Pronoun: _____   Verb: _____

Упражне́ние 1.9   Fill in the blanks with the correct letters.

1. (о/е)   У него́ в ко́мнате есть больш_____е окно́.
    He has a big window in his room.

2. (а/я)   Они́ крич_____ли, но мы их не слы́шали.
    They were shouting, but we couldn't hear them.

3. (о/е)   Мы ча́сто слу́шаем Страви́нск_____го.
    We often listen to Stravinskii.

4. (у/ю)   Они́ сейча́с подхо́дят к гараж_____.
    They are approaching the garage now.

5. (ы/и)   Я никогда́ не ви́дела так_____х краси́в_____х па́рков!
    I never saw such beautiful parks!

Зада́ние 1.1   Prepare a three-minute talk or write a composition, as assigned by your instructor, about the courses you are taking this semester, the kind of homework you have to do, and where you like to do it.

Зада́ние 1.2   Talk with your classmates about the classes they have taken so far in their university careers. Make a list of the classes and compare it with all the classes offered by your school. How are your classmates different from the rest of the students at your school in terms of the classes they take? Prepare a three-minute talk or write a composition, as assigned by your instructor, on the basis of this information.

Фо́то-зада́ние   Look at the photograph on the first page of this unit in the textbook. What do you think the students are discussing? Write a composition or prepare a presentation, as assigned by your instructor, acting out a scene that might be illustrated in this picture.

Glossary

Vocabulary marked with # is found in the main text within the lexicon section of this unit. If no imperative is listed for a particular verb, it means that the verb has no imperative. Verbs are identified as first conjugation (I), second conjugation (II), or irregular (*). Past tense forms are provided only if they feature a shift of stress. Nouns with irregularly formed plurals are listed in both singular and plural forms. Nouns that exist only in the plural are listed in nominative and genitive case (**род.**) forms.

большо́й	*big*
врач	*doctor*
всё у́тро, весь день, весь ве́чер, всю ночь	*all morning, all day, all evening, all night*
# гото́виться/при- (II) [к чему́?]: гото́влюсь, гото́вишься, гото́вится, гото́вимся, гото́витесь, гото́вятся, гото́вься! гото́вьтесь!	*to prepare [for something]*
де́ньги, де́нег (*род.*)	*money*
друг, друзья́	*friend, friends*
е́здить (II): е́зжу, е́здишь, е́здит, е́здим, е́здите, е́здят	*to go (and come back) or make trips (by vehicle)*

жить (I):
    живу́, живёшь, живёт, живём, живёте, живу́т, живи́(те)!,
    жил, жила́, жи́ли

to live

занима́ться (I) [где? чем?]:
    занима́юсь, занима́ешься, занима́ется, занима́емся,
    занима́етесь, занима́ются, занима́йся! занима́йтесь!

to study, to do homework [where? in what subject?]

заня́тия, заня́тий (род.)

classes

звони́ть/по- (II) [кому́? куда́?]:
    звоню́, звони́шь, звони́т, звони́м, звони́те, звоня́т, звони́(те)!

to call on the phone [whom? where?]

изуча́ть (I) [что?]:
    изуча́ю, изуча́ешь, изуча́ет, изуча́ем, изуча́ете, изуча́ют,
    изуча́й(те)!

to major or specialize [in something]

ка́ждый день, ка́ждую неде́лю, ка́ждый ме́сяц, ка́ждый год

every day, week, month, year

лаборато́рия

laboratory

люби́ть (II) [кого́? что?]:
    люблю́, лю́бишь, лю́бит, лю́бим, лю́бите, лю́бят, люби́(те)!

to love [someone, something]

ма́ленький

small

медсестра́, медбра́т

nurse

мочь (I):
    могу́, мо́жешь, мо́жет, мо́жете, мо́жем, мо́гут, мог, могла́,
    могли́

can, to be able

музе́й

museum

недалеко́ от [чего́?]

not far from [what?]

перево́дчик

translator

письмо́, пи́сьма

letter, letters

писа́ть/на- (I) [кому́? что? о чём?]:
    пишу́, пи́шешь, пи́шет, пи́шем, пи́шете, пи́шут, пиши́(те)!

to write [whom? what? about what?]

плащ

raincoat

преподава́ть (I) [что? кому́?]:
    преподаю́, преподаёшь, преподаёт, преподаём, преподаёте,
    преподаю́т, преподава́й(те)!

to teach [what? to whom?]

[на] про́шлой/сле́дующей неде́ле

last/next week

[в] про́шлом/сле́дующем году́

last/next year

профе́ссор, профессора́

professor, professors

рабо́тать (I) [где? кем?]:
    рабо́таю, рабо́таешь, рабо́тает, рабо́таем, рабо́таете,
    рабо́тают, рабо́тай(те)!

to work [where? in what capacity?]

рассказа́ть (I) [кому́? о чём?]:
    расскажу́, расска́жешь, расска́жет, расска́жем,
    расска́жете, расска́жут, расскажи́(те)!

to tell [whom? about what?]

ре́дко

rarely, seldom

роди́тели, роди́телей (*род.*)	*parents*
на сле́дующей/про́шлой неде́ле	*next/last week*
в сле́дующем/про́шлом году́	*next/last year*
# слу́шать (I) [курс по чему́?]: слу́шаю, слу́шаешь, слу́шает, слу́шаем, слу́шаете, слу́шают, слу́шай(те)!	*to listen, to take a class [in what?]*
# учи́ть/вы– (II) [что?]: учу́, у́чишь, у́чит, у́чим, у́чите, у́чат, учи́(те)!	*to study a subject or to memorize (by heart)*
# учи́ться/на– (II) [где? де́лать что?]: учу́сь, у́чишься, у́чится, у́чимся, у́читесь, у́чатся, учи́сь! учи́тесь!	*to study, to be a student, to learn to do something*
фи́зик	*physicist*
ча́сто	*frequently*
челове́к, лю́ди	*person, people*
язы́к	*language*

UNIT 2

Lexicon: Telephone Etiquette

Russians use particular expressions when they talk with one another on the phone. They generally recite telephone numbers as follows.

273-42-07: Двéсти сéмьдесят три, сóрок два, ноль семь
458-19-36: Четы́реста пятьдеся́т вóсемь, девятнáдцать, три́дцать шесть
821-00-69: Восемьсóт двáдцать оди́н, два нуля́, шестьдеся́т дéвять

Позови́(те), пожáлуйста, [когó?] к телефóну
  To call someone to the phone, to ask someone to pick up the phone

Сергéй Антóнович, бýдьте добры́, позови́те, пожáлуйста, Ни́ну к телефóну.
Sergey Antonovich, please be so kind as to ask Nina to pick up the phone.

Попáсть не тудá, ошиби́ться нóмером, не тот нóмер набрáть
  To get a wrong number

— Э́то Сергéевы?
— Нет, вы не тудá попáли.
Is this the Sergeevs?
No, you have the wrong number.

— Э́то Тáня?
— Нет, вы оши́блись нóмером.
Is this Tania?
No, you have the wrong number.

— Э́то Ми́ша Соколóв?
— Нет, вы не тот нóмер набрáли.
Is this Misha Sokolov?
No, you have the wrong number.

Тут нет такóго, такóй, таки́х
  There's no one here by that name

— Позови́те, пожáлуйста, Ми́шу Соколóва.
— Тут нет такóго.
Please ask Misha Sokolov to pick up the phone.
There's no one here by that name.

Передáй(те), пожáлуйста, [комý?], что звони́л/а [кто?]. Попроси́(те) [когó?] перезвони́ть мне по телефóну...
  Please tell [whom] that _____ called. Ask [whom] to call me back at the following number...

— Передáйте, пожáлуйста, Лари́се Влади́мировне, что звони́л Бóря. Попроси́те её перезвони́ть мне по телефóну 712-21-38.
Please tell Larisa Vladimirovna that Boria called. Please ask her to call me back at 712-2138.

У телефóна, Слýшаю Вас.
To say you are on the phone

> — Позовúте, пожáлуйста, Татьяну Сергéевну.
> — Я у телефóна.
> *Please ask Tat'iana Sergeevna to pick up the phone.*
> *This is she.*

> — Позовúте, пожáлуйста, Михаúла Борúсовича.
> — Слýшаю вас.
> *Please ask Mikhail Borisovich to pick up the phone.*
> *This is he.*

Вас беспокóит [кто?] (формáльно) / Это говорúт [кто?] (мéнее формáльно)/ Это - [кто?] (ещё мéнее формáльно)
To say someone is calling

> — Вас беспокóит Úгорь Матвéев.
> *This is Igor' Matveev calling. [lit.: This is Igor' Matveev bothering you.]*

> — Это Тáнечка.
> *It's Tanechka calling.*

Передавáть/передáть привéт [комý? от когó?]
To convey greetings to someone from someone

> — Вам передаю́т большóй привéт Михáйловы.
> *The Mikhailovs said to give you a big hello.*

Встречáться/встрéтиться [с кем? где? когдá?]
To meet up with someone where and when

> — Давáй встрéтимся с нúми у пáмятника Пýшкину в семь часóв.
> *Let's meet them at the Pushkin monument at seven o'clock.*

Договорúться [с кем?]
To agree with someone to do something

> — Хорошó, тогдá мы договорúлись встрéтиться в семь?
> — Да, договорúлись.
> *Okay, so we agreed to meet at seven?*
> *Yes, agreed.*

До встрéчи, до звонкá (*colloquial*), созвонúмся (*colloquial*), до свидáнья, покá
To say good-bye: until we meet, until our next call, until we see each other next, bye-bye

> — Ну лáдно, до встрéчи.
> *Okay, see you later.*

> — Ну хорошó, ты мне потóм позвонúшь?
> — Конéчно, созвонúмся.
> *Okay, so you'll call me later?*
> *Of course, good-bye until we talk later.*

Задáние 2.1 Practice giving and taking down phone numbers in Russian with your classmates.

Задáние 2.2 Practice making telephone calls with classmates in which you arrange to meet. Use the preceding vocabulary.

Listing Tasks

The listening text for this unit consists of three dialogues between different pairs of people talking on the telephone. The dialogues are not related to one another.

PRE-LISTENING TASK

How many phone calls did you make last week? Whom did you call and why? What are some of the reasons you make phone calls in general?

LISTENING TASK

Listen to the text and then answer questions 1 through 10 in English and 11 through 14 in Russian.

1. Summarize dialogue 1.
2. In dialogue 1, who is being asked to come to the phone?
3. In dialogue 1, who is calling this person?
4. In dialogue 1, what is the phone number and whose phone number is it?
5. Summarize dialogue 2.
6. In dialogue 2, who is being asked to come to the phone?
7. Summarize dialogue 3.
8. In dialogue 3, who is talking?
9. In dialogue 3, what is playing at the movie theater? Where is the movie theater located?
10. In dialogue 3, at what time will they meet?
11. How do people answer the phone in the dialogues?
12. How do people ask for someone to be called to the phone?
13. How do people say good-bye?
14. In one of the dialogues someone is asked to convey a message. How is this expressed?

DICTATION

Replay the tape and, as you listen, write out each of the dialogues in full.

PERFORMANCE

Practice reciting the dialogues.

POST-LISTENING TASK

Using the dialogues as models, work in groups of three to create and perform your own dialogues in which you call one another up and get wrong numbers, ask to leave a message for one another, introduce yourself as a friend of a mutual acquaintance, and invite one another to a movie at a nearby theater.

CULTURAL PROBLEM

How is Russian telephone etiquette different from North American telephone etiquette?

Lexicon: Verbs of Asking and Answering

The verbs of asking and answering take special grammatical constructions in Russian.

Спрáшивать/спросúть [когó? о чём?]
   To ask someone for information, to ask someone about something

> Он навéрно спрóсит нас, почемý мы не бы́ли на заня́тиях.
> *He'll probably ask us why we weren't at class.*

Просúть/по– [когó? дéлать/с- что?]
   To ask someone to do something

> Он чáсто прóсит нас не говорúть об э́том при дéтях.
> *He often asks us not to talk about this in front of the children.*

Просúть/по– [что? у когó?]
   To ask someone for something, to ask someone to borrow something

> Мы попрóсим маши́ну у роди́телей.
> *We'll ask our parents to borrow the car.*

Задавáть/задáть вопрóс/-ы [комý?]
   To pose a question to someone

> Корреспондéнт зáдал Петрóвской нéсколько слóжных вопрóсов.
> *The correspondent asked Petrovskaia several complicated questions.*

Отвечáть/отвéтить [комý? на что?]
   To answer someone's letter or question

> Áлла Петрóвна зáвтра отвéтит вам на вопрóс.
> *Alla Petrovna will answer your question tomorrow.*

> Пáша сейчáс отвечáет роди́телям на письмó.
> *Pasha is answering his parents' letter now.*

Говорúть/по– [с кем? о чём?]
   To talk or chat with someone about something

> Мы поговорúм с Марúей Пáвловной о нём зáвтра.
> *We'll talk with [have a chat with] Maria Pavlovna about him tomorrow.*

Говорúть/сказáть [комý? что?]
   To tell someone about something in particular

> Скóлько раз я тебé говорúла, что здесь нельзя́ курúть?!
> *How many times have I told you that there's no smoking here!*

> Мы сказáли Óльге Сергéевне, что Пéтя бóлен.
> *We told Ol'ga Sergeevna that Petia is sick.*

Расскáзывать/рассказáть [комý? о чём?]
   To tell someone more about something

> Как тóлько мы приéдем домóй, мы тебé обо всём расскáжем.
> *As soon as we get home we'll tell you about everything.*

It is important to remember that the verbs **спрáшивать/спросúть** can never be used with the word **вопрóс;** use the verbs **задавáть/задáть** if you must use the word **вопрóс**. The conjugations for these verbs may be found in the glossary for this unit.

Упражне́ние 2.1 Fill in the blanks with the Russian equivalent of the English word or phrase in parentheses.

1. Мы заблуди́лись [*got lost*] и (*asked*) _____, как дое́хать до

   Пу́шкинской пло́щади.

2. Мой сосе́д по ко́мнате всё вре́мя (*asks*) _____ у меня́ де́нег.

3. Вчера́ по телеви́зору Ба́рбара Уа́лтерс (*asked*) _____ Ра́йсе

   Горбачёвой интере́сные вопро́сы. Ра́йса ча́сто не понима́ла и

   (*asked*) _____ Ба́рбару говори́ть ме́дленно.

4. Мы (*asked*) _____ профе́ссора об э́том, и он нам

   (*told*) _____, что экза́мена не бу́дет.

5. Когда́ же ты (*will answer*) _____ на письмо́ ма́тери?

6. Она́ (*told*) _____ нам дли́нную исто́рию о том, как она́ доста́ла

   биле́ты в Большо́й теа́тр.

Текст 2.1 This song is by contemporary Russian poet Evtushenko.

PRE-READING TASK

The title of the song is *Do the Russians Want War?* Based on the title and the fact that the author spent some of his childhood in evacuation during World War II, what do you think you might find in the song? Make some predictions and see if you're right.

Хотя́т ли ру́сские во́йны?

Хотя́т ли ру́сские во́йны?
Спроси́те вы у тишины́[1]
над ши́рью па́шен и поле́й[2]
и у берёз, и тополе́й.[3]

[1]*the silence*
[2]над... *above the vastness of the plowed fields and meadows*
[3]берёз... *birch trees and poplar trees*

Спроси́те вы у те́х солда́т,
что под берёзами лежа́т,
и пусть вам ска́жут их сыны́,[4]
хотя́т ли ру́сские во́йны.

[4]пусть... *may their sons answer you* (**сыны́** is colloquial for **сыновья́**)

Не то́лько за свою́ страну́[5]
солда́ты ги́бли[6] в ту войну́,—
а что́бы лю́ди всей земли́[7]
споко́йно ви́деть сны могли́.[8]

[5]за... *for their country*
[6]*fell, perished*
[7]всей... *of all the earth*
[8]споко́йно... *could dream in tranquillity*

Под ше́лест ли́стьев и афи́ш[9]
ты спи́шь, Нью–Йо́рк, ты спи́шь, Пари́ж...
Пусть ва́м отве́тят ва́ши сны́,
хотя́т ли ру́сские во́йны.

[9]Под... *Under the murmur of leaves and posters*

Да, мы умеем воевать,[10]
но не хотим, чтобы опять
солдаты падали в бою[11]
на землю грустную свою.[12]

Спросите вы у матерей,
спросите у жены моей,
и вы тогда понять должны,[13]
хотят ли русские войны!

— Е. А. Евтушенко, 1961

[10]умеем... *know how to fight*
[11]падали... *fell in battle*
[12]на... *on their sad land*

[13]понять... *must understand*

 ## POST-READING TASKS

1. Write a 2-3 sentence summary of the song.
2. Find all the 2nd conjugation verbs in the song and identify their infinitives.
3. Find all the images from nature associated with Russia.

Note: You can hear Evtushenko singing this song in the film *Kindergarten,* directed by the poet himself (available in the United States on video).

Упражнение 2.2 Fill in the blanks with the correct verb of asking and answering, using the following cues (not necessarily in this order): *asked, asked/borrowed, asked, answered, asked, answered.*

Вчера Маргарита зашла и _____,[1] не знаю ли я, когда сегодня

вечером будет филбм «Санта–Барбара». Я _____,[2] что не знаю, но

что у Ирины Васильевны наверно есть программа. Мы вместе пошли к Ирине Васильевне

и _____[3] у неё программу. Она _____,[4] что

дочь _____[5] программу и отнесла её в школу. Мы

_____[6] Ирину Васильевну, не знает ли она, когда будет «Санта–

Барбара». Она сказала, что сейчас смотрит этот фильм, и пригласила нас посмотреть

вместе с ней.

Phonetics and Intonation

Introduction to Lexical Stress

Russian, like English, has a system of lexical stress. Consider, for example, the pronunciation of the English word *garage,* a two-syllable word with a silent *e* in word-final position. The other two vowels in the word, *a,* are written the same but pronounced differently. In the first syllable, *a* is pronounced like "uh," as in *but,* while in the second syllable, the *a* is pronounced like "ah," as in *hot.* Now consider the English word *garbage.* This, too, is a two-syllable word with a silent *e* in word-final position and two other vowels, both written as *a,* but pronounced differently. Here the pronunciation of the first *a* is like *hot,* while the pronunciation of the second *a* is like *but.* The difference in the pronunciation of these words is due to the difference in the lexical stress of the word. We pronounce these words differently because the stress in one word falls on the first syllable (g*a*rbage), while the stress in the other word falls on the second syllable (gar*a*ge). The vowel that is not stressed has a pronunciation different from the vowel that is stressed.

You will now hear some Russian words that illustrate lexical stress.

1. за́мок   замо́к
2. о́рган   орга́н

Russian has a similar system of lexical stress, in that unstressed vowels **a, o, e,** and **я** have different sounds than their stressed counterparts. One of the key differences between the Russian and English systems of lexical stress is that English allows for more than one stress in most words, whereas Russian allows for *only* one stress in a word (except for compound or foreign words, which may have more than one stress).

The pronunciation of unstressed vowels **a, o, e,** and **я** in Russian depends, in part, on the position of the unstressed vowel in the word. Is it before or after the stressed vowel? Is it in word-initial position? Is it preceded by another vowel?

This unit and the units that follow will explore the different types of *reduction* of unstressed vowels in Russian.

FULL REDUCTION OF UNSTRESSED a AND o AFTER HARD CONSONANTS

Russian vowels **a** and **o** are fully reduced when they are

1. not in word-initial position *and*
2. before the stressed syllable *but not* in the syllable immediately preceding the stress, or
3. following the stressed syllable.

These vowels, when fully reduced, are indistinguishable from one another. It is impossible to listen to the sounds they make and distinguish **a** from **o** when both are fully reduced.

Listen to the tape and note that the bold vowels in the following list are fully reduced. The fully reduced **a** and **o** sound like the slightest pause between consonants or after a consonant.

1. контрабáнда   6. панорáма
2. пропагáнда   7. фотогрáфия
3. катарáкта   8. парадóкс
4. гонорáр   9. саксофóн
5. моногрáмма   10. монопóлия

REDUCTION OF UNSTRESSED a AND o AFTER THE STRESS

Remember that Russian vowels **a** and **o** are fully reduced when they occur after the stress. These vowels, when fully reduced, are indistinguishable from one another. It is impossible to listen to the sounds they make and distinguish **a** from **o** when both are fully reduced.

Listen to the tape and note that the bold vowels in the following list are fully reduced. The fully reduced **a** and **o** sound like the slightest pause between consonants or after a consonant.

1. за́мок   6. бáза
2. о́рган   7. пáфос
3. áстма   8. трáнспорт
4. áтлас   9. дóгма
5. áтом   10. póбот

PARTIAL REDUCTION OF UNSTRESSED a AND o AFTER HARD CONSONANTS

Russian vowels **a** and **o** are partially reduced when they are:

1. in word-initial position or
2. in the syllable immediately preceding the stress.

These vowels, when partially reduced, are indistinguishable from one another. It is impossible to listen to the sounds they make and distinguish **a** from **o** when both are partially reduced.
     Partially reduced **a** and **o** sound like "uh" in the words *but* or *nut*, except when in word-initial position in which case they may be pronounced as "ah" (as in *lot*) in Muscovite pronunciation.

Listen to the tape and note that bold vowels in the following list are partially reduced. Some of the words are pronounced in Muscovite pronunciation.

1.	ав**а**нгáрд	10.	п**а**рáграф	18.	**а**стрóлог
2.	**а**квалáнг	11.	н**о**вáтор	19.	**а**втóбус
3.	**а**ромáт	12.	р**а**бóта	20.	**а**втóграф
4.	**а**стронáвт	13.	т**а**бáк	21.	**а**крóполь
5.	ш**о**колáд	14.	ф**о**тóграф	22.	б**а**рóн
6.	б**а**лáнс	15.	**а**стронóм	23.	**а**втостóп
7.	б**а**рáк	16.	**а**нтр**о**пóлог	24.	**а**налóгия
8.	г**а**рáж	17.	**о**ктагóн	25.	**а**натóмия
9.	**о**ктáва				

PRACTICE WITH NON-WORDS

In the following exercise, in the two sounds for each number, the unstressed vowels have the same pronunciation. This means that a native speaker of Russian, hearing an unfamiliar or new word (such as these nonsense syllables), would not know how to spell this word, because either of the two spellings would be possible given the word's pronunciation.

Listen to and practice these sounds, which feature reduced vowels **a** and **o**.

	STRESS ON 1ST SYLLABLE		**STRESS ON 2ND SYLLABLE**		**STRESS ON 3RD SYLLABLE**
1.	нáнана нáноно	2.	нанáна нонáно	3.	нананá нононá
4.	вáвава вáвово	5.	вавáва вовáво	6.	вававá вововá
7.	зáзаза зáзозо	8.	зазáза зозáзо	9.	зазазá зозозá
10.	дáдада дáдодо	11.	дадáда додáдо	12.	дададá дододá

SELF-QUIZ

Listen to the pronunciation of the geographical names and mark the stress.

1.	Орландо	11.	Огайо
2.	Батон–Руж	12.	Айова
3.	Оттава	13.	Алабама
4.	Гонолулу	14.	Бостон
5.	Давенпорт	15.	Вологда
6.	Даллас	16.	Кострома
7.	Колорадо	17.	Ялта
8.	Торонто	18.	Волгоград
9.	Канада	19.	Ярославль
10.	Канзас	20.	Москва

Exercises and Activities

Упражнéние 2.3   Look at the list of infinitives and find their conjugations by checking the index in the textbook and the corresponding unit glossary in the workbook to determine the prototype verb to which they belong. Then write out the conjugation of the verbs for the **я, ты,** and **онú** forms, and past-tense forms for **он, онá,** and **онú,** indicating stress as you do so. (These conjugation patterns will help you with **Упражнéние 4.4.**)

1.	носúть	11.	заплатúть
2.	купúть	12.	ходúть
3.	лежáть	13.	сидéть
4.	познакóмиться	14.	учúться
5.	беспокóиться	15.	обúдеться
6.	женúться	16.	кричáть
7.	просúть	17.	говорúть
8.	возúть	18.	готóвить
9.	отвéтить	19.	остановúть
10.	летéть	20.	спросúть

Упражнéние 2.4   Answer the following questions for each prototype verb you identified in the previous exercise.

1. Does each verb prototype feature a mutation? If so, in what conjugated forms does it occur?
2. Does each verb prototype feature a shifting stress pattern in either the nonpast or past-tense forms? If so, in which?
3. Does each verb prototype feature a syllabic alternation?

Задáние 2.3   Select at least five verbs in **Упражнéние 2.3** and write a story of two or more paragraphs using those verbs.

Упражнéние 2.5   Fill in the blanks with the correct form of the missing irregular verbs, **бежáть, дать, хотéть,** and **есть.**

Мы с Андрюшей (*want*) _____[1] помогáть бездóмным [*homeless*] в

райóнном приюте для нúщих [*regional shelter for poor people*]. Чáсто бывáет, что бéдные

(*eat*) _____[2] тóлько в такúх райóнных лриюгах, потомý что у нúх

нет дéнег на продýкты. Сейчáс мы (*are running*) _____[3] тудá, чтóбы

помогáть с приготовлéнием обéда [*with the preparation of a meal*]. Мы решúли [*decided*], что (*will give*) _____[4] не только своё время, но и деньги. Нужно

помогать бедным.

 Упражнение 2.6 Translate the paragraph, changing the passive constructions into idiomatic English.

Говорят, что на нашей улице построят новый дом для бывших заключённых (*former convicts*), которые только что освободились. Думают, что этим людям нужно спокойно жить в обычном районе, чтобы потом совершенно самостоятельно войти в нормальную жизнь. Считается, что мы не будем возражать против того, чтобы эти люди жили в нашем районе. В газете было опубликовано объявление районного совета, в котором приглашали всех жителей района на обсуждение этой проблемы. Говорят, что смогут построить такой дом в другом месте далеко от нас, но я не знаю, правильно ли это. Мне кажется, что и там будут возражения со стороны местных жителей.

 Задание 2.4 Watch or listen to an interview on the television or radio and prepare a short oral or written summary of the interview, as assigned by your instructor.

 Фото-задание Look at the photograph on the first page of Unit 2 in the textbook and write up what could be a "transcript" of the American journalist's interview with the Russian veteran.

Glossary

Beginning with the glossary for this unit, all regular second-conjugation verbs and the four irregular verbs will be given only in the **я, ты, они**, and imperative forms. Full information will be given for first conjugation verbs. If no imperative is provided, there is no imperative for the given verb. Past tense forms are listed *only* when they are in some way irregular. Verbs marked M are multidirectional, U are unidirectional (see Unit 23).

бежать (U-*)/по– (*) [куда?]:
  бегу, бежишь, бегут, беги(те)!

to run [where?] (not in the sense of jogging on a track)

бояться (II) [кого? чего?]:
  боюсь, бойшься, боятся, бойся! бойтесь!

to be afraid [of someone, something]

вас беспокоит... [кто?]

it's . . . calling (more formal)

видеть/у– (II) [кого? что?]:
  вижу, видишь, видят

to see, to catch sight of [whom? what?]

возвращаться (I)/вернуться (I) [куда?]:
  возвращаюсь, возвращаешься, возвращается,
  возвращаемся, возвращаетесь, возвращаются,
  возвращайся! возвращайтесь!; вернусь, вернёшься,
  вернётся, вернёмся, вернётесь, вернутся, вернись!
  вернитесь!

to return [where]

возить (M-II)/везти (U-I)/по– (I) [что? куда?]:
  вожу, возишь, возят, вози(те)!; везу, везёшь, везёт, везём,
  везёте, везут, вези(те)! вёз, везла, везли

to carry, to transport [what? where?] by vehicle or conveyance встреча́ться (I)/встре́титься (II) [с кем? где? когда́?]: встреча́юсь, встреча́ешься, встреча́ется, встреча́емся, встреча́етесь, встреча́ются, встреча́йся! встреча́йтесь!; встре́чусь, встре́тишься, встре́тятся, встре́ться! встре́тьтесь! — *to meet [with whom? where? when?]*

говори́ть/по– (II), [с кем? о чём?]: говорю́, говори́шь, говоря́т, говори́(те)! — *to chat, to have a chat [with whom? about what?]*

говори́ть (II) / сказа́ть (I) [кому́? о чём?]: скажу́, ска́жешь, ска́жет, ска́жем, ска́жете, ска́жут, скажи́(те)! — *to say, to tell [whom? about what?]*

гото́вить/при– (II) [что?]: гото́влю, гото́вишь, гото́вят, гото́вь(те)! — *to prepare [what?]*

дава́ть (I)/дать (*) [кому́? что?]: даю́, даёшь, даёт, даём, даёте, даю́т, дава́й(те)!; дам, дашь, даду́т, да́й(те)! — *to give [whom? what?]*

держа́ть/по– (II) [что? где?]: держу́, де́ржишь, де́ржат, держи́(те)! — *to hold [what? where?]*

до встре́чи, до звонка́ (созвони́мся), до свида́нья — *until we meet up, until the next call, goodbye*

договори́ться (II) [с кем?]: договорю́сь, довори́шься, договоря́тся, договори́сь! договори́тесь! — *to agree [with whom]*

есть/съ– (*) [что?]: ем, ешь, едя́т, ешь(те)! — *to eat [what?]*

жить (I) [где?]: живу́, живёшь, живёт, живём, живёте, живу́т, живи́(те)!, жил, жила́, жи́ли — *to live [where?]*

задава́ть (I)/зада́ть (*) вопро́с [кому́?]: задаю́, задаёшь, задаёт, задаём, задаёте, задаю́т, задава́й(те)!; зада́м, зада́шь, зададу́т, зада́й(те)! за́дал, задала́, за́дали — *to assign, to pose [a question to whom?]*

замеча́ть (I)/заме́тить (II) [кого́? что?]: замеча́ю, замеча́ешь, замеча́ет, замеча́ем, замеча́ете, замеча́ют, замеча́й(те)!; заме́чу, заме́тишь, заме́тят, заме́ть(те)! — *to notice [whom? what?]*

знако́мить/по– (II) [кого́? с кем?]: знако́млю, знако́мишь, знако́мят, знако́мь(те)! — *to acquaint [whom? with whom?]*

знако́миться/по– (II): знако́млюсь, знако́мишься, знако́мятся, знако́мься! знако́мьтесь! — *to become acquainted [with whom?]*

идти́ (U-I)/пойти́ (I) [куда́?]: иду́, идёшь, идёт, идём, идёте, иду́т, иди́(те)!; пойду́, пойдёшь, пойдёт, пойдём, пойдёте, пойду́т, пойди́(те)!, пошёл, пошла́, пошли́ — *to go on foot (use in present or future tense only for the time being)*

крича́ть/за– (II) [что? на кого́? кому́?]: кричу́, кричи́шь, крича́т, кричи́(те)! — *to yell, to shout [what? at whom? to whom?]*

купи́ть — *см.* покупа́ть

                                                    to buy; see **покупа́ть**

лежа́ть/по– (II) [где?]:
    лежу́, лежи́шь, лежа́т, лежи́(те)!

to lie/be lying down [where?]

лови́ть (II)/пойма́ть (I) [кого́? что?]:
    ловлю́, ло́вишь, ло́вят, лови́(те)!; пойма́ю, пойма́ешь,
    пойма́ет, пойма́ем, пойма́ете, пойма́ют, пойма́й(те)!

to catch [whom? what?]

люби́ть/по– (II) [кого́? что?]:
    люблю́, лю́бишь, лю́бят, люби́(те)

to love [whom? what?]

ненави́деть/воз– (II) [кого́? что?]:
    ненави́жу, ненави́дишь, ненави́дят, ненави́дь(те)!

to hate, to come to hate [whom? what?]

\# не туда́ попа́сть

to get a wrong number (use the past tense only for now)

\# отвеча́ть (I)/отве́тить (II) [кому́? на письмо́ и́ли на вопро́с]:
    отвеча́ю, отвеча́ешь, отвеча́ет, отвеча́ем, отвеча́ете,
    отвеча́ют, отвеча́й(те)!; отве́чу, отве́тишь, отве́тят,
    отве́ть(те)!

to answer someone's letter or question

открыва́ть (I)/откры́ть (I) [что?]:
    открыва́ю, открыва́ешь, открыва́ет, открыва́ем,
    открыва́ете, открыва́ют, открыва́й(те)!; откро́ю, откро́ешь,
    откро́ет, откро́ем, откро́ете, откро́ют, откро́й(те)!

to open [what?]

пить/вы́– (I) [что?]:
    пью, пьёшь, пьёт, пьём, пьёте, пьют, пей(те)!

to drink [what?]

покупа́ть (I)/купи́ть (II) [что? кому́? для кого́?]:
    покупа́ю, покупа́ешь, покупа́ет, покупа́ем, покупа́ете,
    покупа́ют, покупа́й(те)!; куплю́, ку́пишь, ку́пят, купи́(те)!

to buy [what? for whom?]

\# позови́(те) [кого́?] к телефо́ну

to ask someone to pick up the phone

\# проси́ть/по– (II) [кого́? де́лать/с– что? *or* у кого́? что?]:
    прошу́, про́сишь, про́сят, проси́(те)!

to ask [whom? to do what?] [someone for what?]

\# расска́зывать (I)/рассказа́ть (I) [кому́? о чём?]:
    расска́зываю, расска́зываешь, расска́зывает,
    расска́зываем, расска́зываете, расска́зывают,
    расска́зывай(те)!; расскажу́, расска́жешь, расска́жет,
    расска́жем, расска́жете, расска́жут, расскажи́(те)!

to tell [whom? about what?]

слы́шать/у– (II) [что?]:
    слы́шу, слы́шишь, слы́шат

to hear [what?]

смотре́ть/по– (II) [что?]:
    смотрю́, смо́тришь, смо́трят, смотри́(те)!

to watch [what?]

сове́товать/по– (II) [кому́? де́лать/с– что?]:
    сове́тую, сове́туешь, сове́тует, сове́туем, сове́туете,
    сове́туют, сове́туй(те)!

to advise [whom to do what?]

спать/по– (II) [где?]:
    сплю, спишь, спят, спи(те)!

to sleep [where?]

спрáшивать (I) /спросúть (II) [когó? о чём?]:
   спрáшиваю, спрáшиваешь, спрáшивает, спрáшиваем,
   спрáшиваете, спрáшивают, спрáшивай(те)!; спрошý,
   спрóсишь, спрóсят, спросú(те)!

to ask [whom about what?]
(request for information only)

стоя́ть/по– (II) [где?]:
   стою́, стои́шь, стоя́т, стóй(те)!

to stand, to be standing [where?]

теря́ть/по– (I) [что?]:
   теря́ю, теря́ешь, теря́ет, теря́ем, теря́ете, теря́ют, теря́й(те)!

to lose [what?]

умéть/с– (I) [дéлать что?]:
   умéю, умéешь, умéет, умéем, умéете, умéют, умéй(те)!

to be able to do [what?]

хотéть/за– (*) [что? дéлать/с– что?]:
   хочý, хóчешь, хотя́т

to want [what? or to do what?]

чи́стить/по– (II) [что?]:
   чи́щу, чи́стишь, чи́стят, чи́сти(те)!

to clean [what?]

читáть/про– (I) [что?]:
   читáю, читáешь, читáет, читáем, читáете, читáют, читáй(те)!

to read [what?]

UNIT 3

Lexicon: Family

Russians commonly use certain words and expressions when they describe their families.

Состоя́ть [из чего́?] (из двух, трёх, четырёх, пяти́, шести́, семи́, восьми́, девяти́, десяти́ челове́к)
To consist of something, to consist of two to ten people

> Моя́ семья́ состои́т из четырёх челове́к.
> *My family consists of four people.*

Оди́н брат, два, (три, четы́ре) бра́та, пять бра́тьев, нет бра́тьев
One brother, two (three, four) brothers, five brothers, no brothers

> Мла́дшие бра́тья ещё хо́дят в шко́лу, а ста́ршие бра́тья уже́ рабо́тают.
> *My younger brothers still go to school, but my older brothers already work.*

Одна́ сестра́, две (три, четы́ре) сестры́, пять сестёр, нет сестёр
One sister, two (three, four) sisters, five sisters, no sisters

> Ста́ршие сёстры поступи́ли в аспиранту́ру, а мла́дшие сёстры ещё у́чатся в
> университе́те.
> *My older sisters are in graduate school, but my younger sisters are still students at the
> university.*

Мла́дшего/ста́ршего/сре́днего бра́та зову́т...
Мла́дшую/ста́ршую/сре́днюю сестру́ зову́т...
[My] younger/older/middle brother's/sister's name is . . .

> Ста́ршую сестру́ зову́т А́нна, а мла́дшего бра́та — Серге́й.
> *My older sister's name is Anna, and my younger brother's name is Sergei.*

Кем он/она́ вам/тебе́ прихо́дится?
Он мне прихо́дится двою́родным бра́том./Она́ мне прихо́дится двою́родной сестро́й.
How are you related to him/her? He's my cousin./She's my cousin.

> Вита́лий ей прихо́дится дя́дей.
> *Vitalii is her uncle.*

Жить вме́сте [с кем?], жить отде́льно [от кого́?]
To live together [with whom], to live separately [from whom?]

> Я живу́ вме́сте с ма́терью, а оте́ц живёт отде́льно от нас.
> *I live with my mother, but my father lives separately from us.*

Жив/жива́/жи́вы и́ли у́мер/умерла́/у́мерли
To be alive, to be dead

> Ба́бушка, сла́ва Бо́гу, ещё жива́, но де́душка у́мер в про́шлом году́.
> *My grandmother, thank God, is still alive, but my grandfather died last year.*

Жени́ться/по-
To get married (said only of couples)

> На́до спеши́ть! Па́вел и Лари́са же́нятся сего́дня в три часа́.
> *We have to hurry! Pavel and Larisa are getting married today at three o'clock.*

Жени́ться [на ком?] Быть жена́тым [на ком?]
To get married, to be married (said only of a man)

> Бра́т жени́лся на Ната́ше, когда́ он жил в Петербу́рге.
> *My brother got married to Natasha when he was living in Petersburg.*

Выходи́ть/вы́йти за́муж [за кого́?] Быть за́мужем [за кем?]
To get married, to be married (said only of a woman)

> Ната́ша вы́шла за́муж за моего́ бра́та де́вять лет наза́д.
> *Natasha married my brother nine years ago.*

Разводи́ться/развести́сь, подава́ть/пода́ть на разво́д
To get divorced, to file for divorce

> Та́ня и Ми́ша сейча́с разво́дятся: они́, наве́рно, разлюби́ли друг дру́га.
> *Tania and Misha are getting divorced: apparently, they fell out of love.*

Ма́чеха/о́тчим/сво́дные бра́тья, сёстры
Stepmother/stepfather/stepbrothers, stepsisters

> Ма́чеха нас о́чень лю́бит.
> *Our stepmother loves us very much.*

Рожда́ться/роди́ться
To be born (usually used only in perfective)

> У Петро́вых родила́сь де́вочка! У Па́вловых роди́лся ма́льчик!
> *The Petrovs had a baby girl! The Pavlovs had a baby boy!*

Умира́ть/умере́ть
To die

> Де́душка у́мер, когда́ мне бы́ло 15 лет.
> *My grandfather died when I was 15 years old.*

ДРУГИ́Е РО́ДСТВЕННИКИ	OTHER RELATIVES
дя́дя, тётя	*uncle, aunt*
племя́нник, племя́нница	*nephew, niece*
двою́родный брат, двою́родная сестра́	*cousin*
внук, вну́чка	*grandson, granddaughter*
прадеде́душка, прабабу́шка	*great-grandfather, great-grandmother*
пра́внук, пра́внучка	*great-grandson, great-granddaughter*
тесть, тёща	*father-in-law, mother-in-law of the husband,* i.e, *the wife's father and mother*
свёкор, свекро́вь	*father-in-law, mother-in-law of the wife,* i.e., *the husband's father and mother*

Possessive modifiers, **мой**, **твой**, **его́/её**, **наш**, **ваш**, and **их**, are *not* used with family members if the relationship is the subject of the sentence. If you use **я** to talk about your family, don't use the possessive modifier *my* to refer to your relatives. Also note that Russians often refer to all adults as "aunts" and "uncles" or "grandparents" (depending on their age) when talking to children

Упражне́ние 3.1   Fill in the blanks with the correct "family" word, using the following cues, though not necessarily in this order: *niece, was born, got married, had died, stepfather, brothers, sisters, consists.*

Мари́на _____¹ за Андре́я, когда́ она́ зако́нчила университе́т. Че́рез

два го́да, у них _____² до́чка, кото́рую назва́ли Э́лла.

_____³ Мари́ны помога́л расти́ть Э́ллочку. Мари́на ча́сто ду́мала о

свое́й ма́тери, кото́рая _____,⁴ когда́ Мари́на ещё учи́лась в шко́ле.

У Андре́я три_____⁵ и два/две _____:⁶ его́

семья́ _____⁷ из восьми́ челове́к. В его́ семье́ все лю́бят

_____.⁸

Listening Tasks

The listening text for this unit consists of a description of one family.

PRE-LISTENING TASK

Draw a diagram depicting the relationships among people in your extended family, indicating their ages and professions (or educational status). How would you describe this diagram orally in Russian? Make a list of the words you would need to learn in order to do this.

LISTENING TASK

Listen to the text and then answer questions 1 through 5 in English and 6 through 9 in Russian. Then make a list of all the members of the family and list their ages and professions.

1. For what occasion did people gather?
2. Make a list of the places from which various relatives traveled. Find all the cities mentioned on the map of Russia on the inside cover of the textbook.
3. Who made a very touching toast?
4. Who told everyone how someone was nervous?
5. Where does the young couple live now and where do they hope to live?
6. What is the Russian term for *young married couple*, used to describe the family?
7. The speaker says that two people were *delighted*. How is this expressed?
8. What is the Russian equivalent of the word *apparently*?
9. What is the Russian equivalent of *to make a toast*?

DICTATION

Replay the tape and, as you listen, write out a description of the family in full.

PERFORMANCE

Practice reciting the description you wrote out.

POST-LISTENING TASK

Using the description as a model, write a description of your family based on the diagram you drew in the pre-listening task.

CULTURAL PROBLEM

What are some of the differences between American and Russian family structures as illustrated in the description you listened to on the tape and the description you wrote of your own family?

Phonetics and Intonation

Lexical Stress Continued

REDUCTION OF UNSTRESSED a AFTER SOFT CONSONANTS

In Unit 2, we examined the reduction of vowels **a** and **o** when preceded by hard consonants. When preceded by soft consonants, the reduction of **a** is somewhat different. When partially reduced, it sounds not like "uh" (as in *but* or *nut*), but like "ih," as in *bit* or *knit*. When fully reduced, it sounds less distinguishable.

Listen to the words on the tape.

PARTIAL REDUCTION

1.	часы́	6.	часа́ми
2.	часа́	7.	щаве́ль
3.	Чайко́вский	8.	щаве́левый
4.	часо́в	9.	щади́ть
5.	чаду́	10.	щади́ли

FULL REDUCTION

1.	частота́	6.	чароде́й
2.	часово́й	7.	часовщи́к
3.	чаёвничать	8.	часосло́в
4.	чаевы́е	9.	часосло́ва
5.	чаево́д	10.	частоко́л

REDUCTION OF UNSTRESSED VOWELS e AND я

The vowels **e** and **я** sound similar to the partially and fully reduced **a** after a soft consonant in most circumstances, but there are two important exceptions, which will be discussed later in this unit.

Listen to the words on the tape.

PARTIAL REDUCTION

1. вельвéт
2. депрéссия
3. герóй
4. геóграф
5. Еврóпа
6. календáрь
7. медбрáт[1]
8. метáлл
9. пейзáж
10. семéстр
11. сестрá
12. взялá
13. лягýшка
14. январь
15. язы́к

FULL REDUCTION

1. вертикáль
2. ветеринáр
3. генерáл
4. желатúн
5. керосúн
6. легиóн
7. медсестрá[2]
8. пессимúзм
9. револьвéр
10. сегрегáция
11. телевúзор
12. телегрáф
13. телегрáмма
14. телефóн
15. телепáт

REDUCTION OF UNSTRESSED VOWEL я IN THE REFLEXIVE ENDING -ся

In the reflexive ending -ся, the vowel я does not signify that the previous consonant is soft. In fact, the vowel я in the reflexive ending -ся is pronounced like a fully reduced a or o preceded by a hard consonant.

Listen to the words on the tape.

1. учúться
2. ýчится
3. ýчатся
4. вернýться
5. вернётся
6. вернýтся
7. одевáться
8. одевáется
9. одевáются
10. улыбáться
11. улыбáется
12. улыбáются

PRACTICE WITH NONWORDS

The two sounds for each number sound alike, despite the fact that they are spelled differently. Practice the reduction of е and я with these nonsense syllables:

STRESS ON 1ST SYLLABLE	STRESS ON 2ND SYLLABLE	STRESS ON 3RD SYLLABLE
1. нéнене нéняня	2. ненéне нянéня	3. ненené нянянé
4. вéвеве вéвявя	5. вевéве вявéвя	6. вевевé вявявé
7. зéзезе зéзязя	8. зезéзе зязéзя	9. зезезé зязязé

---

[1]Some speakers may not reduce the vowel in the first syllable of this word because it is a compound word (*medical brother*), while other speakers may reduce the vowel according to the rules of reduction of unstressed vowels.

[2]See footnote 1.

UNSTRESSED VOWELS e AND я PRECEDED BY ANOTHER VOWEL

When **e** and **я** are preceded by another vowel, they sound like "uh" (as in *but* or *nut*) preceded by a y-glide: "yuh" (as in *yummy*).

Listen to the tape and note that the two vowels (**e** and **я**) sound indistinguishable in this position.

1. зда́ние	7. упражне́ние
2. зда́ния	8. упражне́ния
3. зада́ние	9. зре́ние
4. зада́ния	10. зре́ния
5. заня́тие	11. написа́ние
6. заня́тия	12. написа́ния

SELF-QUIZ

Listen to the pronunciation of the geographical names on the tape, write the English equivalents, and mark the stress in the Russian names.

	PLACE NAME IN RUSSIAN	PLACE NAME IN ENGLISH		PLACE NAME IN RUSSIAN	PLACE NAME IN ENGLISH
1.	Техас	_____	11.	Япония	_____
2.	Галифакс	_____	12.	Тегеран	_____
3.	Детройт	_____	13.	Ямайка	_____
4.	Орегон	_____	14.	Аргентина	_____
5.	Петербург	_____	15.	Египет	_____
6.	Киев	_____	16.	Швейцария	_____
7.	Нева	_____	17.	Непал	_____
8.	Рязань	_____	18.	Амстердам	_____
9.	Германия	_____	19.	Сенегал	_____
10.	Венеция	_____	20.	Россия	_____

Exercises and Activities

Упражне́ние 3.2   Look at the list of infinitives and find their conjugations by checking the index in the textbook and the corresponding unit glossary in the workbook to determine the prototype verb to which they belong. Then write out the conjugation of the verbs for the **я, ты,** and **они́** forms, and the past-tense forms for **он, она́,** and **они́,** indicating stress as you do so. Then answer the questions in **Упражне́ние 2.4,** p. 19, for the first conjugation prototypes. (The conjugation patterns will help you with **Упражне́ние 4.3.**)

1. ксерокопи́ровать
2. вы́пить
3. приня́ть
4. потеря́ть
5. везти́
6. мочь
7. сове́товать
8. заказа́ть
9. зака́зывать
10. рабо́тать

11. танцева́ть
12. писа́ть
13. обману́ть
14. успе́ть
15. плыть
16. оде́ться
17. одева́ться
18. снима́ть
19. снять
20. здра́вствовать

Зада́ние 3.1 Select at least five verbs in **Упражне́ние 3.2** and write a story of two or more paragraphs using those verbs.

Зада́ние 3.2 Prepare a three-minute talk or write a composition, as assigned by your instructor, about your family or the family of a famous individual.

Фо́то-зада́ние Look at the photograph on the first page of this unit in the textbook. Write a paragraph or prepare a presentation, as assigned by your instructor, describing the ages and occupations of the Andreevs and who might be in their extended family.

Glossary

Beginning with this unit, listings for all regular first conjugation verbs will be given only in the **я, ты, они́** and imperative forms. If no imperative is provided, there is no imperative for the given verb. Past tense forms are listed only when they are in some way irregular.

брать (I)/взять (I) [кого́? что?]:
  беру́, берёшь, беру́т, бери́(те)! брал, брала́, бра́ли; возьму́, возьмёшь, возьму́т, возьми́(те)! взял, взяла́, взя́ли

to take (only with reference to a physical removal of an object from one location to another, not with reference to a course at school or to medicine) [whom? what?]

внук, вну́чка

grandson, granddaughter

води́ть (M-II)/вести́ (U-I) [кого́? что? куда́? к чему́?]:
  вожу́, во́дишь, во́дят, води́(те)!; веду́, ведёшь, веду́т, веди́(те)! вёл, вела́, вели́

to take by foot or lead [whom? where? to what?]

возвраща́ться (I)/верну́ться (I):
  возвраща́юсь, возвраща́ешься, возвраща́ются, возвраща́йся! возвраща́йтесь!; верну́сь, вернёшься, верну́тся, верни́сь! верни́тесь!

to return

выходи́ть (II)/вы́йти (I) за́муж [за кого́?]:
  выхожу́, выхо́дишь, выхо́дят, выходи́(те); вы́йду, вы́йдешь, вы́йдут, вы́йди(те)! вы́шел, вы́шла, вы́шли

to get married to someone (said of a woman only)

говори́ть (II)/сказа́ть (I) [кому́? что?]:
  говорю́, говори́шь, говоря́т, говори́(те)!; скажу́, ска́жешь, ска́жут, скажи́(те)!

to say [what? to whom?]

давáть (I)/дать (*) [что? комý?]:   *to give [what? whom?]*
     даю́, даёшь, даю́т, давáй(те)!; дам, дашь, даст, дади́м,
     дади́те, даду́т, дáй(те)! дал, далá, дáли

\# двою́родный брат, двою́родная сестрá   *cousin (m, f)*

дéлать/с- (I) [что?]:   *to do [what?]*
     дéлаю, дéлаешь, дéлают, дéлай(те)!

\# дя́дя   *uncle*

ждать/подо-(I) [когó? что?]:   *to wait for [whom? for*
     жду, ждёшь, ждут, жди́(те)! ждал, ждалá, ждáли   *what?] (no preposition is*
                                                     used in Russian)

\# жени́ться/по-(II):   *to get married (said only of*
     женю́сь, жéнишься, жéнятся, жени́сь! жени́тесь!   *couples)*

\# жени́ться (II):   *to get married (said only of*
     женю́сь, жéнишься, жéнятся, жени́сь! жени́тесь!   *men, no perfective)*

\# жив, живá, жи́вы   *alive, living*

\# жить [где?] (I):   *to live [where?]*
     живу́, живёшь, живу́т, живи́(те)! жил, жилá, жи́ли

закрывáть (I)/закры́ть (I) [что?]:   *to close [what?]*
     закрывáю, закрывáешь, закрывáют, закрывáй(те)!;
     закрóю, закрóешь, закрóют, закрóй(те)!

здрáвствовать (I): здрáвствуй(те)!   *to be healthy (greetings!)*

знáть (I)/узнáть (I) [что?]:   *to know/to find out [what?]*
     знáю, знáешь, знáют, знáй(те)!; узнáю, узнáешь, узнáют,
     узнáй(те)!

искáть/по-(I) [что?]:   *to look [for something]/to*
     ищу́, и́щешь, и́щут, ищи́(те)!   *search [for something] for*
                                                       a while

\# мáчеха   *stepmother*

\# млáдший [брат/сестрá]   *younger [brother/sister]*

мочь/с- (I) [дéлать что?]:   *can*
     могу́, мóжешь, мóгут

начинáть (I)/начáть (I) [дéлать что?]:   *to begin [what?]*
     начинáю, начинáешь, начинáют, начинáй(те)!; начну́,
     начнёшь, начну́т, начни́(те)! нáчал, началá, нáчали

находи́ть (I)/найти́ (I) [что? где?]:   *to find [what? where?]*
     нахожу́, нахóдишь, нахóдят, находи́(те)!; найду́, найдёшь,
     найду́т, найди́(те)! нашёл, нашлá, нашли́

окáзываться (I)/оказáться (I) [каки́м/какóй? кем? чем?]:   *to turn out to be something:*
     окáзывается, окáзываются; окáжется, окáжутся   *use third person forms*
                                                       only for most contexts

\# отдéльно [от когó?]   *separately*

открывáть (I)/откры́ть (I) [что?]:   *to open [what?]*
     открывáю, открывáешь, открывáют, открывáй(те)!;
     открóю, открóешь, открóют, открóй(те)!

отноше́ние/отноше́ния [к чему́? кому́?]:
  междунаро́дные отноше́ния

attitude [toward what? whom?] or relationship toward/between things or people; international relations

о́тчим

stepfather

писа́ть/на-(I) [кому́? о чём?]:
  пишу́, пи́шешь, пи́шут, пиши́(те)

to write [whom? what?]

пить/вы́-(I) [что?]:
  пью, пьёшь, пьют, пей(те)! пил, пила́, пи́ли; вы́пью,
  вы́пьецб, вы́пьют, вы́пей(те)! вы́пил, вы́пила, вы́пили

to drink [what?] or take medicine

пла́кать/за-(I):
  пла́чу, пла́чешь, пла́чут, пла́чь(те)!

to cry

племя́нник, племя́нница

nephew, niece

понима́ть (I)/поня́ть (I) [кого́? что?]:
  понима́ю, понима́ешь, понима́ют, понима́й(те)!; пойму́,
  поймёшь, пойму́т, пойми́(те)! по́нял, поняла́, по́няли

to understand [whom? what?]

привыка́ть (I)/привы́кнуть (I) [к кому́? чему́?]:
  привыка́ю, привыка́ешь, привыка́ют, привыка́й(те)!;
  привы́кну, привы́кнешь, привы́кнут, привы́кни(те)!
  привы́к, привы́кла, привы́кли

to get used to [whom? what?]

принима́ть (I)/приня́ть (I) [кого́? что?]:
  принима́ю, принима́ешь, принима́ют, принима́й(те)!;
  приму́, при́мешь, при́мут, прими́(те)! при́нял, приняла́,
  при́няли

to take/accept [whom? what?] (may be used with medicine)

разводи́ться (II) /развести́сь (I):
  развожу́сь, разво́дишься, разво́дятся, разводи́сь!
  разводи́тесь!; разведу́сь, разведёшься, разведу́тся,
  разведи́сь! разведи́тесь!

to get divorced

рожда́ться (I)/роди́ться (II):
  роди́тся, родя́тся, роди́лся, родила́сь, роди́лись

to be born (use perfective in almost all contexts)

сове́товать/по-(I) [кому́? де́лать что?]:
  сове́тую, сове́туешь, сове́туют, сове́туй(те)!

to advise [whom to do what?]

согла́сен/согла́сна/согла́сны [с кем? с чем?]

agreed

состоя́ть (I) [из чего́?]:
  состои́т, состоя́т

to consist [of what?] (use imperfective third person only in almost all contexts)

сре́дний [брат/сестра́]

middle [brother/sister]

станови́ться (II)/ста́ть (I) [каки́м/како́й? кем? чем?]:
  становлю́сь, стано́вишься, стано́вятся, станови́сь!
  станови́тесь!; ста́ну, ста́нешь, ста́нут, ста́нь(те)!

to become [what?]

ста́рший [брат/сестра́]

older or oldest [brother/sister]

танцева́ть/по-(I):
  танцу́ю, танцу́ешь, танцу́ют, танцу́й(те)!

to dance

тётя

aunt

узнава́ть (I)/узна́ть (I) [кого́? что?]:
    узнаю́, узнаёшь, узнаю́т, узнава́й(те)!; узна́ю, узна́ешь,
    узна́ют, узна́й(те)!

to recognize [*whom? what?*]

уме́ние [де́лать что?]

ability or know-how to do something

уме́ть/с- (I) [де́лать что?]:
    уме́ю, уме́ешь, уме́ют

to know how to do something

умира́ть (I)/умере́ть (I):
    умира́ю, умира́ешь, умира́ют; умру́, умрёшь, умру́т, у́мер,
    умерла́, у́мерли

to die

UNIT 4

Lexicon: Cultural Activities

Russians have traditionally enjoyed "high culture"—including art, ballet, opera, literature, theater, and so forth—as important leisure activities. Russians often memorize many works of poetry, both short and long, and entertain themselves by reciting poetry for one another. It is commonly believed that the ability to recite poetry is one of the characteristics of an educated person, because the memorization of poetry has been part of the regular school program for most Russian children. Here are some of the words and expressions you would use to describe the cultural activities you like most.

Проводить/провести свободное время [как? где?]
To spend free time

> Сергей Васильевич часто проводит свободное время в театре.
> *Sergey Vasil'evich often spends his free time at the theater.*

Ходить [куда?]
To go (frequently) somewhere or to have gone somewhere (and returned)

> Вчера мы ходили на премьеру нового итальянского фильма.
> *Yesterday we went to the premiere of a new Italian film.*

Билет [куда?]
A ticket to what?

> У меня три билета на оперу. Хотите пойти?
> *I have three tickets for the opera. Would you like to go?*

Я очень люблю, как играет/танцует...
I love the way someone acts/dances

> Мне нравится, как играет Валентин Гафт.
> *I love the way Valentin Gaft acts.*

Выступать [где?]
To perform

> Сегодня в Большом театре выступает Смирновская!
> *Smirnovskaia is performing tonight at the Bol'shoi theater.*

Артист(-ка)
Performing artist

> Алла Пугачёва – одна из его любимых артисток.
> *Alla Pugachova is one of his favorite performers.*

Спектакль
Performance (dramatic or musical)

> Этот спектакль очень популярен: на него ходит вся Москва!
> *This performance is very popular: all Moscow is going to see it!*

Игра́ть роль
To perform a role

Смоктуно́вский и Высо́цкий игра́ли роль Га́млета, ка́ждый по-своему.
Smoktunovskii and Vysotskii played the role of Hamlet, each in his own way.

Режиссёр
Director of a play or film

Тарко́вский, наве́рно, оди́н из са́мых изве́стных ру́сских режиссёров в кино́, а Станисла́вский—в теа́тре.
Tarkovskii is probably one of the most famous Russian directors in cinema, and Stanislavskii in theater.

Худо́жник
Artist (painter or sculptor)

Мой люби́мый францу́зский худо́жник — Ренуа́р, а Ре́пин — мой люби́мый ру́сский худо́жник.
My favorite French artist is Renoir, but Repin is my favorite Russian artist.

The conjugations for these verbs may be found in the glossary for this unit.

Упражне́ние 4.1   Fill in the blanks with the correct word or expression, using the following cues, though not necessarily in this order: *tickets, went, performance, to spend, artist, performers, plays a role.*

— Как _____[1] свобо́дный ве́чер в Москве́? Мо́жет быть, пойти́ в кино́?

— Но мы _____[2] в кино́ вчера́ ве́чером. Мо́жет быть на бале́т?

— Ты всё вре́мя _____[3] на бале́т. А мне не интере́сно. Дава́й пойдём на _____[4] в теа́тр «Совреме́нник».

— У тебя́ есть _____[5] в теа́тр?

— Да, и мне сказа́ли, что _____,[6] кото́рый де́лал декора́ции для э́того спекта́кля, то́же _____[7] в спекта́кле.

— Да, но я бы хоте́ла пойти́ в Большо́й теа́тр, где танцу́ют _____[8] из наро́дного анса́мбля «Руста́ви».

 Зада́ние 4.1   Prepare a three-minute talk or write a composition, as assigned by your instructor, about cultural activities you have enjoyed recently.

Listening Tasks

The listening text for this unit is a radio announcement about an important exhibit in an art museum.

PRE-LISTENING TASK

You're about to listen to an announcement of an important art exhibit. Imagine that you're the curator of the exhibit. What information would you want to include in your announcement?

LISTENING TASK

Listen to the text and then answer questions 1 through 8 in English and 9 through 11 in Russian.

1. Write a two-sentence summary of the radio announcement.
2. When did the exhibit open?
3. Where is the exhibit being held?
4. What artists are featured in the exhibit?
5. Why is the exhibit important?
6. Until what date will the exhibit be at this site?
7. What are the hours when one can see the exhibit?
8. What kind of lecture will Shuvalova be giving?
9. Listen closely to find the Russian equivalent of *in connection with*.
10. What is the Russian equivalent of *will give a lecture on the topic*?
11. What is the Russian equivalent of *interesting for all those who are interested in Russian painting*?

DICTATION

Replay the tape and, as you listen, write out the announcement in full.

PERFORMANCE

Practice reciting the announcement.

POST-LISTENING TASK

Using the announcement as a model, work with a classmate to create and perform your own announcement in which you state: the name of cultural event, when and where it will occur, its significance, and for whom it will be particularly interesting.

CULTURAL PROBLEM

What do you know about Kandinskii and Malevich? Why wasn't their work frequently displayed during the Soviet era? Look at some reproductions of their paintings before answering this question.

Lexicon: To Stop

Russian uses several different verbs to convey the notion of stopping.

Остана́вливаться/останови́ться
To come to a stop or to stay in a hotel

> Авто́бус подошёл и останови́лся на остано́вке.
> *The bus came up and stopped at the bus stop.*

> Когда́ я быва́ю в Москве́, я всегда́ остана́вливаюсь в гости́нице «Мир».
> *Whenever I'm in Moscow I always stay at the hotel Mir.*

Остана́вливать/останови́ть [кого?]
To stop someone or something in motion

> Нас останови́л милиционе́р.
> *A policeman stopped us.*

Переставáть/перестáть [дéлать что?]
To stop doing something

> Я перестáл смотрéть телеви́зор: у меня́ прóсто нет врéмени!
> *I stopped watching television: I just have no time!*

> Перестáньте э́то дéлать!
> *Stop doing that!*

> Дéти не перестаю́т шумéть! Перестáньте шумéть!
> *The children won't stop making noise! Stop making noise!*

Прекращáть/прекрати́ть [что? дéлать что?]
To stop a process

> Они́ не прекращáют говори́ть об э́том.
> *They won't stop talking about this.*

Бросáть/брóсить [дéлать что?]
To quit doing something

> Моя́ тёща наконéц брóсила кури́ть.
> *My mother-in-law finally quit smoking.*

Упражнéние 4.2 Fill in the blanks with the Russian equivalent of the English word in parentheses.

1. — Где вы бы́ли, когдá (*stopped*) _____ часы́?

2. — Я хотéла вы́йти покури́ть, но меня́ (*stopped*) _____ Сергéй.

3. — Он мне напóмнил, что я (*quit*) _____ кури́ть.

4. — Я ему́ сказáла, чтóбы он (*stopped*) _____ мешáть мне.

5. — Потóм он мне предложи́л поéхать вмéсте в Пари́ж, где мы смогли́ бы (*to stop/stay*)

   _____ в мáленьком пансионáте.

Задáние 4.2 Prepare a three-minute talk or write a composition, as assigned by your instructor, continuing the conversation in **Упражнéние 4.2**. Use as many verbs of stopping and expressions related to cultural activities as you can.

Упражнéние 4.3 Fill in the blanks with the Russian equivalent of the English word in parentheses.

1. Они́ подошли́ к молодóму человéку и (*stopped*) _____, не знáя,

   Фёдоров ли э́то, и́ли нет.

2. Олéг, навéрно, тебя́ (*will stop*) _____, éсли ты начнёшь говори́ть

   об э́том.

3. Мили́ция тут чáсто (*stops*) _____ маши́ны, котóрые превышáют

   скóрость.

4   Они́ (*stop*) _____ кури́ть ка́ждый год, но начина́ют опя́ть кури́ть

че́рез па́ру дней.

Phonetics and Intonation

Russian **у** and **ю** Contrasted with English *u*

The Russian **у** has a much deeper sound than does the English *u*. To pronounce the Russian **у** correctly, you must round your lips and stick them out far enough so that you can *see* them when you look down.

Listen to the Russian and English words and their respective **у**, **ю**, and *u* sounds on the tape.

	RUSSIAN	ENGLISH
1.	бум	boom
2.	дум	doom
3.	тут	toot
4.	мюз	mews
5.	бюро	bureau
6.	бюрократ	bureaucrat
7.	ну	new
8.	губ	goop
9.	буд	boot
10.	гун	goon

SELF-QUIZ

Indicate whether the sound you hear on the tape is the Russian **у**, **ю** or the English *u*.

	RUSSIAN	ENGLISH
1.	бум	boom
2.	дум	doom
3.	руль	rule
4.	тут	toot
5.	мюз	mews
6.	гун	goon
7.	ну	new
8.	губ	goop
9.	буд	boot
10.	дуг	duke

Exercises and Activities

Упражне́ние 4.4   Identify the stress pattern for each of the verbs in **Упражне́ния 2.3** and **3.2**.

Зада́ние 4.3   Choose five verbs from **Упражне́ние 2.3** and five from **Упражне́ние 3.2** and use them to write a three-paragraph story.

Фо́то-зада́ние   Look at the photograph on the first page of this unit in the textbook. Write a paragraph or prepare a presentation, as assigned by your instructor, acting out a scene that might be illustrated in this picture.

Glossary

# арти́ст(-ка)	*performing artist*
# биле́т	*ticket*
брать (I) /взять (I) [кого́? что? куда́?]: беру́, берёшь, беру́т, бери́(те)! брал, брала́, бра́ли; возьму́, возьмёшь, возьму́т, возьми́(те)! взял, взяла́, взя́ли	*to take (physically removing an object from a location) [whom? what?]*
# броса́ть (I) /бро́сить (II) [кого́? что?]: броса́ю, броса́ешь, броса́ют, броса́й(те)!; бро́шу, бро́сишь, бро́сят, брось(те)!	*to quit or abandon [whom? what? to where?]*
ви́деть/у– (II) [кого́? что?]: ви́жу, ви́дишь, ви́дят	*to see, to catch sight of [whom? what?]*
# выступа́ть (I) [где?]: выступа́ю, выступа́ешь, выступа́ют, выступа́й(те)!	*to perform [where?]*
дава́ть (I) /дать (*) [кому́? что?]: даю́, даёшь, даю́т, дава́й(те)!; дам, дашь, даст, дади́м, дади́те, даду́т, дай(те)! дал, дала́, да́ли	*to give something to someone [whom? what?]*
# игра́ть (I) /сыгра́ть роль (I): игра́ю, игра́ешь, игра́ют, игра́й(те)!; сыгра́ю, сыгра́ешь, сыгра́ют, сыгра́й(те)!	*to play a role*
крича́ть/за– (II) [что?]: кричу́, кричи́шь, крича́т, кричи́(те)!	*to yell or shout [what?]*
# остана́вливать (I) /останови́ть (II) [кого́? что?]: остана́вливаю, остана́вливаешь, остана́вливают, остана́вливай(те)!; остановлю́, остано́вишь, остано́вят, останови́(те)!	*to stop [whom? what?] in motion*
# остана́вливаться (I) / останови́ться (II) [где?]: остана́вливаюсь, остана́вливаешься, остана́вливаются, остана́вливайся! остана́вливайтесь!; остановлю́сь, остано́вишься, остано́вятся, остановись! остановитесь!	*to come to a stop, to stop [where?]*
# перестава́ть (I) /переста́ть (I) [де́лать что?]: перестаю́, перестаёшь, перестаю́т, перестава́й(те)!; переста́ну, переста́нешь, переста́нут, переста́нь(те)!	*to stop doing something*
пла́кать/за– (I): пла́чу, пла́чешь, пла́чут, пла́чь(те)!	*to cry*
плати́ть/за– (II) [кому́? ско́лько де́нег? за что?]: плачу́, пла́тишь, пла́тят, плати́(те)!	*to pay [whom? how much? for what?]*
# пойти́ (I) [куда́?]: пойду́, пойдёшь, пойду́т, пойди́(те)! пошёл, пошла́, пошли́	*to go on foot*

приводи́ть (II) /привести́ (I) [кого́? что? куда́? к чему́?]:
  привожу́, приво́дишь, приво́дят, приводи́(те); приведу́,
  приведёшь, приведу́т, приведи́(те)! привёл, привела́,
  привели́

to bring [whom? what? where?]

прекраща́ть (I) /прекрати́ть (I) [что?]:
  прекраща́ю, прекраща́ешь, прекраща́ют, прекраща́й(те)!;
  прекращу́, прекрати́шь, прекратя́т, прекрати́(те)!

to stop (a process) [what?]

проводи́ть (II) /провести́ (I) [свобо́дное вре́мя]:
  провожу́, прово́дишь, прово́дят, проводи́(те)!; проведу́,
  проведёшь, проведу́т, проведи́(те)! провёл, провела́,
  провели́

to spend (free time)

режиссёр

director of a film or play

спекта́кль

performance

ходи́ть (M-II) [куда́?]:
  хожу́, хо́дишь, хо́дят, ходи́(те)!

to go on foot (frequently or roundtrip)

худо́жник

artist (in the sense of painter or sculptor)

UNIT 5

Lexicon: Applying To and Enrolling In a University or Graduate School

The Russian system of education is structured differently from the American system. Russians typically study for five years at the university level. Those who wish to become attorneys or doctors go to institutes of law or medicine, and study for a total of five years before attaining the degree that entitles them to practice. Further study, on the graduate level, is not required for base-level jobs in these fields in Russia at this time. Americans who wish to practice law or medicine, of course, must first get a bachelor's degree (university level diploma) and then continue their studies in graduate school. Graduate studies in Russia are typically for those people who wish to teach on the post-secondary level (i.e., at an institute or university).

If you wish to explain in Russian that an American wants to go to graduate school in law or medicine in America, you must say **поступи́ть в аспиранту́ру на юриди́ческий/ медици́нский факульте́т** or **поступи́ть в аспиранту́ру в юриди́ческий/ медици́нский институ́т.**

The following words and expressions describe the application and matriculation process at a university.

Конча́ть/ко́нчить (Зака́нчивать/зако́нчить, Ока́нчивать/око́нчить) университе́т, Получи́ть дипло́м
   To graduate from the university, to receive one's diploma

   Я зако́нчу университе́т в ма́е, получу́ дипло́м и сра́зу поступлю́ в аспиранту́ру.
   I'll graduate from the university in May, get my diploma, and immediately enroll in graduate school.

Заполня́ть/запо́лнить анке́ты
   To fill out forms

   Я три часа́ заполня́ла э́ту анке́ту: она́ о́чень сло́жная.
   It took me three hours to fill out this form: it's very complicated.

Подава́ть/пода́ть заявле́ние
   To submit an application

   Ви́ка подала́ заявле́ние в три университе́та.
   Vika submitted applications to three universities.

Поступа́ть/поступи́ть в аспиранту́ру
   To apply to or enroll in graduate school (note aspectual difference)

   Серге́й поступа́л в аспиранту́ру в про́шлом году́, но не поступи́л.
   Sergei applied to graduate school last year, but didn't enroll (i.e., wasn't accepted.)

   Ла́ра посту́пит в аспиранту́ру в сентябре́.
   Lara will enroll in graduate school in September.

Принима́ть/приня́ть [кого́?] в аспиранту́ру
To accept someone into graduate school

Я сейча́с поступа́ю в аспиранту́ру: наде́юсь, что меня́ при́мут.
I'm applying to graduate school now: I hope that I will be accepted.

Поступи́ть [на како́й факульте́т?]
To enter a department

Татья́на посту́пит на факульте́т хи́мии (на химфа́к).
Tat'iana will enroll in the chemistry department.

Сдава́ть/сдать вступи́тельные экза́мены [куда́?]
To take or pass entrance examinations (note the aspectual difference)

Ни́на сего́дня сдаёт вступи́тельный экза́мен в МГУ.
Nina is taking her entrance exam for Moscow University today.

Ми́ша сдава́л вступи́тельный экза́мен на про́шлой неде́ле.
Misha took the entrance exam last week.

Мы о́чень наде́емся, что Ни́на сдаст э́тот экза́мен.
We are really hoping that Nina will pass this exam.

Упражне́ние 5.1   Fill in the blanks with the correct words or expressions, using the following cues, though not necessarily in this order: *will accept, enroll, filled out the form, will take/write, submitted an application, will pass.*

Ла́ра хо́чет _____[1] в университе́т: она́

_____[2] на про́шлой неде́ле и вчера́

_____.[3] Она́

_____[4] вступи́тельный экза́мен на бу́дущей неде́ле. Я

наде́юсь, что она́ _____[5] э́тот экза́мен и что её

_____.[6]

Зада́ние 5.1   Prepare a three-minute talk or write a composition, as assigned by your instructor, about your plans to go to college, graduate school, or professional school or about the plans of a friend or friends.

Listening Tasks

The listening text for this unit consists of a conversation between two people who haven't seen each other in a long time. One asks the other about his daughter and learns that she has grown up and is almost ready to graduate from an institute.

PRE-LISTENING TASK

What would your parents tell an old friend of theirs who asks about you? Imagine the friend hasn't seen you since you were twelve years old. What sorts of things would your parents and/or the friend say? Write down at least four likely comments.

LISTENING TASK

Listen to the text and then answer questions 1 through 5 in English and 6 through 10 in Russian.

1. Summarize the dialogue in three or four sentences.
2. What are the names of the two speakers?
3. What is the daughter's name?
4. What is she doing these days?
5. What are her plans? (Answer as fully as possible.)
6. How does the woman indicate that it's been a long time since she and the man have seen each other?
7. How does the woman express surprise at what the daughter is doing? (Find two different expressions that indicate surprise.)
8. What is the woman's appraisal of the daughter's talent?
9. How does the woman ask to visit the man and his family?
10. How does the woman promise to visit the man and his family?

DICTATION

Replay the tape and, as you listen, write out the dialogue in full.

PERFORMANCE

Practice reciting the dialogue.

POST-LISTENING TASK

Using the dialogue as a model, work with a classmate to create and perform your own dialogue in which you do the following: assume the role of one of your parents and an old friend of that parent, inquire about one another's children and their educational/professional status, and express surprise at the passing of time.

CULTURAL PROBLEM

Would an American go through the same process for entering graduate school as that described here? What would be different?

Lexicon: Almost

There are two different ways to express the concept of *almost* in Russian: **почти** and **чуть не** + *past tense*. The first, **почти**, is used for positive situations and contexts, while the second, **чуть не** + *past tense*, is used for negative situations and contexts.

> Светлана Михайловна почти закончила проект: она наверно закончит его завтра.
> *Svetlana Mikhailovna has almost finished the project: she'll probably finish it tomorrow.*

> Александр Анатольевич чуть не упал здесь.
> *Aleksandr Anatol'evich almost fell here.*

Упражнéние 5.2   Fill in the blanks with the correct equivalent of *almost*. You may need to provide the negative particle **не**.

1. Мы _____ провалились на экзамене.

2. Он _____ всё сделал: остаётся совсем немного работы.

3. Я _____ вы́учила все слова́ на за́втра.

4. Све́та _____ забы́ла, что за́втра бу́дет собра́ние в декана́те.

5. Ди́ма _____ получи́л пятёрку: е́сли бы он ещё немно́го бо́льше

   позанима́лся, он бы и получи́л её!

Phonetics and Intonation

Intonation Pattern 1: Simple Declarative Sentences

Intonation pattern 1 features a fall in pitch on the stressed syllable of the word that is at the very center of meaning in the utterance. Once the pitch falls on this syllable it does not rise again.

 Listen to intonation pattern 1 in the sentences on the tape.

1. Я учу́сь в Виско́нсинском университе́те.
2. Я америка́нец/америка́нка.
3. Мои́ роди́тели живу́т в Мичига́не.
4. Ма́ма рабо́тает в э́том институ́те.

In the following sentences, notice how the pitch falls on different words as the center of meaning in the sentence is shifted. The pitch falls on the stressed syllable in the underlined words.

5. <u>Обяза́тельно</u>.
6. Обяза́тельно <u>помо́жет</u>.
7. <u>Со́ня</u> обяза́тельно помо́жет.
8. Со́ня обяза́тельно <u>нам</u> помо́жет.
9. Со́ня обяза́тельно нам помо́жет <u>за́втра ве́чером</u>.
10. Со́ня обяза́тельно нам помо́жет за́втра ве́чером реши́ть <u>э́тот вопро́с</u>.

 SELF-QUIZ

Listen to each statement on the tape and underline the word on which the pitch falls. Then write a question in Russian that might elicit the statement.

1. Уже́ пошла́.
2. Уже́ пошла́ на рабо́ту.
3. В институ́т.
4. Е́дут в институ́т.
5 Е́дут в институ́т ру́сского языка́.
6. Е́дут в институ́т ру́сского языка́ на у́лицу Во́лгина.
7. Не рабо́тает.
8. Сего́дня не рабо́тает.
9. Лифт сего́дня не рабо́тает.
10. Э́тот лифт сего́дня не рабо́тает.

Exercises and Activities

Упражне́ние 5.3 Read the story of the wedding of two Russians living in New York. Choose the correct future-tense form of the verbs in parentheses as required by context.

Ки́ра Медве́дева и То́ля Андре́ев реши́ли пожени́ться: они́ (бу́дут приглаша́ть/пригласи́т)

_____[1] всех родны́х и друзе́й на венча́ние, кото́рое (бу́дет

происходи́ть/произойдёт) _____[2] деся́того а́вгуста в ма́ленькой

це́ркви недалеко́ от кварти́ры Ки́риной ма́тери. По́сле венча́ния бу́дет сва́дебный у́жин в

рестора́не «Москва́». Ки́ра, наве́рно, до́лго (бу́дет ду́мать/поду́мает)

_____[3] обо всех подро́бностях свя́занных со сва́дьбой. Она́ уже́

беспоко́ится о том, как (бу́дут вести́/поведу́т) _____[4] себя́ её

со́бственные роди́тели, кото́рые развели́сь де́сять лет наза́д и о́чень ре́дко ви́дятся друг с

дру́гом. На сва́дьбе они́ (бу́дут ви́деться/уви́дятся) _____[5] в пе́рвый

раз за три го́да. Есте́ственно, Ки́ра бои́тся, что они́ (бу́дут ссо́риться/поссо́рятся)

_____[6] при гостя́х. То́ля стара́ется успока́ивать свою́ неве́сту. Он

уверя́ет, что её роди́тели не (бу́дут руга́ться/поруга́ются) _____[7] ни в

це́ркви, ни в рестора́не. То́ля наде́ется, что Ки́ра (бу́дет понима́ть/поймёт)

_____,[8] что да́же е́сли её роди́тели (бу́дут вести́/поведу́т)

_____[9] себя́ некраси́во, никто́ из госте́й не (бу́дет осужда́ть/осу́дит)

_____[10] Ки́ру и То́лю за поведе́ние Ки́риных роди́телей. Ки́ра

говори́т, что То́ля прав, но всё равно́ она́ (бу́дет успока́иваться/успоко́ится)

_____[11] то́лько по́сле сва́дьбы.

Упражне́ние 5.4 The story of Kira and Tolia's wedding continues. Choose the correct past-tense form of the verbs in parentheses as required by context.

Наконе́ц всё (быва́ло/бы́ло) _____[1] гото́во. То́лины друзья́, Ви́тя и

Оле́г, (стоя́ли/постоя́ли) _____[2] пе́ред це́рковью и

(встреча́ли/встре́тили) _____[3] родны́х и госте́и, кото́рых Ки́ра и

То́ля (приглаша́ли/пригласи́ли) _____[4] на сва́дьбу. То́лин дя́дя,

Михаи́л Петро́вич, (приезжа́л/прие́хал) _____[5] пе́рвым: он

(говори́л/сказа́л) _____,[6] что не (хоте́л/захоте́л)

_____[7] опа́здывать. Он был в джи́нсах и футбо́лке, но нёс с собо́й

чемода́н. Ви́тя и Оле́г (удивля́лись/удиви́лись) _____[8] тому́, что

Михаи́л Петро́вич был в тако́й просто́й оде́жде и

(приезжа́л/прие́хал) _____⁹ с чемода́ном. Как то́лько Михаи́л

Петро́вич (знако́мился/познако́мился) _____¹⁰ с Ви́тей и Оле́гом, он

(спра́шивал/спроси́л) _____,¹¹ где мо́жно переоде́ться. Ему́

говори́ли/сказа́ли _____,¹² что наве́рно мо́жно переоде́тбся в тчале́те

·в кафе́ за угло́м.

Упражне́ние 5.5   The story of Kira and Tolia's wedding continues. Choose the correct past-tense form of the verbs in parentheses as required by context.

Че́рез де́сять мину́т Михаи́л Петро́вич (выходи́л/вы́шел) _____¹ из

кафе́ в элега́нтном се́ром костю́ме. В э́то вре́мя (приходи́ла/пришла́)

_____² Ки́рина ма́ма, Кла́вдия Ива́новна. (Приходи́л/пришёл)

_____³ и свяще́нник, с кото́рым Кла́вдия Ива́новна

(начина́ла/начала́) _____⁴ говори́ть об обря́де венча́ния в

правосла́вной це́ркви. Пока́ они́ увлечённо (говори́ли/поговори́ли)

_____⁵ на э́ту те́му, (приходи́л/пришёл) _____⁶

Ки́рин оте́ц, Алекса́ндр Па́влович. Он о́чень ти́хо (входи́л/вошёл)

_____⁷ в це́рковь и (остана́вливался/останови́лся)

_____⁸ спра́ва. Он _____⁹ (говори́л/сказа́л)

Ви́те, что специа́льно не (здоро́вался/поздоро́вался) _____¹⁰ с

бы́вшей жено́й, потому́ что не (хоте́л/захоте́л) _____¹¹ меша́ть ей.

Упражне́ние 5.6   The story of Kira and Tolia's wedding continues. Choose the correct past-tense form of the verbs in parentheses as required by context.

Наконе́ц (приходи́ли/пришли́) _____¹ Ки́ра и То́ля: Ки́ра в бе́лом

пла́тье, а То́ля в си́нем костю́ме. Все го́сти (входи́ли/вошли́) _____² в

це́рковь и (смотре́ли/посмотре́ли) _____³ на ико́ны. Че́рез не́сколько

мину́т (начина́лось/начало́сь) _____⁴ венча́ние. Свяще́нник

(говори́л/поговори́л) _____⁵ гро́мко, что́бы всем бы́ло слы́шно. Ки́ра

то́же (отвеча́ла/отве́тила) _____⁶ гро́мко, но То́ля

(говори́л/поговори́л) _____⁷ о́чень ти́хо. Каза́лось, что он

(пла́кал/запла́кал) _____⁸ от сча́стья во вре́мя венча́ния. Когда́

слу́жба (зака́нчивалась/зако́нчилась) _____⁹ и То́ля и Ки́ра

(станови́лись/ста́ли) _____¹⁰ му́жем и жено́й, вдруг

(прибегáл/прибежáл) _____[11] их друг, Серёжа: он

(опáздывал/опоздáл) _____[12]!

Упражнéние 5.7 The story of Kira and Tolia's wedding continues. Choose the correct past-tense form of the verbs in parentheses as required by context.

Серёжа был в ýжасе и дóлго (извиня́лся/извини́лся) _____,[1] говоря́,

что он не (ви́дел/уви́дел) _____[2] ресторáн на проспéкте, где нýжно

бы́ло поверну́ть напрáво. Он (объясня́л/объясни́л) _____,[3] что он

цéлый час (искáл/поискáл) _____[4] цéрковь в другóм райóне, покá не

(понимáл/пóнял) _____,[5] где он (дéлал/сдéлал) _____[6] оши́бку. Молодожёны (предлагáли/предложи́ли)

_____[7] своемý дрýгу посмотрéть видеозáпись их бракосочетáния,

котóрую (дéлала/сдéлала) _____[8] их подрýга, Тáня, и все

(отправля́лись/отпрáвились) _____[9] на нáбережную

фотографи́роваться.

Упражнéние 5.8 The following are some of the comments made by guests at the party Kira and Tolia held at the restaurant after the wedding ceremony. Choose the correct negative past-tense form of the verbs in parentheses as required by context.

1. Михаи́л Петрóвич не (спрáшивал/спроси́л) _____ об обря́де

   венчáния: он хотéл узнáть, где мóжно переодевáться.

2. Ки́рин отéц не (здорóвался/поздорóвался) _____ с Ки́риной

   мáтерью.

3. Ки́рины роди́тели не (ссóрились/поссóрились) _____ на свáдьбе

   своéй дóчери.

4. Серёжа не (ви́дел/уви́дел) _____ ресторáн, у котóрого он дóлжен

   был поверну́ть напрáво.

5. Серёжа не (приезжáл/приéхал) _____ вóвремя на свáдьбу.

6. Ви́тя и Олéг не (замечáли/замéтили) _____, что Серёжа ещё не

   (приезжáл/приéхал) _____, когдá началáсь свáдьба.

7. Когдá все вошли́ в цéрковь, никтó не (дýмал/подýмал) _____ о

   том, что Серёжи ещё нет.

8. Тóля не (говори́л/поговори́л) _____ грóмко во врéмя венчáния.

9. Ки́ра не (плáкала/заплáкала) _____ во врéмя венчáния.

10. Тóля рад, что в концé концóв Кúра не (обижáлась/обúделась)

_____ на свойх родúтелей.

Упражнéние 5.9 Here are some of the questions asked by guests at Kira and Tolia's wedding party at the restaurant. Choose the correct infinitive in parentheses as required by context.

1. Когдá молодожёны должны́ (уезжáть/уéхать) _____ в свáдебное

   путешéствие?

2. Когдá наконéц начнýт (подавáть/подáть) _____ обéд?

3. Почемý оркéстр кóнчил (игрáть/поигрáть) _____?

4. Тут мóжно (курúть/покурúть) _____?

5. Рáзве в э́том зáле нельзя́ (танцевáть/потанцевáть) _____?

6. Почемý Кúра и Тóля бýдут продолжáть (жить/пожúть) _____

   вмéсте с Тóлиными родúтелями?

7. Вам нрáвится (танцевáть/потанцевáть) _____ под такýю мýзыку?

8. Кто помóжет молодожёнам (добирáться/добрáться) _____ до

   аэропóрта пóсле свáдьбы?

9. Не хотúте ли вы (вы́ходить/вы́йти) _____ из зáла и тúхо

   (говорúть/поговорúть) _____ обо всём?

10. Зачéм нам (выходúть/вы́йти) _____, когдá мóжно и тут хорошó

    (говорúть/поговорúть) _____?

Bonus Question: Try to determine who among the identified guests might have posed some or all of the preceding questions and to whom the questions might have been addressed.

Фóто-задáние Look at the photograph on the first page of this unit in the textbook. Write a paragraph or prepare a presentation, as assigned by your instructor, describing the party at which this photograph was taken.

Glossary

вдруг	*suddenly (usually with perfective)*
всегдá	*always (usually with imperfective)*
дóлго	*for a long time (usually with imperfective)*
допускáть (I) /допустúть (II) [, что...]: допускáю, допускáешь, допускáют, допускáй(те)!; допущý, допýстишь, допýстят, допустú(те)!	*to assume, suppose that . . .*
допýстим	*let's suppose . . .*

заполня́ть (I) /запо́лнить (II) [анке́ту]:
заполня́ю, заполня́ешь, заполня́ют, заполня́й(те)!; запо́лню,
запо́лнишь, запо́лнят, запо́лни(те)!

to fill out [a form]

иногда́

*sometimes (usually with
imperfective)*

когда́–нибудь

sometime

конча́ть (I) /ко́нчить (II) [де́лать что́–нибудь]:
конча́ю, конча́ешь, конча́ют, конча́й(те)!; ко́нчу, ко́нчишь,
ко́нчат, ко́нчи(те)!

to finish doing something

начина́ть (I) /нача́ть (I) [де́лать что́–нибудь]:
начина́ю, начина́ешь, начина́ют, начина́й(те)!; начну́,
начнёшь, начну́т, начни́(те)! на́чал, начала́, на́чали

to begin doing something

наконе́ц

*finally (usually with
perfective)*

никогда́

never

печа́тать/на– (I) [что?]:
печа́таю, печа́таешь, печа́тают, печа́тай(те)!

to type [what?]

подава́ть (I) /пода́ть (*) [заявле́ние]:
подаю́, подаёшь, подаю́т, подава́й(те)!; пода́м, пода́шь,
пода́ст, подади́м, подади́те, подаду́т, пода́й(те)! по́дал,
подала́, по́дали

to submit [an application]

поступа́ть (I) /поступи́ть (II) [куда́?]:
поступа́ю, поступа́ешь, поступа́ют, поступа́й(те)!; поступлю́,
посту́пишь, посту́пят, поступи́(те)!

*to apply to/enroll in
[where?]*

предполага́ть (I) /предположи́ть (II) [что?]:
предполага́ю, предполага́ешь, предполага́ют; предположу́,
предположи́шь, предполо́жат

to assume

предположи́м

let's assume . . .

принима́ть (I) /приня́ть (I) [кого́? куда́?]:
принима́ю, принима́ешь, принима́ют, принима́й(те)!; приму́,
при́мешь, при́мут, прими́(те)! при́нял, приняла́, при́няли

to accept [whom? where?]

привыка́ть (I) /привы́кнуть (I) [к кому́? чему́?]:
привыка́ю, привыка́ешь, привыка́ют, привыка́й(те);
привы́кну, привы́кнешь, привы́кнут, привы́кни(те)!
привы́к, привы́кла, привы́кли

*to get used [to whom?
what?]*

продолжа́ть (I) /продо́лжить (II) [де́лать что́–нибудь]:
продолжа́ю, продолжа́ешь, продолжа́ют, продолжа́й(те)!;
продо́лжу, продо́лжишь, продо́лжат, продо́лжи(те)!

*to continue doing
something*

ре́дко

*infrequently (usually with
imperfective)*

сдава́ть (I) /сдать (*) экза́мен [куда́?]:
сдаю́, сдаёшь, сдаю́т, сдава́й(те)!; сдам, сдашь, сдаст,
сдади́м, сдади́те, сдаду́т, сдал, сдала́, сда́ли

*to take an exam/to pass an
exam [entrance exam
into what?]*

сказа́ть (I) [что? кому́?]:
    скажу́, ска́жешь, ска́жут

to say

ска́жем

let's say . . .

убира́ть (I) /убра́ть (I) [что?]:
    убира́ю, убира́ешь, убира́ют, убира́й(те)!; уберу́, уберёшь,
    уберу́т, убери́(те)! убра́л, убрала́, убра́ли

to clean something up in the sense of straightening up and/or removing things

учи́ться/на– (II) [де́лать что?]:
    учу́сь, у́чишься, у́чатся, учи́сь! учи́тесь!

to learn to do something

це́лую неде́лю, це́лый ме́сяц, це́лый день

a whole week, month, day (used with the imperfective)

ча́сто

frequently (used with the imperfective)

UNIT 6

Lexicon: Hospitality

Russians use certain terms and expressions to greet and entertain guests in their homes. When you visit a Russian friend, you will surely experience the warmth and hospitality for which Russians are famous. Remember, however, never to offer to shake hands over the threshold of someone's home: this is a violation of Russian custom. If you try to do this, your Russian hosts may pull you inside before shaking your hand. Also remember that it is a tradition to bring a small gift such as flowers, candy or cookies, fresh fruit, tea or coffee, wine or cognac, or a book. If you bring flowers, remember to bring an odd number of them, as an even number is considered bad luck.

Ходи́ть в го́сти, быть в гостя́х
To go visiting, to be visiting with friends

> Ру́сские о́чень лю́бят ходи́ть в го́сти.
> *Russians love to go visiting friends.*

> Ми́ша вчера́ был в гостя́х у Петро́вых.
> *Yesterday Misha visited with the Petrovs.*

Заходи́ть/зайти́ [к кому́? куда́?]
To drop by at someone's home

> Заходи́те к нам за́втра, пожа́луйста, о́коло семи́.
> *Please drop by our place tomorrow around 7 o'clock.*

Раздева́ться/разде́ться
To take off one's outer clothing

> Здра́вствуйте! Раздева́йтесь, пожа́луйста!
> *Hello! Please take off your coat and hat!*

Снима́ть/снять о́бувь, ту́фли
To take off one's shoes

> Сними́те, пожа́луйста, ту́фли. Вот вам та́почки.
> *Please take off your shoes. Here are some slippers for you.*

Проходи́ть/пройти́ [куда́?]
To walk through (from the entrance hall to the living room or kitchen)

> Здра́вствуйте! Проходи́те, пожа́луйста!
> *Hello! Please come in!*

Передава́ть/переда́ть [что? кому́? от кого́?]
To convey a greeting or gift from someone to someone else

> Переда́йте ва́шим роди́телям большо́й приве́т от нас.
> *Please give your parents a big hello from us.*

Садиться/сесть за стол
To sit down at the table

> Обед готов. Садитесь, пожалуйста, за стол!
> *Dinner is ready. Please sit down at the table!*

Сидеть/по– за столом
To be seated at the table

> Когда мы пришли, все гости уже сидели за столом.
> *When we arrived, all the guests were already seated at the table.*

Брать/взять [что? чего?]
To take something (sometimes used with the partitive genitive, described in Unit 8 of your textbook)

> Берите, пожалуйста, конфеты.
> *Please take some candies.*

Есть/съесть [что?]
To eat something

> Не стесняйтесь: ешьте пирог!
> *Don't be ashamed: eat some pie!*

Пить/выпить [что? за кого? что?]
To drink something for something or someone (in the sense of a toast)

> Давайте выпьем за ваше здоровье!
> *Let's drink to your health!*

> Извините, но я не пью водку.
> *Excuse me, but I don't drink vodka.*

Предлагать/предложить тост [за что? кого?]
To make or propose a toast for something or someone

> Я хочу предложить тост за Сашу.
> *I want to make a toast for Sasha.*

> Я предлагаю тост за то, чтобы всё хорошо получилось.
> *I propose a toast: may everything turn out okay.*

Упражнение 6.1 Fill in the blanks with the correct word or expression, using the following cues, though not necessarily in this order: *walked through, were visiting, to drink, propose, went visiting, take off, to eat, dropped by, sit down, take off our coats.*

Вчера мы _____[1] к Беловым. Как только мы вошли в квартиру,

Марина Белова воскликнула: «Как хорошо, что вы _____[2]!» Она

попросила нас _____·_____[3] и _____[4] туфли. Она

дала нам хорошие, тёплые тапочки и сказала, чтобы мы _____[5] в

комнату. Там все уже _____[6] за столом. Борис сказал, — Что же вы

стесняетесь?! _____[7] за стол! Я _____[8] тост за

наших новых друзей! Итак, мы начали _____[9] и

_____.[10] Ско́лько всего́ бы́ло на столе́! Мы до́лго _____

_____[11] у Бе́ловых и верну́лись домо́й о́чень по́здно.

Зада́ние 6.1   Prepare a three-minute talk or write a composition, as assigned by your instructor, about how you would entertain a Russian friend in your home or dorm. Try to use as many hospitality words as you can.

Зада́ние 6.2   Prepare a three-minute talk or write a composition, as assigned by your instructor, describing what some strange hosts, such as the Addams family, want(ed) their guests to do.

Фо́то-зада́ние   Look at the photograph on the first page of this unit in the textbook. Write a paragraph or prepare a presentation, as assigned by your instructor, describing the dinner party in the picture.

Listening Tasks

The listening text for this unit consists of a conversation about the strangeness of foreigners and their behavior.

PRE-LISTENING TASK

How might people in other countries think Americans and their behavior are strange? Make a list of things that Americans consider *normal* but people in Russia, Japan, Senegal, or Venezuela might not.

LISTENING TASK

Listen to the text and answer questions 1 through 5 in English and 6 through 10 in Russian.

1. Summarize the dialogue in two or three sentences.
2. What are the names of the two speakers?
3. Which speaker is more understanding or tolerant of foreigners' "strange ways"?
4. Which speaker is less understanding?
5. Name three things the Americans did that surprised the Russians.
6. What is the Russian expression meaning *offering one's hand [in order to shake hands]*? (Provide both imperfective and perfective verbs.)
7. What is the Russian expression meaning *customary* or *accepted*?
8. What is the Russian expression meaning *to pay attention to something*?
9. How does one speaker complain that the other is being too harsh on the Americans?
10. What is the Russian equivalent of the expression *this is done throughout the world*?

DICTATION

Replay the tape and, as you listen, write out the dialogue in full.

PERFORMANCE

Create a dialogue of your own, using the one on the tape as a model. Then perform it with a classmate.

POST-LISTENING TASK

Using the dialogue as a model, work with one or more classmates to create and perform your own dialogue in which you play Americans talking about the strange behavior of a visiting Russian acquaintance.

CULTURAL PROBLEM

What might be some of the beliefs, customs, or superstitions underlying the Russian behavior that the American students violated as discussed in the dialogue?

Phonetics and Intonation

Intonation Pattern 2: Questions with a Question Word and Other Constructions

In Russian, questions with a question word (such as **кто, что, где, куда, почему, когда** and **зачём**) require intonation pattern 2. In this pattern, the pitch of the intonation rises on the stressed syllable of the question word and then falls immediately. This is very different from English interrogative intonation: English questions with a question word have a rising pitch at the end of the question. For example, in the question, *When are they coming?* the pitch rises on the word *coming*, however, in the Russian question **Когда они придут?** the pitch rises on the second (stressed) syllable of the question word **когда**, and falls immediately for the rest of the question.

Intonation pattern 2 is used to indicate:

- Semantic emphasis of a particular word in a sentence; for example, in the sentence **Он уже ушёл!** the pattern emphasizes the meaning of the word **ушёл**.
- Imperatives, especially for hospitality imperatives such as **Здравствуйте! Садитесь!**
- Either/or expressions; for example, in the sentence **Она зайдёт в четверг или в пятницу?** the pattern is used for the second item in a pair of either/or options.
- Expressions of surprise, such as **неужели!**
- Pointing something out with the particle **вот!**
- Expressions with **ведь, же,** and **однако.**

Listen to the questions and statements on the tape and practice using intonation pattern 2.

RUSSIAN QUESTION OR STATEMENT

1. **Кто** она?
2. **Где** работает Паша?
3. **Когда** они придут?
4. **Что** это такое?
5. **Как** это сказать по-русски?
6. **Как** зовут её **отца?**
7. **Чья** это книга?
8. **Куда** вы идёте?
9. **Здравствуйте!**
10. **Садитесь!**
11. **Вот** газета!
12. **Сегодня** не можешь? Тогда во вторник или в среду?
13. Мы опоздали! Поезд уже **ушёл!**
14. **Неужели** это ваш сын?
15. Ведь он совсем ничего не **знает!**

SELF-QUIZ

Listen to the sentences on the tape and circle the word or words that feature intonation pattern 2.

1. **Куда** вы ездили?
2. **Куда** вы ездили в прошлом году?

3. Здра́вствуйте, Тама́ра Васи́льевна!
4. Раздева́йтесь и проходи́те, пожа́луйста!
5. Неуже́ли э́то ва́ша дочь?
6. В пя́тницу не смо́жете? Вы смо́жете э́то сде́лать в суббо́ту и́ли в воскресе́нье?
7. Вот Ива́н!
8. Она́ говори́т по–францу́ски и́ли по–испа́нски?
9. Ведь она́ говори́т и по–францу́зски, и по–испа́нски!
10. Как зову́т его́ сестру́?
11. Бо́льше нет биле́тов!?
12. Ле́кция уже́ начала́сь!
13. Ведь они́ уже́ смотре́ли э́тот фильм!
14. Она́ счита́ет, одна́ко, что мо́жно посмотре́ть его́ ещё раз.
15. Он же сказа́л, что придёт!

Exercises and Activities

Упражне́ние 6.2   Complete the chart by providing the impertive form of each verb as in the example.

INFINITIVE	ОНИ́ FORM	IMPERATIVE
Образе́ц: рассказа́ть	расска́жут	расскажи́(те)
1. не пла́кать	не пла́чут	_____
2. заплати́ть	запла́тят	_____
3. переписа́ть	перепи́шут	_____
4. стать	ста́нут	_____
5. потанцева́ть	потанцу́ют	_____
6. познако́мить	познако́мят	_____
7. спроси́ть	спро́сят	_____
8. отве́тить	отве́тят	_____
9. здра́вствовать	здра́вствуют	_____
10. верну́ться	верну́тся	_____
11. продава́ть	продаю́т	_____
12. прода́ть	продаду́т	_____
13. не крича́ть	не крича́т	_____
14. не возвраща́ться	не возвраща́ются	_____

Упражне́ние 6.3   Choose the correct aspectual form of the imperative from the verbs in parentheses. Then consult your textbook (pages 66–67) to identify which rule, 1 or 2, or which exception, a, b, or c, supports your choice. Note that the perfective imperative is always first in each pair.

1. (Напиши́те/Пиши́те) письмо́ дире́ктору.
2. (Позвони́те/Звони́те) Кири́ллу Андре́еву на рабо́ту.
3. Не (забу́дьте/забыва́йте) де́ньги!

4. Не (поигра́йте/игра́йте) в америка́нский футбо́л: э́то опа́сный спорт.
5. (Поигра́йте/Игра́йте) в америка́нский футбо́л: э́то – интере́сный спорт!
6. (Поигра́йте/Игра́йте) в футбо́л с на́ми сего́дня! Пого́да – прекра́сная!
7. (Спо́йте/По́йте) с на́ми в хо́ре.
8. Не (скажи́те/говори́те) ему́ об э́том, пожа́луйста!

 Упражне́ние 6.4 Translate the following passage into idiomatic English. Use the transliteration guide in the Appendix to transliterate Russian names.

Любо́вь Влади́мировна сказа́ла, что́бы мы пригласи́ли америка́нских студе́нтов на ве́чер поэ́зии. Я попроси́ла Серге́я Земцо́вского позвони́ть преподава́телям, что́бы узна́ть, когда́ лу́чше провести́ э́тот ве́чер. Преподава́тели сказа́ли Серге́ю, что студе́нты свобо́дны в сре́ду по́сле пяти́, и что четве́рг вообще́ свобо́дный день. Поэ́тому мы реши́ли устро́ить ве́чер в сре́ду ве́чером на сле́дующей неде́ле. Пото́м мы все собрали́сь на ка́федре и реши́ли, кто бу́дет занима́ться ра́зными вопро́сами организа́ции ве́чера.

— Дава́йте пригласи́м и не́мцев и францу́зов.

— Нет, дава́йте лу́чше не приглаша́ть други́х студе́нтов. Пусть э́то бу́дет ве́чер то́лько для америка́нских студе́нтов.

— Ла́дно. Константи́н Миха́йлович! Бу́дьте добры́! Позвони́те руководи́телю америка́нской гру́ппы и сообщи́те ей, что ве́чер поэ́зии состои́тся в сре́ду.

— Хорошо́, позвоню́.

— Еле́на Ильи́нична, пожа́луйста, напиши́те объявле́ние для студе́нтов, кото́рую мо́жно бу́дет раздава́ть на заня́тиях.

— Пусть Алекса́ндр Ива́нович его́ напи́шет. Он лу́чше меня́ разбира́ется в э́том.

— Хорошо́, я согла́сен.

— Ита́к, ну́жно соста́вить програ́мму ве́чера.

— Дава́йте мы не бу́дем занима́ться э́тим вопро́сом. Пусть лу́чше Дми́трий Константи́нович и Верони́ка Никола́евна вме́сте реша́т э́тот вопро́с.

— Дми́трий Константи́нович и Верони́ка Никола́евна! Вы согла́сны с э́тим предложе́нием?

— Согла́сны.

— Посиди́те, поговори́те, поду́майте и предложи́те спи́сок поэ́тов и конкре́тных стихотворе́ний, пожа́луйста. Учти́те, пожа́луйста, что студе́нты наве́рно уже́ чита́ли, и не ограни́чивайтесь в отбо́ре поэ́тов.

— И не забу́дьте, что Любо́вь Влади́мировна о́чень лю́бит Маяко́вского.

— Да что вы! Я не хоте́ла, что́бы ду́мали то́лько обо мне. Де́лайте, как хоти́те!

Упражне́ние 6.5 Fill in the blanks with the correct form of one of the verbs in parentheses. Remember that after **дава́йте**, perfective verbs are in the **мы** form, while imperfective verbs take the infinitive or **бу́дем** + *infinitive*.

1. Дава́йте сейча́с же (написа́ть/писа́ть) _____ письмо́ Татья́не

   Кири́лловне.

2. Дава́йте не (написа́ть/писа́ть) _____ письмо́ Татья́не

   Кири́лловне сейча́с. Дава́йте (подожда́ть/ждать) _____, пока́ не

   вернётся Екатери́на Станисла́вовна.

3. Дава́йте тогда́ (перечита́ть/перечи́тывать) _____ письмо́ от

   Татья́ны Кири́лловны, пока́ не вернётся Екатери́на Станисла́вовна.

4. Дава́йте не (перечита́ть/перечи́тывать) _____ письмо́ от Татья́ны

   Кири́лловны; дава́йте лу́чше (найти́/находи́ть) _____ все

   докуме́нты, кото́рые нам нужны́, и (соста́вить/составля́ть) _____

   план сле́дующего прое́кта.

5. Дава́йте я (найти́/находи́ть) _____ докуме́нты, но пусть Анто́н

   Анато́льевич (соста́вить/составля́ть) _____ план.

6. Нет, пусть Мари́на Дми́триевна и Па́вел Васи́льевич (соста́вить/составля́ть)

   _____ э́тот план. Пусть Анто́н Анато́льевич

   (пригото́вить/гото́вить) _____ ко́фе!

7. Анто́н Анато́льевич! Не (пригото́вить/гото́вить) _____ ко́фе в

   э́той кофева́рке! Она́ слома́лась! (Пригото́вить/Гото́вить) _____

   его́ в но́вой кофева́рке, кото́рая на ве́рхней по́лке.

Упражне́ние 6.6 Translate the following passage into Russian.

> "Please tell me, have you invited the Russian students to visit with us?"
> "Yes. I told them not to avoid us, to visit us more often (**ча́ще**)."
> "When they were visiting with us on Tuesday I told them to eat and drink."
> "What an evening that was! I remember, you said 'Let's drink to [our] meeting!'"
> "Before leaving (**russian**) the Russian students, they began . . ."
> "Yes, and you said, 'Let's speak only Russian tonight!'"
> "But then Kostia said, 'Let's not speak Russian tonight. Let's speak English.'"
> "Masha said, 'Let Kostia speak English while we will speak Russian.'"
> "Then Kostia said, 'All right. Let me speak English, while everyone else speaks Russian.'"
> "We made toasts and talked very late."
> "Before leaving (**пре́жде чем уйти́**), the Russian students, they began to clean up. We told
> them, 'Don't clean up! We'll clean everything up!'"
> "What an evening that was!"

Зада́ние 6.3 Choose five verbs in **Упражне́ние 6.2** and write a story of at least three paragraphs using those verbs in an imperative form.

Зада́ние 6.4 Imagine that you are the head of a family and that you are going away for a few days on a business trip. Prepare a three-minute talk or write a composition, as assigned by your instructor, in which you leave instructions to the other members of your family about what they should or should not do while you are gone. Mention at least three "one-time" tasks that must be completed in your absence, as well as at least three "frequent" tasks that must be completed once daily, if not more frequently.

Glossary

\# брать (I) /взять (I) [что? чего́?]:   *to take*
   беру́, берёшь, беру́т, бери́(те)! брал, брала́, бра́ли; возьму́,
   возьмёшь, возьму́т, возьми́(те)! взял, взяла́, взя́ли

быть (I) в гостях:
бу́ду, бу́дешь, бу́дут, бу́дь(те)! был, была́, бы́ли

to be visiting with friends

включа́ть (I) /включи́ть (II) [что? во что?]:
включа́ю, включа́ешь, включа́ют, включа́й(те)!; включу́,
включи́шь, включа́т, включи́(те)!

to turn on (e.g., the television or any electrical mechanism) or to include something in something else

говори́ть (II) /сказа́ть (I) [кому́, что́бы... + *past tense*]:
говорю́, говори́шь, говоря́т, говори́(те)!; скажу́, ска́жешь,
ска́жут, скажи́(те)!

to tell someone to do something

есть (*) /съесть (*) [что?]:
ем, ешь, ест, еди́м, еди́те, едя́т, ешь(те)!

to eat

забыва́ть (I) /забы́ть (I) [кого́? что? о ком? о чём?]:
забыва́ю, забыва́ешь, забыва́ют, забыва́й(те)!; забу́ду,
забу́дешь, забу́дут, забу́дь(те)!

to forget someone or something or about someone or something

заходи́ть (II) /зайти́ (I) [к кому́? куда́?]:
захожу́, захо́дишь, захо́дят, заходи́(те)!; зайду́, зайдёшь,
зайду́т, зайди́(те)! зашёл, зашла́, зашли́

to drop in at someone's home

избега́ть (I) /избежа́ть (*) [кого́? чего́?]:
избега́ю, избега́ешь, избега́ют, избега́й(те)!; избегу́,
избежи́шь, избежи́т, избежи́м, избежи́те, избегу́т,
избеги́(те)!

to avoid something or someone

ограни́чивать (I) /ограни́чить (II) [что?]:
ограни́чиваю, ограни́чиваешь, ограни́чивают,
ограни́чивай(те)!; ограни́чу, ограни́чишь, ограни́чат,
ограни́чь(те)!

to limit or restrict something

передава́ть (I) /переда́ть (*) [что? кому́? от кого́?]:
передаю́, передаёшь, передаю́т, передава́й(те)!; переда́м,
переда́шь, переда́ст, передади́м, передади́те, передаду́т,
переда́й(те)! пе́редал, передала́, пе́редали

to convey or pass something on to someone from someone else (note 2 possible stress options in past tense perf.)

пить/вы́– (I) [что? за кого́? что?]:
пью, пьёшь, пьют, пей(те)!; пил, пила́, пи́ли

to drink (for someone or something)

предлага́ть (I) /предложи́ть (II) [тост за кого́? что?]:
предлага́ю, предлага́ешь, предлага́ют, предлага́й(те)!;
предложу́, предло́жишь, предло́жат, предложи́(те)!

to make or propose a toast for someone or something

проходи́ть (II) /пройти́ (I) [куда́?]:
прохожу́, прохо́дишь, прохо́дят, проходи́(те)!; пройду́,
пройдёшь, пройду́т, пройди́(те)! прошёл, прошла́, прошли́

to walk through (from an entranceway to another room in a home)

раздева́ться (I) /разде́ться (I):
раздева́юсь, раздева́ешься, раздева́ются, раздева́йся!
раздева́йтесь!; разде́нусь, разде́нешься, разде́нутся,
разде́нься! разде́ньтесь!

to take off one's outer clothes

сади́ться (II) /сесть (I) за стол:
сажу́сь, сади́шься, садя́тся, сади́сь! сади́тесь!; ся́ду,
ся́дешь, ся́дут, ся́дь(те)! [*This command is often rude.*]

to take a seat at a table

сиде́ть/по– (II) за столо́м:
сижу́, сиди́шь, сидя́т, сиди́(те)! [*This command means: don't get up from your seated position!*]

to be seated at a table

снима́ть (I) /снять (I) [ту́фли]:
снима́ю, снима́ешь, снима́ют, снима́й(те)!; сниму́, сни́мешь, сни́мут, сними́(те)! снял, сняла́, сня́ли

to take off [one's shoes]

·убира́ть (I) /убра́ть (I):
убира́ю, убира́ешь, убира́ют, убира́й(те)!; уберу́, уберёшь, уберу́т, убери́(те)! убра́л, убрала́, убра́ли

to clean or straighten up

увели́чивать (I) /увели́чить (II) [что?]:
увели́чиваю, увели́чиваешь, увели́чивают, увели́чивай(те)!; увели́чу, увели́чишь, увели́чат, увели́чь(те)!

to increase something

учи́тывать (I) /уче́сть (I) [что?]:
учи́тываю, учи́тываешь, учи́тывают, учи́тывай(те)!; учту́, учтёшь, учту́т, учти́(те)! учёл, учла́, учли́

to bear or keep something in mind, to be aware of something

уменьша́ть (I) /уме́ньшить (II) [что?]:
уменьша́ю, уменьша́ешь, уменьша́ют, уменьша́й(те)!; уме́ньшу, уме́ньшишь, уме́ньшат, уме́ньши(те)!

to reduce something

ходи́ть в го́сти:
хожу́, хо́дишь, хо́дят, ходи́(те)!

to go visiting friends

хоте́ть/за– (*) [что, де́лать/с- что, что́бы кто... + *past tense*]:
хочу́, хо́чешь, хо́чет, хоти́м, хоти́те, хотя́т

to want something, to want to do something, to want someone to do something

UNIT 7

Lexicon: Shopping for Food and Ordering Food

Here are some of the expressions you may need to shop for food and to order food in restaurants.

Взвéшивать/взвéсить [что?]
To weigh out (an amount of food)

Продавéц взвéшивает огурцы́ для покупáтеля.
The salesman is weighing out cucumbers for the customer.

Взвéсьте, пожáлуйста, три килó апельси́нов.
Please weigh out three kilos of oranges for me.

Магази́н (в), ры́нок (на)
Store, market

В продовóльственных магази́нах появи́лось мнóго продýктов.
A lot of goods have appeared in the grocery stores.

Цéны на ры́нке остáлись óчень высóкими.
Prices at the market have remained very high.

Скóлько стóит... ?
How much does it cost?

— Скóлько стóит эта буты́лка пепси–кóлы?
How much does this bottle of Pepsi cost?

— Дéсять (ты́сяч) пятьсóт пятьдесят [рублéй].
Ten (thousand) five hundred fifty [rubles].

Сдáча, мéлочь, монéта
Change from a purchase, small change, coin(s)

Вы мне дáли дéсять ты́сяч рублéй. Вот вáша сдáча.
You gave me ten thousand rubles. Here's your change.

Нет ли у вас мéлочи? Хочý купи́ть жетóн для телефóна.
Do you have any change? I want to buy a token for the (public) telephone.

Скóлько у вас краси́вых инострáнных монéт! Давнó собирáете?
You have so many beautiful foreign coins. Have you been collecting (them) for long?

Размéнивать/разменя́ть дéньги
To change money within a currency

Вы не разменя́ете мне пятьсóт ты́сяч рублéй?
Do you have change for five hundred thousand rubles?

Помéнивать/поменя́ть дéньги
To change money from one currency to another

Вы не поменя́ете сто дóлларов США?
Can you change one hundred U.S. dollars for me?

Цéны в дóлларах и́ли в рубля́х
Prices in dollars or rubles

— Цéны в э́том магази́не в дóлларах и́ли в рубля́х?
Are the prices in this store in dollars or in rubles?

— Цéны у нас напи́саны в дóлларах, но плáтят рубля́ми по кýрсу.
The prices are written in dollars, but one pays in rubles according to the current exchange rate.

Плати́ть/за– [скóлько? за что? кудá?]
To pay how much for something and where to pay

— Кудá мне заплати́ть?
Where should I pay?
— Заплати́те в кáссу.
Pay at the cashier's.

Едá
Food (as a category of things vs. clothing and shelter)

Человéку же нужнá едá!
A person needs food!

Пи́ща
Food (as nourishment)

Пи́ща в америкáнских забегáловках óчень жи́рная.
The food in American fast-food restaurants is very fatty.

Продýкты
Food items, groceries

Мы зайдём в магази́н за продýктами, а потóм пойдём домóй.
We'll stop in at the store for some groceries, and then we'll go home.

Покупáть/купи́ть [что? где? в магази́не? на ры́нке?]
To buy something

Я обы́чно покупáю молóчные продýкты в магази́не на Тверскóй.
I usually buy dairy products in a store on Tverskaia Street.

Закáзывать/заказáть, брать/взять [что? где?]
To order something

Я обы́чно закáзываю блины́ в э́том ресторáне.
I usually order bliny in this restaurant.

На пéрвое, на вторóе [горя́чее], на трéтье [слáдкое]
For the first course, entrée, dessert

Я возьмý салáт по–москóвски на пéрвое, кýрицу по–ки́евски на вторóе, морóженое на трéтье.
I'll order Moscow salad for my appetizer, chicken á la Kiev for my main course, and ice cream for dessert.

Официáнт -ка, счёт, с вас..., чаевы́е
Waiter/waitress, bill (in a restaurant), you owe . . ., tip

Бýдьте добры́, принеси́те, пожáлуйста, счёт.
Please bring the bill.

Вот, пожа́луйста, счёт: с вас сто два́дцать ты́сяч три́ста пятьдеся́т рубле́й.
Here's the bill: it comes to 120,350 rubles.

Официа́нт хорошо́ рабо́тал сего́дня: дава́йте оста́вим ему́ хоро́шие чаевы́е.
The waiter worked well today: let's give him a good tip.

Упражне́ние 7.1 Fill in the blanks with the correct word or phrase, using the following cues, though not necessarily in this order: *the bill, buys, change (from his purchase), changes, for dessert, drink, market, ordered (twice), will take, the waiter, was weighing out.*

Оле́г хо́чет пригото́вить большо́й обе́д для свои́х друзе́й: он _____¹

100 до́лларов США на рубли́ и идёт на _____.² Там он

_____³ о́вощи, фру́кты, моло́чные проду́кты и говя́дину. Продаве́ц,

кото́рый _____⁴ капу́сту и лук для друго́го клие́нта, напо́мнил Оле́гу,

что он забы́л _____.⁵ До́ма Оле́г гото́вит о́вощи на пару́, жа́рит

говя́дину. Обе́д гото́в, но где друзья́? Они́ заказа́ли стол в рестора́не «Пра́га»! Оле́г

побежа́л в рестора́н и нашёл свои́х друзе́й. Они́ уже́ _____⁶ обе́д, но

ещё не на́чали обе́дать. Оле́г _____⁷ сала́т по–моско́вски, ку́рицу по–

ки́евски, моро́женое. _____⁸ спроси́л, что он бу́дет (*drink*)

_____?⁹ Оле́г сказа́л, что _____¹⁰ во́дку. Всё

хорошо́ обе́дали и бы́ли в хоро́шем настрое́нии, но пото́м принесли́

_____¡¹¹

Зада́ние 7.1 Prepare a three-minute talk or write a composition, as assigned by your instructor, about your own plan to prepare an elaborate meal for some friends. Explain what you'll serve for each course, using the Russian terms **на пе́рвое, на второ́е, на тре́тье,** and so forth.

Зада́ние 7.2 Prepare a three-minute talk or write a composition, as assigned by your instructor, about an elaborate meal you had or will have in a restaurant. Explain what you ordered or will order for each course using the Russian terms **на пе́рвое, на второ́е, на тре́тье,** and so forth.

Зада́ние 7.3 List the foods you would need to prepare a favorite dish. Read the items to your classmates and have them guess what dish you are making.

Зада́ние 7.4 Prepare a three-minute talk or write a composition, as assigned by your instructor, about the meal you are preparing for friends in **Зада́ние 7.1.** List what you'll need to buy and where you'll buy it.

Фо́то-зада́ние Look at the photograph on the first page of this unit in the textbook. Write a paragraph or prepare a presentation, as assigned by your instructor, describing how the market in the picture seems different from or similar to the places where you usually buy fruits and vegetables.

Listening Tasks

The listening text for this unit consists of a description of old-fashioned and newer grocery stores in Russia.

PRE-LISTENING TASK

Imagine explaining to a foreigner how to shop for food in a modern American supermarket. What would you have to explain to him or her?

LISTENING TASK

Listen to the text and answer questions 1 through 3 in English and 4 through 8 in Russian.

1. Write a brief description explaining how old-fashioned stores still operate in Russia.
2. How many rubles worth of groceries is the customer buying in the first department, the second department, and the third department?
3. Do you have to stand in line again if you have to pay up a balance?
4. What is the Russian expression for *in the old way*?
5. What is the Russian expression for *getting in line*?
6. What is the Russian term for *cashier*?
7. What is the Russian expression for *the corresponding department*?
8. What is the Russian word meaning *to pay up, pay extra, pay the balance*?

DICTATION

Replay the tape and, as you listen, write out the text in full.

PERFORMANCE

Practice reciting the text.

POST-LISTENING TASK

Using the text as a model, work with a classmate to create and recite your own text about how a modern American supermarket operates.

CULTURAL PROBLEM

Why do you think some Russians might prefer the old-fashioned stores to the newer kinds of stores, which operate on the American model?

Phonetics and Intonation

Intonation Pattern 3: Questions Without a Question Word and Other Constructions

Intonation pattern 3 is used for questions that lack a question word. In this intonation pattern, the pitch rises on the stressed syllable of the word about which the question is being asked. This pattern is also used for the first element in an either/or construction as well as for the last word in a clause interrupted by a subordinate clause.

Listen to the questions and statements on the tape. The boldfaced Russian words are at the center of the questions in which they occur

1. Она́ рабо́тает в **Петербу́рге**?
   She's working in Petersburg? (I thought she was working in <u>Moscow</u>!)

2. Она́ **рабо́тает** в Петербу́рге?
   She's working in Petersburg? (I thought she was <u>studying</u> there.)

3. **Она́** рабо́тает в Петербу́рге?
   She's working in Petersburg? (I thought <u>he</u> was working in Petersburg!)

4. — Они́ пое́хали в Москву́. — Куда́? **В Москву́**?
   They've gone to Moscow.
   Where? To Moscow?

5. **Закро́йте** окно́.
   Close the window.

6. Ты не **закро́ешь** окно́?
   Won't you close the window?

7. Она говори́т **по–францу́зски** и́ли по–испа́нски?
   Does she speak French or Spanish?

8. Э́то **Серге́й** вон там говори́т с Мари́ной?
   Is that Sergei talking with Marina over there?

9. **Молодо́й челове́к**, кото́рый стои́т ря́дом с Мари́ной, её муж.
   The young man standing next to Marina is her husband.

10. **Де́вушка**, кото́рая пе́ла в хо́ре, сестра́ Кири́лла.
    The girl who was singing in the chorus is Kirill's sister.

11. **Профе́ссор**, о кото́ром мы говори́ли, изве́стный специали́ст по кита́йской исто́рии.
    The professor about whom we were talking is a well-known specialist in Chinese History.

12. **Студе́нты**, кото́рые опозда́ли на ле́кцию, пото́м **объясни́ли**, что слома́лся **авто́бус**, на кото́ром они́ е́хали в университе́т.
    The students who missed the lecture explained that the bus on which they were going to the university broke down.

SELF-QUIZ

Listen to the tape and circle the word that is the emphasis of the question as determined by intonation. Then write another sentence that clarifies meaning.

1. Они́ говоря́т по–испа́нски?
2. Они́ говоря́т по–испа́нски?
3. Они́ говоря́т по–испа́нски?
4. Вы не зна́ете моего́ профе́ссора?
5. Вы не зна́ете моего́ профе́ссора?
6. Вы не зна́ете моего́ профе́ссора?
7. Кири́лл помо́жет тебе́ за́втра с э́тим зада́нием?
8. Кири́лл помо́жет тебе́ за́втра с э́тим зада́нием?
9. Кири́лл помо́жет тебе́ за́втра с э́тим зада́нием?
10. Кири́лл помо́жет тебе́ за́втра с э́тим зада́нием?

Exercises and Activities

Упражнёние 7.2 The following is a list of nouns in the nominative case singular. Mark the gender of each noun with the Russian letter **М** (masculine), **Ж** (feminine), or **С** (neuter) and the type of stem with the English letter **H** (hard) or **S** (soft) in the appropriate column. Then provide the nominative case plural form. Words marked with an asterisk [*] have a stress shift in the nominative plural; words marked with a double asterisk [**] are end-stressed; words marked (I) have some other irregularity.

	NOUN	GENDER	STEM	NOMINATIVE CASE PLURAL FORM
1.	стул (I)			_____
2.	друг**			_____
3.	учёный			_____
4.	сын (I)			_____
5.	человёк (I)			_____
6.	сестра́*			_____
7.	сло́во*			_____
8.	письмо́*			_____
9.	глаз**			_____
10.	го́род**			_____
11.	учи́тель*			_____
12.	знако́мая			_____

Упражнёние 7.3 Review **Упражнёние 7.2** and make a list of the inanimate nouns.

Упражнёние 7.4 Combine the phrases into complex or compound sentences, using the word **кото́рый** to replace repeated subjects wherever you see three dots (...). Try to make a story out of the sentences. All verbs should be in the past tense and agree with subjects separated from the verbs by a plus sign (+), except those verbs that are underlined (which should remain in the infinitive).

1. вчера́ мы + познако́миться с инженёрами из О́мска ... инженёры + говори́ть по–ру́сски
2. по у́лицам броди́ть + инженёры ... инженёры + не хотёть сидёть в гости́нице
3. инженёры + говорить о том, где мо́жно <u>закуси́ть</u>
4. студёнты из на́шей гру́ппы... студёнты + <u>изуча́ть</u> ру́сский язы́к, + услы́шать, как они́ + говори́ть по–ру́сски.
5. мы + спроси́ть инженёров, не хотёть + ли они́ <u>пойти́</u> в студёнческий клуб.
6. они́ + согласи́ться, и мы все вмёсте + пойти́ в студёнческий клуб.
7. мы + до́лго говори́ть с инженёрами о жи́зни в Росси́и ... жизнь в Росси́и ста́ла о́чень интерёсной в послёднее врёмя
8. они́ + показа́ть нам фотогра́фии ... фотогра́фии они́ + снять в О́мске пёред отъёздом из Росси́и
9. ста́ло по́здно и мы должны́ + быть <u>верну́ться</u> домо́й
10. пёред тем, как мы попроща́лись с но́выми друзья́ми ... но́вые друзья́ + приёхать ненадо́лго из О́мска, мы + обменя́ться адрёсами

Упражнéние 7.5   Use a **котóрый** clause, a **все/кто** or **всё/что** clause to combine the two simple sentences in each pair of sentences below.

1. Андрéева ушлá с рабóты. Ей не понрáвилась э́та рабóта.
2. Онá взялá все вéщи [*all these things*]. Э́ти вéщи принадлежáли ей [*belonged to her*].
3. Онá поговорила с Михáйловым и БелЯ́евой. Они знáли о другóй рабóте по специáльности Андрéевой.
4. Андрéева позвонила в нóвую лаборатóрию. Нóвая лаборатóрия нахóдится в Новосибирске.
5. Там её знáют [*all those who*] ... рабóтает в óбласти структурной механики.
6. В Новосибирске давнó высокó оценили талáнт и спосóбности Андрéевой, Михáйлова и БелЯ́евой. Андрéева, Михáйлов и БелЯ́ева чáсто публикуют статьи в извéстных научных журнáлах.
7. Когдá Андрéева поговорила с дирéктором, он ей предложил [*everything*] онá хóчет. Андрéева срáзу согласилась поступить тудá на рабóту.

Задáние 7.6   Imagine that you are going to Russia for a four-month stay, but you can take only two suitcases. What will you take with you? Make a list of the items you'll need. Then write a paragraph describing what you would buy (**покупáть/купить** + *accusative*) to take with you (**брать/взять с собóй в Россию**).

Many, Some, and Few

Мнóго ~ Мнóгие
Нéсколько ~ Нéкоторые
Немнóго ~ Немнóгие

Use the words **мнóго, нéсколько,** and **немнóго** when you want to emphasize the notions *many, some* and *few*, respectively, without referring to other members of the same class. The words they modify all take the genitive case plural form.

Мнóго **студéнтов** бы́ло на лéкции.
Many students were at the lecture.

Нéсколько **человéк** уже сидéло в зáле.
A few people were already sitting in the hall.

Существует **немнóго** книг на э́ту тéму.
There are [exist] only a few books on this topic.

The words **мнóгие, нéкоторые,** and **немнóгие**, on the other hand, emphasize the relationship of the *many, some,* and *few* in comparison with other members of the same class. These words modify an expression and are in the same case as the expression they modify. In the examples below, these modifiers and the words they modify are all in the nominative case. Note that when these words do not modify a subject, the implied subject is *people*.

На лéкции бы́ли **мнóгие студéнты** из нáшей группы, [но другие пошли на концéрт].
Many of the students from our class were at the lecture [but some went to the concert].

Нéкоторые профессорá чáсто хóдят в э́тот клуб, [но другие тудá хóдят рéдко].
Some of the professors often go to this club [but others go there infrequently].

Немнóгие знáют об э́том ресторáне, [но, конéчно, мы–то знáем!].
Few people know about this restaurant [but of course we know about it!]

The distinction between these two groups of words is eliminated when the words are used in a construction that requires an oblique case ending (i.e., a case ending other than the nominative or accusative case). In instances when you need an oblique case ending, you must use a form of the words **мно́гие, не́которые,** or **немно́гие.**

> Мно́гим понра́вится э́тот но́вый слова́рь!
> *Many people will like this new dictionary!*

> Я не люблю́ ходи́ть в го́сти к не́которым друзья́м без Па́ши.
> *I don't like to go visiting some friends without Pasha.*

> Та́ня зна́ет немно́гих специали́стов по э́тому вопро́су.
> *Tanya knows the few specialists in this area.*

Упражне́ние 7.6   Fill in the blanks with the Russian equivalent of English word in parentheses.

Я о́чень люблю́ я́блоки. (*Many [people]*) _____[1] счита́ют, что

хорошо́ есть по одному́ я́блоку в де́нь. Но (*some*) _____[2]

специали́сты предупрежда́ют, что на (*many*) _____[3] я́блоках мо́гут

быть оста́тки хими́ческих веще́ств, кото́рые испо́льзуют (*many*) _____[4]

фе́рмеры в сада́х. В связи́ с э́тим, не рекоменду́ется есть (*many*) _____[5]

фру́ктов из одного́ ме́ста, одно́й фе́рмы. В (*few*) _____[6] магази́нах,

продаётся (*some/several*) _____[7] сорто́в фру́ктов и овоще́й, кото́рые

выра́щиваются [*are cultivated*] без ядохимика́тов [*pesticides*].

Glossary

Starting with this chapter, the glossary listings will not include regular imperative forms that are formed according to the rules explained in Unit 6. Nominative case plural forms are provided when irregular in some way. Genitive case plural forms are provided for words that have no singular form.

больно́й	*patient (adjectival declension)*
брат, бра́тья	*brother, brothers*
# взве́шивать (I) /взве́сить (II) [что?]: взве́шиваю, взве́шиваешь, взве́шивают; взве́шу, взве́сишь, взве́сят	*to weigh out*
вре́мя, времена́	*time, times*
глаз, глаза́	*eye, eyes*
го́род, города́	*city, cities*
де́ло, дела́	*matter, matters, thing, things*
де́ньги, де́нег (*род.*)	*money*
дом, дома́	*home, homes; building, buildings*
друг, друзья́	*friend, friends*
# еда́	*food (always singular)*

# есть/съ– (*) [что?]: ем, ешь, ест, едим, едите, едят, ешь(те)!	*to eat*
жена́, жёны	*wife, wives*
зда́ние	*building*
знако́мый	*acquaintance (adjectival declension)*
и́мя, имена́	*name, names*
кафе́	*cafe (indecl.)*
ко́фе (м.)	*coffee (masculine, indecl.)*
ку́хня	*kitchen or cuisine*
магази́н	*store*
мать, ма́тери	*mother, mothers*
ме́бель (ж.)	*furniture (always sl.)*
ме́лочь	*small change*
мно́го, мно́гие	*many, many of*
# моне́та	*coin*
муж, мужья́	*husband, husbands*
музе́й	*museum*
немно́го, немно́гие	*few*
не́сколько, не́которые	*some, several*
но́мер, номера́	*hotel room, hotel rooms*

# обме́нивать (I) /обменя́ть (I) де́ньги: 	
   обме́ниваю, обме́ниваешь, обме́нивают; обменя́ю,
   обменя́ешь, обменя́ют
	to exchange money (from one currency to another)

оде́жда	*clothing (always singular)*
оте́ц, отцы́	*father, fathers*
очки́, очко́в (род.)	*glasses (spectacles)*
# пи́ща	*food (as nourishment) (always singular)*
# плати́ть/за– (II) [ско́лько? за что?]: плачу́, пла́тишь, пла́тят	*to pay how much for something*
# покупа́ть (I) /купи́ть (II) [что?]: покупа́ю, покупа́ешь, покупа́ют; куплю́, ку́пишь, ку́пят	*to buy something*
по́хороны, похоро́н (род.)	*funeral*
# проду́кты	*food items*
профе́ссор, профессора́	*professor, professors*

# разме́нивать (I) /разменя́ть (I) де́ньги: 	
   разме́ниваю, разме́ниваешь, разме́нивают; разменя́ю,
   разменя́ешь, разменя́ют
	to change money (within one currency), to make change

ребёнок, де́ти	child, children
россия́нин, россия́не	citizen(s) of Russia (not necessarily ethnic Russian)
# ры́нок (на)	market
сда́ча	change (from a purchase)
сестра́, сёстры	sister, sisters
# Ско́лько сто́ит ... ?	how much does it cost?
соображе́ние, из э́тих соображе́ний	principle, from these principles
стул, сту́лья	chair, chairs
сын, сыновья́	son, sons
упражне́ние	exercise
учёный	scholar/scientist (adjectival declension)
учи́тель, учителя́	teacher, teachers
# цена́, це́ны (в до́лларах/рубля́х)	price, prices
# чай	tea
челове́к, лю́ди	person, people

UNIT 8

Lexicon: Nationality and Citizenship

Russians distinguish between the concepts of nationality and citizenship. If you look again at **текст 8a** in the textbook, you will see that the author, Aleksei Demidov, describes a situation as **российская**, not **русская**. The former term refers to the Russian Federation, which includes people of many nationalities (Russians, Ukrainians, Tatars, Jews, and so forth), while the latter term refers only to people who are considered ethnic Russians. The notion of nationality is closely tied to native language and heredity. For example, Jews or Tatars whose native language is Russian may consider themselves Russian, but Russian society may *not* consider them as such if they have a clearly identifiable Jewish or Tatar first or last name. Any citizen of the Russian Federation whose native language is *not* Russian is usually considered non-Russian. On the other hand, according to Russian Federation law, people born on the territory of the Russian Federation or the former Soviet Union may claim Russian citizenship, even if they are not of Russian nationality.

When Russians want to talk about nationality and citizenship with Americans, they may begin by asking about ethnic background, using the expression **Откуда приехали ваши предки?** or **Кто вы по национальности?** Russians use the following words and expressions to describe nationality and citizenship:

Гражданин/гражданка (*nom. pl.* граждане *gen. pl.* граждан) какой страны?
Citizen of what country?

> Он американский гражданин, но живёт постоянно в Москве.
> *He's an American citizen, but he lives permanently in Moscow.*

> Извините, вы — гражданка какой страны?
> *Excuse me, but of what country are you a citizen?*

Получать/получить гражданство
To receive citizenship

> Они прожили в США уже пять лет и вчера получили гражданство.
> *They have lived in the USA for 5 years already and yesterday received citizenship.*

Национальность: Кто вы по национальности?
Nationality

> Она по национальности украинка, но живёт в Петербурге.
> *She is Ukrainian, but she lives in Petersburg.*

Россиянин/россияне
Citizen(s) of the Russian Federation

> Эти татары и грузины всю жизнь живут в Екатеринбурге: конечно, они россияне.
> *These Tatars and Georgians have been living their entire lives in Ekaterinburg: of course they are citizens of the Russian Federation.*

Российский
Relating to the Russian Federation (not necessarily ethnic Russian)

> Российские солдаты не хотят воевать в Чечне.
> *The soldiers of the Russian Federation do not want to fight in Chechnya.*

Происхожде́ние (Кто вы по этни́ческому происхожде́нию? Вы — како́го этни́ческого происхожде́ния?)

Ancestry and ethnic background

Я америка́нка, но я — ирла́ндского и италья́нского происхожде́ния.
I am American, but I am of Irish and Italian descent.

Here is a list of some of the nationalities and their languages represented by people living in the Russian Federation; all of these peoples are **россия́не** if they are citizens of the Russian Federation. (Note that nationalities and languages are *not* capitalized unless they are the first word of a sentence.)

MASCULINE/PLURAL	FEMININE	LANGUAGE
ру́сский/ру́сские	ру́сская	по-ру́сски
украи́нец/украи́нцы	украи́нка	по-украи́нски
белору́с/белору́сы	белору́ска	по-белору́сски
тата́рин/тата́ры	тата́рка	по-тата́рски
каза́х/каза́хи	каза́чка	по-каза́хски
узбе́к/узбе́ки	узбе́чка	по-узбе́кски
азербайджа́нец/ азербайджа́нцы	азербайджа́нка	по-азербайджа́нски
армяни́н/армя́не	армя́нка	по-армя́нски
грузи́н/грузи́ны	грузи́нка	по-грузи́нски
латы́ш/латыши́	латы́шка	по-латы́шски
лито́вец/лито́вцы	лито́вка	по-лито́вски
эсто́нец/эсто́нцы	эсто́нка	по-эсто́нски
евре́й/евре́и	евре́йка	на и́диш, на иври́т

Упражне́ние 8.1   Find as many of the nations (former republics of the USSR), represented in the list of nationalities above, on the map on the inside cover of the textbook. The last nationality does not have its own state, but continues to have an autonomous republic—Birobidjan—within the Russian Federation.

Зада́ние 8.1   Prepare a three-minute talk or write a composition, as assigned by your instructor, in which you discuss your ethnic background or the ethnic background of someone you know.

Зада́ние 8.2   Interview your classmates or friends to learn about their ethnic backgrounds or the ethnic backgrounds of some of their friends; then prepare a three-minute talk or write a composition, as assigned by your instructor, based on what you learn.

Фо́то-зада́ние   Look at the photograph on the first page of this unit in the textbook. The women in the photograph are singing Russian folk songs. Write a paragraph or prepare a presentation, as assigned by your instructor, about someone you know who is interested in the folk music or folk art of any culture.

Listening Tasks

The listening text for this unit consists of a description of the rules on how to become a citizen of various countries in the world.

PRE-LISTENING TASK

What do you think the requirements are for becoming a citizen of the United States or Canada? How might a Russian become a citizen of the United States or Canada?

LISTENING TASK

Listen to the text and then answer questions 1 through 11 in English and 12 through 15 in Russian.

1. Which countries provide for a simplified naturalization process for foreigners who marry citizens?
2. Which country allows for this simplified naturalization process only for foreign women who marry male citizens?
3. Which countries allow/provide for naturalization of a foreign spouse upon the registration of the marriage?
4. Which countries shorten the time period for naturalization upon registration of the marriage?
5. How old does one have to be, generally speaking, to apply for citizenship?
6. What are two countries that require applicants for citizenship to be at least twenty-one years old?
7. How long does one have to live in Switzerland, Austria and Spain or Italy, Finland, Sweden, and the United States in order to become a citizen?
8. Name at least three countries that require applicants for citizenship to lead a decent lifestyle.
9. Name at least three countries that demand a certain competency in the language as a requirement for citizenship.
10. In which two countries are special benefits available to entice people to become citizens?
11. If **добрый** means *good* and **порядок** means *order*, what is a **добропорядочный образ жизни**?
12. What is the Russian expression for *in certain [or some] cases/situations*?
13. What is the Russian expression for *the time period is considerably/significantly reduced*?
14. What is the Russian expression for *constant/permanent residence*?
15. What is the Russian expression for *first and foremost*?

DICTATION

Replay the text and, as you listen, write out the names of the countries each time they are mentioned. Which countries are mentioned most frequently? Which countries are mentioned least frequently?

PERFORMANCE

Practice reciting the names of the countries.

POST-LISTENING TASK

Using the information in the text, work with a classmate and role-play a situation in which one of you is a naturalization officer of the United States and the other is a Russian who wishes to emigrate to the U.S. and become a U.S. citizen, or reverse the direction of emigration.

CULTURAL PROBLEM

Why do you think the question of foreign citizenship is of increasing interest to many Russians these days? What does it mean for Russia?

Phonetics and Intonation

Intonation Pattern 4

Intonation pattern 4 is used for follow-up questions and for certain bureaucratic requests for information.

Listen to the questions. Intonation pattern 4 is used for the boldfaced words and phrases.

1. Ната́ша сейча́с на рабо́те. **А Со́ня?**
2. Сего́дня они́ не мо́гут. **А за́втра?**
3. Я о́чень люблю́ Достое́вского. **А Толсто́го?**
4. В тре́тьем за́ле идёт ремо́нт. **А в четвёртом?**
5. В три часа́ мы ещё бу́дем на рабо́те. **А в четы́ре?**
6. Ей не нра́вится Страви́нский. **А вам?**
7. А́нна сего́дня не придёт. **А Серге́й?**
8. **Ва́ши докуме́нты?**
9. **Ва́ша фами́лия, и́мя?**
10. **Год рожде́ния?**

SELF-QUIZ

Listen to the sentences and write a follow-up question for each of them on a separate piece of paper.

Exercises and Activities

Упражне́ние 8.2 Complete the sentence **Здесь нет сейча́с...** with the genitive case form of each phrase.

1. большо́й сканда́л _____
2. ужа́сная ситуа́ция _____
3. бе́лое бельё _____
4. хоро́ший санато́рий _____
5. интере́сный преподава́тель _____
6. истори́ческий музе́й _____
7. ваш де́душка _____
8. Мари́на Анто́новна _____

Зада́ние 8.3 Select one of the individuals or items named in **Упражне́ние 8.2** and write a paragraph explaining or justifying his, her, or its absence. Be persuasive!

Упражне́ние 8.3 Complete the sentence **Здесь нет сейча́с...** with the genitive case form of each phrase.

1. плохи́е преподава́тели _____
2. бы́вшие учителя́ _____

3. ва́ши сыновья́ _____

4. твои́ друзья́ _____

5. их до́чери _____

6. краси́вые о́кна _____

7. дли́нные пи́сьма _____

8. на́ши де́душки и ба́бушки _____

9. э́ти америка́нцы _____

10. истори́ческие музе́и _____

11. совреме́нные лаборато́рии _____

12. высо́кие зда́ния _____

Упражне́ние 8.4 Fill in the blanks with the genitive case form of the personal pronoun.

1. Когда́ (вы) _____ не́ было в лаборато́рии, мы зако́нчили э́ту

   рабо́ту.

2. Когда́ (он) _____ не́ было, заходи́л И́горь.

3. Вчера́ все кро́ме (они́) _____ бы́ли на собра́нии.

4. Она́ бу́дет в Во́логде в сре́ду, так что (она́) _____не бу́дет до́ма

   в э́тот день.

5. Мы бы́ли у Бо́ри два часа́, а когда́ мы возвраща́лись домо́й от (он)

   _____, встре́тили его́ отца́.

Упражне́ние 8.5 Complete the sentence **Э́то соба́ка...** with the correct form of each name. Remember that names ending in **-ский/-стый/-стой, -цкий/-цкой, -ская/-стая/-цкая,** or **-ские/ -стые/-цкие** are always adjectival (whether masculine, feminine or plural.)

1. Кири́лл Андре́ев _____

2. Татья́на Андре́ева _____

3. Кири́лл и Татья́на Андре́евы _____

4. Анато́лий Пастерна́к _____

5. Лари́са Пастерна́к _____

6. Анато́лий и Лари́са Патерна́к _____

7. Пол Бра́ун _____

8. Па́ула Бра́ун _____

9. Фёдоровы _____

10. Зина́ида Тури́цына _____

11. Верони́ка Верби́цкая _____

12. Влади́мир Высо́цкий _____

13. Пётр Чайко́вский _____

14. И́горь Страви́нский _____

15. Татья́на Толста́я _____

16. Гали́на Исако́вская _____

17. Бори́с и Верони́ка Верби́цкие _____

18. Лев Тро́цкий _____

19. Еле́на Ястре́мская _____

20. Анато́лий и Мари́на Зели́нские _____

Зада́ние 8.4   Make a list of five to ten items you have purchased in the last two weeks, including food, items of clothing, school supplies, and so forth. Write down how much you paid (**плати́ть/заплати́ть**) for each of these items, being careful to use the correct genitive case forms for the words **до́ллар** (**оди́н до́ллар, два до́ллара, пять до́лларов**) and **цент** (**оди́н цент, два це́нта, пять це́нтов**).

Упражне́ние 8.6   Reverse the direction of the sentences, replacing the preposition and changing the construction from the accusative case to the genitive case.

> **Образе́ц:**   Мы сейча́с идём в теа́тр.
> Мы сейча́с **идём из теа́тра.**

1. Мы е́дем на Чёрное мо́ре.

   _____

2. Мы уе́хали в Ту́лу. (Мы прие́хали...)

   _____

3. Бо́ря е́дет в Петрозаво́дск.

   _____

4. О́ля уе́хала в Челя́бинск. (О́ля прие́хала...)

   _____

5. Э́ти студе́нты иду́т на конце́рт.

   _____

6. А́нна — почтальо́н. Она́ сейча́с идёт на по́чту.

   _____

7. Я обы́чно ухожу́ на рабо́ту в 8 часо́в. (Я обы́чно прихожу́...)

   _____

8. Мы сейча́с идём к Га́ле.

   _____

9. Олéг éдет к бáбушке.

_____

10. Мы éдем к Васи́лию Влади́мировичу.

_____

Упражнéние 8.7 Fill in the blanks with the correct expression of possession. Note that some sentences will require **есть** and others may require a form of the verb **имéться** or no verb at all.

1. (*Dina Ivanova has a car*) _____ и мы на ней поéдем

в Ту́лу.

2. (*Tula [a city] has*) _____ прекрáсные пáмятники

архитекту́ры.

3. (*Tula used to have*) _____ ещё бóльше церквéй,

мнóгие из них бы́ли разру́шены в пéрвые гóды совéтской влáсти.

4. Ди́на должнá пробы́ть в Ту́ле дóльше нас, и поэ́тому (*we won't have a car*)

_____ на обрáтном пути́.

5. Обрáтно мы поéдем на пóезде, но мы бои́мся, что (*there won't be tickets*)

_____ на пóезд Ту́ла-Москвá.

6. Поэ́тому мы хоти́м поговори́ть с Кóлей: (*he had a car*) _____

_____ и, мóжет быть, (*he still has it*)

_____.

7. Éсли (*Kolia doesn't have a car anymore*) _____

_____, мóжет быть придётся подождáть Ди́ну.

8. Конéчно, мóжет быть (*there will be tickets*) _____

и́ли на пóезд, и́ли на автóбус.

9. В Ту́ле мы надéемся жить в гости́нице в цéнтре гóрода: (*the hotel has*)

_____ прекрáсные номерá и краси́вый ресторáн.

10. Éсли (*this hotel won't have any rooms*) _____, мы

бу́дем жить в гости́нице далекó от цéнтра: (*that hotel always has rooms*)

_____.

11. (*That hotel doesn't have telephones*) _____ в

номерáх и э́то, конéчно, неудóбно.

12. (*Vitia has an aunt*) _____, котóрая живёт в Ту́ле, и

мы смóжем звони́ть от неё.

13. (*Vera Borisovna, Vitia's aunt, has a great apartment*) _____

    _____ в це́нтре.

14. (*She used to have an apartment*) _____

    на окра́ине го́рода без телефо́на, но неда́вно она́ перее́хала в центр.

15. Она́ наде́ется, что (*she will have a dacha*) _____

    недалеко́ от того́ ме́ста, где она́ ра́ньше жила́, потому́ что там о́чень краси́во.

 Упражне́ние 8.8   Combine the phrases to form complex or compound sentences using the word **кото́рый** or a **кто/что** clause to replace a repeated subject wherever you see three dots (...) or a phrase in brackets. Try to make a story out of the sentences.

1. На про́шлой неде́ле Зи́на ... Зи́на рабо́тает в институ́те вме́сте с И́горем ... [Зи́на] пригласи́ла нас прийти́ к ней на день рожде́ния.
2. И́горь ча́сто говори́т, что Зи́на хоро́ший друг ... без [Зи́ны] бы́ло бы тру́дно, де́лать всё, (*which is*) ну́жно
3. Зи́на хорошо́ рабо́тает да́же с Па́шей ... все боя́тся Па́ши
4. Па́ша о́чень мно́го тре́бует от всех рабо́тников ... занима́ется/занима́ются вопро́сами перево́да с францу́зского
5. Зи́на та́кже хорошо́ рабо́тает с Верони́кой Никола́евной ... мы все избега́ем разгово́ров с Верони́кой Никола́евной
6. Верони́ка Никола́евна всё вре́мя стои́т пе́ред же́нским туале́том ... о́коло же́нского туале́та ра́ньше собира́лись же́нщины институ́та во вре́мя переры́ва.
7. У Зи́ны на дне рожде́ния бы́ли и Па́ша и Верони́ка Никола́евна ... специа́льно ра́ди Па́ши и Верони́ки Никола́евны Зи́на да́же сказа́ла, что́бы никто́ не кури́л
8. Когда́ мы пришли́ в рестора́н, мы заме́тили, что забы́ли у Зи́ны всё ... без (*which*) нельзя́ поздравля́ть с днём рожде́ния
9. Одни́м сло́вом мы забы́ли в кварти́ре все пода́рки ... пода́рки мы купи́ли Зи́не на день рожде́ния
10. Все ... (*who*) оста́вил пода́рки у Зи́ны, бы́ли возмущены́
11. Мы попроси́ли Ди́му и Ле́ру, ... у Ди́мы и Ле́ры ключ от кварти́ры Зи́ны, тихо́нько верну́ться к Зи́не за пода́рками
12. Зи́на была́ занята́ гостя́ми ... о́коло госте́й она́ сиде́ла, и не заме́тила, что нет ни Ди́мы, ни Ле́ры
13. К тому́ же ря́дом с ней сиде́ла Та́ня ... у Та́ни всегда́ сто́йкие францу́зские духи́
14. Все ... о́коло (*whom*) сиде́ла Та́ня, бы́ли привлечены́ си́льным за́пахом её духо́в
15. Верну́лись Ди́ма и Ле́ра с пода́рками ... без пода́рков нельзя́ бы́ло поздравля́ть Зи́ну, и все бы́ли в восто́рге
16. По́сле того́, как Зи́на откры́ла пода́рки, она́ поблагодари́ла всех ... (*who*) пришёл и поздра́вил её с днём рожде́ния.

 Упражне́ние 8.9   Translate into Russian.

Arkadii Smirnov, from Samara, has a problem: he is afraid of his professors. From my point of view, he avoids Kuznetsova and Vasil'evskaia, professors who demand a lot from him. On the one hand, good professors, without whom it is impossible to learn (**невозмо́жно учи́ться**) demand a lot from their students. On the other hand, Arkadii did not have good professors last year (**в про́шлом году́**). He will have two good professors next year (**в сле́дующем году́**), but maybe he will avoid them, too. Nina says that until Arkadii reads a book for people who avoid problems, he will not have the opportunities (**возмо́жности**) that he seeks. Arkadii's sister, Svetlana, also wants to help him (**помога́ть ему́**), but their mother can't live without her.

Упражнёние 8.10   Translate the following passage into Russian.

Irina Beliaeva, from the Ukraine, has three bad professors this year, but she does not avoid them. After classes end this year (**в э́том году́**), she will even work for one of them in the laboratory. (She received a letter from Denisova about the job in the laboratory on the twelfth of April). Before she knew that she will be working in the laboratory this summer (**э́тим ле́том**), Irina hoped to find a job in the hospital. A lot of the students work at the hospital in the summer and Irina wanted to work near them. Now Irina has a problem, because without her, Denisova won't have an assistant (**помо́щник**) in the laboratory.

These two students have very different problems!

Зада́ние 8.5   Write a story consisting of 2 or more paragraphs using six of the following phrases in any order:

до э́того, мы реши́ли	*before which we decided*
по́сле э́того, мы пошли́	*after which we went*
из/с кото́рого/кото́рой/кото́рых	*from which*
от кото́рого/кото́рой/кото́рых	*from whom*
у кото́рого/кото́рой/кото́рых	*at whose home*
кро́ме того́, что	*beside which/whom*
до того́, как...	*before (something happens/ed)*
по́сле того́, как...	*after (something happens/ed)*
без кото́рого/кото́рой/кото́рых	*without which/whom*
для кото́рого/кото́рой/кото́рых	*for which/whom*
кото́рых он бои́тся	*which/whom he is afraid of*
кото́рых она́ избега́ет	*which/whom she avoids*
о́коло кото́рого/кото́рой/кото́рых	*around which/whom*
кото́рого/кото́рой/кото́рых они́ тре́буют	*which they demand*

Glossary

без [кого́? чего́?]	*without someone or something*
боя́ться (II) [кого́? чего́?]: бо́юсь, бои́шься, боя́тся	*to fear someone or something*
вро́де [чего́?]	*like or similar to something*
# граждани́н/гражда́нка/гра́ждане	*citizen(s)*
# гражда́нство: получа́ть/получи́ть гражда́нство	*citizenship: to receive citizenship*
для [кого́? чего́?]	*[designated] for someone or something*
до [кого́? чего́?]	*up until someone or something*
е́хать/по- (I) [куда́? отку́да?]: е́ду, е́дешь, е́дут, поезжа́йте!	*to travel by conveyance [where? from where?]*
идти́/пойти́ (I) [куда́? отку́да?]: иду́, идёшь, иду́т, шёл, шла́, шли́	*to travel on foot [where? from where?]*
из [чего́?]	*from something*

избегáть (I) /избежáть (*) [когó? чегó?]:
    избегáю, избегáешь, избегáют; избегý, избежúшь, избегýт

to avoid someone (acc.) or something (gen.)

искáть/по- (I) [когó? что? когó? чегó?]:
    ищý, úщешь, úщут

to search for something [use accusative for concrete or specific object, genitive for abstract object]

крóме [когó? чегó?]

beside or except someone or something

мéсяц(ы):
    янвáрь, феврáль, март, апрéль, май, июнь, июль, áвгуст, сентя́брь, октя́брь, ноя́брь, декáбрь

month(s) of the year

национáльность:
    Кто вы по национáльности?

nationality: What is your nationality?

от [когó? чегó?]

from someone or something

платúть/за- (II) [комý? скóлько дéнег? за что?]:
    плачý, плáтишь, плáтят

to pay someone how much money for something

пóсле [когó? чегó?]

after someone or something

прéдок

ancestor

происхождéние (зтнúческое): Я немéцкого происхождéния.

ethnic background: I am of German ancestry.

с(о) [чегó?]

from or down off of something

с однóй стороны́..., с другóй стороны́...

on the one hand, on the other hand

с тóчки зрéния (с чьей тóчки зрéния, с тóчки зрéния когó?)

from whose point of view

трéбовать (I) [когó? чегó?]:
    трéбую, трéбуешь, трéбуют

to require someone or something

у [когó? чегó?]

near someone or something (also used to convey possession or lack)

UNIT 9

Lexicon: Cooking

Many Russians love to entertain at home and to be entertained at their friends' homes.

Блю́до
Dish (type of food)

> Суп из грибо́в — моё фи́рменное блю́до.
> *Mushroom soup is my specialty (special dish).*

Ку́хня
Kitchen or cuisine

> Мне о́чень нра́вится францу́зская ку́хня.
> *I like French cuisine a lot.*

Нареза́ть/наре́зать [что?]
To cut, chop, or slice something

> Когда́ ты наре́жешь лук, положи́ его́ сра́зу на сковоро́дку.
> *As soon as you cut the onion, put it immediately into the frying pan.*

Тере́ть (растира́ть/растере́ть) [что?]
To grate something

> Я обы́чно тру сыр и посыпа́ю его́ на макаро́ны.
> *I usually grate cheese and sprinkle it on the pasta.*

Сме́шивать/смеша́ть [что?]
To mix something

> Сме́шивайте муку́ и соль.
> *Mix the flour and the salt.*

Гото́вить/при– [что?]
To prepare something (generic cooking verb)

> Анто́н прекра́сно гото́вит.
> *Anton is a great cook.*

Жа́рить/по– [что?]
To fry something

> Я обы́чно жа́рю ры́бу на сли́вочном ма́сле на ма́леньком огне́.
> *I usually fry fish in butter on a small light (flame).*

Вари́ть/с– [что?]
To boil something

> Я сварю́ карто́шку и́ли макаро́ны.
> *I'll boil up some potatoes or some pasta.*

Подогрева́ть/подогре́ть [что?]
  To heat up something

>Я сейча́с подогре́ю мя́со.
>*I'll warm up the meat [that was already cooked].*

Туши́ть/по– [что?]
  To roast or stew something

>Вади́м ту́шит говя́дину с помидо́рами и чесноко́м.
>*Vadim roasts the beef with tomatoes and garlic.*

Гото́вить [что?] на пару́
  To steam something

>Све́та обы́чно гото́вит о́вощи на пару́.
>*Sveta usually steams the vegetables.*

Печь/ис– [что?]
  To bake something

>Оте́ц ча́сто печёт пече́нье.
>*My father often bakes cookies.*

О́стрый, сла́дкий, го́рький, ки́слый, солёный
  The five major tastes: hot (spicy), sweet, bitter, sour, salty

>Э́тот суп о́чень о́стрый! Он с кра́сным пе́рцем!
>*This soup is very hot (spicy)! It has red pepper!*

>Э́то вино́ о́чень го́рькое: оно́ наве́рно испо́ртилось.
>*The wine is bitter: it's probably gone bad.*

Есть/съ– [что?]
  To eat something

>Они́ вегетариа́нцы и поэ́тому не едя́т мя́са.
>*They're vegetarians and therefore don't eat meat.*

Food is cooked on the stovetop (**на плите́**), in the oven (**в духо́вке**) or, less often, in the microwave (**в микроволно́вой пе́чке**). Food is cooked in a frying pan (**на сковоро́дке**) or in a pot (**в кастрю́ле**). Food items are placed (**класть/положи́ть, ста́вить/поста́вить**) either horizontally or vertically, respectively; sprinkled (**посыпа́ть/посы́пать**); or poured (**налива́ть/нали́ть**) into vessels. These verbs are described in greater detail in Unit 22.

Russians usually order their entire meal at once in a restaurant, from the appetizers to the dessert. (Americans often order dessert only after completing the main course.) Russians consider appetizers the first course, (**пе́рвое**), which may be hot or cold hors d'oeuvres (**горя́чие и́ли холо́дные заку́ски**), the second course (**второ́е** or **горя́чее**) the main course or entrée, and the dessert the third course (**тре́тье**), also called **сла́дкое** or **дессе́рт**.

Зада́ние 9.1   Write about a favorite recipe that you might like to share with Russian friends some day.

Зада́ние 9.2   Prepare a three-minute talk or write a composition, as assigned by your instructor, about an elaborate meal you had or will have in a restaurant. Explain what you ordered or will order for each course, using the Russian terms **на пе́рвое, на второ́е, на тре́тье,** and so forth.

Фо́то-зада́ние   Look at the photograph on the first page of this unit in the textbook. You're making a cup of tea for yourself when suddenly some friends (pictured in the photograph on the first page of unit 5) drop by. Write a paragraph or prepare a presentation, as assigned by your instructor, describing what you will serve them (**к ча́ю**).

Listening Tasks

The listening text for this unit consists of a recipe.

PRE-LISTENING TASK

This recipe is for a traditional Russian food, either a dessert, or an appetizer. What are your favorite desserts or appetizers? What would you expect to hear in a recipe for a dessert? For an appetizer? Make a list of criteria to help you decide what this is a recipe for.

LISTENING TASK

Listen to the text and answer questions 1 through 5 in English and 6 through 8 in Russian.

1.   Name all the ingredients.
2.   Name the cooking utensils you would need to make this recipe.
3.   Given the instructions, what do you think a **ватру́шка** is?
4.   How long and at what temperature does this item need to be baked?
5.   If **вдоба́вок** means *in addition to*, what does **добавля́йте** mean?
6.   What is the Russian word for *filling*?
7.   Find the Russian equivalent for the expression *in a size a little bigger than the frying pan.*
8.   Find the Russian equivalent for the expression *grease the frying pan with butter.*

DICTATION

Replay the tape and, as you listen, write out each recipe in full.

PERFORMANCE

Practice reciting the recipe.

POST-LISTENING TASK

Using the recipe as a model, work with a classmate (and your favorite English-language cookbook, if you wish) to write up recipes in Russian for one of the following: pizza, chocolate chip cookies, cheeseburger and french fries, apple pie, turkey with stuffing and cranberry sauce, corn chowder, or a favorite dish of your choice.

CULTURAL PROBLEM

Traditional Russian cuisine might seem to be higher in fat than other ethnic cuisines. Why do you think that might be so? Traditional Russian cuisine may also seem to feature fewer fresh vegetables and fruits than other cuisines. Why?

Phonetics and Intonation

Intonation Pattern 5

Intonation pattern 5 is used for exclamations. A high pitch is maintained throughout the utterance.

 Listen to intonation pattern 5 in the sentences on the tape.

1. Кака́я она́ у́мная!
2. Каки́е у него́ краси́вые во́лосы!
3. Како́е интере́сное письмо́!
4. Каки́е стра́шные фотогра́фии!
5. Кака́я краси́вая маши́на!
6. Како́е большо́е окно́!
7. Каки́е хоро́шие де́ти!
8. Како́й ужа́сный челове́к!
9. Како́й тро́гательный фильм!
10. Кака́я ужа́сная пого́да!

SELF-QUIZ

Listen to the tape and create (say and write) a positive and a negative exclamation for each noun. Use intonation pattern 5.

1. _____
2. _____
3. _____
4. _____
5. _____
6. _____
7. _____
8. _____
9. _____
10. _____

Exercises and Activities

Упражне́ние 9.1 Complete the sentence **Я ви́жу** _____ with the accusative case form of each phrase.

1. э́та прекра́сная газе́та _____
2. э́та краси́вая ло́шадь _____
3. э́тот но́вый журна́л _____

4. э́та спосо́бная студе́нтка _____

5. э́тот отли́чный студе́нт _____

6. интере́сный преподава́тель _____

7. истори́ческий музе́й _____

8. ваш де́душка _____

9. ва́ша ба́бушка _____

10. Мари́я Васи́льевна _____

Упражне́ние 9.2   Complete the sentence **Я ненави́жу** _____ with the plural form of each phrase. Check for stress shifts in the nouns and spelling.

Образе́ц: ма́ленькая кварти́ра
Я ненави́жу ма́ленькие кварти́ры.

1. э́та но́вая библиоте́ка _____

2. э́тот неудо́бный дива́н _____

3. францу́зкое вино́ _____

4. э́тот ста́рый самова́р _____

5. э́тот ужа́сный слова́рь _____

6. э́то некраси́вое зда́ние _____

7. э́то дли́нное упражне́ние _____

8. э́тот гнило́й пе́рсик _____

9. э́тот кра́сный каранда́ш _____

10. э́тот отврати́тельный дом _____

Упражне́ние 9.3   Answer the question **Кто жа́луется на** _____? with the plural form of each phrase. Check for spelling.

Образе́ц: роди́тели
Сыновья́ жа́луются на роди́телей.

1. твои́ до́чери _____

2. ва́ши сыновья́ _____

3. тала́нтливые худо́жники _____

4. интере́сные лю́ди _____

5. краси́вые ма́льчики _____

6. у́мные де́вушки _____

7. на́ши дя́ди _____

8. ла́сковые ко́шки _____

9. бе́лые ло́шади _____

10. серьёзные адвока́ты _____

Зада́ние 9.3 Choose one or two of the individuals named in **Упражне́ние 9.3** and write a paragraph explaining why you like or love them, using the construction **Я его́/её/их люблю́ за то, что он/-а́/-и** _____.

Упражне́ние 9.4 Complete the sentence **Я ре́дко обижа́юсь на** _____ with the correct form of the names. Remember that names ending in **–ский/-стый/-стой, –цкий/-цкой, –ская/-стая/-цкая, and –ские/-стые/-цкие** are always adjectival.

1. Кири́лл Андре́ев _____

2. Татья́на Андре́ева _____

3. Кири́лл и Татья́на Андре́евы _____

4. Анато́лий Пастерна́к _____

5. Лари́са Пастерна́к _____

6. Анато́лий и Лари́са Пастерна́к _____

7. Пол Бра́ун _____

8. Па́ула Бра́ун _____

9. Зинаи́да Тури́цына _____

10. Влади́мир Высо́цкий _____

Упражне́ние 9.5 Combine the phrases to form complex or compound sentences, using the word **кото́рый** or а **кто/что, то/что** clause to replace repeated subject wherever you see three dots (...). Try to make a story out of the sentences.

1. Ни́на должна́ была́ встре́титься с Ва́ней в семь часо́в во́зле кинотеа́тра «Ви́тязь» ... они́ ча́сто хо́дят в э́тот кинотеа́тр смотре́ть иностра́нные фи́льмы
2. Ни́на до́лго ждала́ Ва́ню ... Ва́ня ре́дко опа́здывает
3. Ни́на да́же лю́бит Ва́ню за ... он ре́дко опа́здывает
4. Она́ ненави́дит мужчи́н ... мужчи́ны ча́сто опа́здывают
5. Она́ счита́ет, что мужчи́на ... ча́сто опа́здывает, не уважа́ет же́нщин
6. Ещё Ни́на лю́бит Ва́ню за то, что он понима́ет всё ... (_which_) ва́жно для Ни́ны.
7. Ни́на начала́ волнова́ться о Ва́не и хоте́ла позвони́ть ему́ на рабо́ту ... его́ рабо́та нахо́дится далеко́ от кинотеа́тра, что́бы узна́ть, когда́ он ушёл
8. она́ уви́дела телефо́н-автома́т ... на про́шлой неде́ле она́ жа́ловалась на э́тот телефо́н-автома́т, потому́ что он проглоти́л её после́дний жето́н
9. она́ наде́ялась на ... что его́ отремонти́ровали и пошла́ звони́ть.
10. Телефо́н ещё не отремонти́ровали и она́ рассерди́лась на всех ... (_who_) рабо́тает в телефо́нном узле́
11. Ни́на рассерди́лась и на Ва́ню, ... Ва́ня не до́лжен был опа́здывать
12. вдруг пришёл Андре́й, ... Андре́я хорошо́ зна́ет Ва́ня
13. Андре́й принёс цветы́, ... за цветы́ он наве́рно мно́го заплати́л
14. цветы́ бы́ли не от Андре́я, а от Ва́ни ... Ва́ня не смог прийти́ и не смог позвони́ть ей ра́ньше
15. Ещё Андре́й принёс запи́ску от Ва́ни ... у Ва́ни заболе́ла мать
16. как то́лько он узна́л, Ва́ня сра́зу пое́хал к ма́тери, ... он о́чень лю́бит мать
17. Ни́на поняла́ всю ситуа́цию и пригласи́ла Андре́я, ... она́ хорошо́ зна́ла Андре́я, посмотре́ть фильм
18. Андре́й согласи́лся и сказа́л, что все, ... (_who_) уже́ смотре́л э́тот фильм, счита́ли его́ о́чень хоро́шим
19. на сле́дующий день Ни́на встре́тилась с Ва́ней, ... Ва́ня сказа́л, что мать чу́вствует себя́ лу́чше

Упражне́ние 9.6   Translate the following passage into Russian.

I thought that Igor' and Nika were an ideal couple, but they don't love each other anymore. They don't understand each other anymore. And they don't respect each other anymore. They became acquainted three years ago, when Igor' was playing soccer in the park and Nika came to see Maksim play. Three weeks later Igor' fell in love with Nika. Then Nika fell in love with Igor', and they went to Kaluga for three days.

Now Nika complains about Igor' all the time. She says that he wakes her up every night because he likes to watch television despite the fact that the programs are bad. She says that she waits for him every evening, but he comes (**прихо́дит**) home late. She used to rely on Igor', she says, but now she can't rely on him. Nika thinks Igor' falls in love with every woman he sees. Nika says that Igor' wastes money (**тра́тит де́ньги**) and that just yesterday he bought a book that cost five-hundred-twenty-one thousand rubles!

Igor' is really angry at Nika. He says that she hates him, but that he loves her. Igor' says that he is offended at Nika because she doesn't like to watch television with him. He says that she doesn't understand that he has to work in the evening. He says that she yells at him often.

Despite everything, I think they should wait. Maybe they won't be angry and won't take offense at each other tomorrow. If they go to Siberia or Lake Baikal for a week, they can forget everything and fall in love again.

Зада́ние 9.4   Write a story consisting of two or more paragraphs, using six of the following phrases in any order.

в кото́рый/кото́рого/кото́рое/кото́рую	*in/to which*
на кото́рый/кото́рого/кото́рое/кото́рую	*at/to which*
за кото́рый/кото́рого/кото́рое/кото́рую	*for which*
на кото́рого/кото́рую он се́рдится	*at whom he's angry*
на кото́рого/кото́рую он жа́луется	*about whom he complains*
кото́рого/кото́рую/кото́рых она́ уважа́ет	*whom she respects*
кото́рого/кото́рую/кото́рых они́ ненави́дят	*whom they hate*
кото́рого/кото́рую/кото́рых они́ лю́бят	*whom they love*
кото́рого/кото́рую/кото́рых он понима́ет	*whom he understands*
кото́рого/кото́рую/кото́рых она́ ждёт	*for whom she is waiting*
они́ жа́луются на всё, что. . .	*they complain about everything that . . .*
они́ наде́ются на всех, кто. . .	*they rely on everyone who . . .*

Зада́ние 9.5   Imagine that you are a tour guide for some Russian tourists in America, including some of the people in **Упражне́ние 9.4**. The tour group spends a lot of time together in the bus. As the tour moves from city to city, tensions have arisen. Prepare a three-minute talk or write composition, as assigned by your instructor, in which you describe who has come to you to complain about other members of the group (**жа́ловаться на кого́**) and who is angry at whom (**серди́ться/рас-на кого́**) and why.

Directional Adverbs

Russian uses special directional adverbs after verbs expressing movement in a direction (as opposed to verbs expressing only a location). The verbs requiring such adverbs include all verbs of motion (such as **ходи́ть, идти́, пойти́, е́здить, е́хать, пое́хать, бе́гать, бежа́ть, побежа́ть, лета́ть, лете́ть, полете́ть, пла́вать, плыть, поплы́ть**[1]) and all the verbs of motion with spatial prefixes (such as **приходи́ть/прийти́, уезжа́ть/уе́хать, пробега́ть/пробежа́ть, вылета́ть/вы́лететь,**

---

[1]These verbs are described in Units 23.

подплыва́ть/подплы́ть[1]), verbs of placement (such as класть/положи́ть, ста́вить/поста́вить, ве́шать/пове́сить, сажа́ть/посади́ть[2]), verbs of position (such as сади́ться/сесть, ложи́ться/лечь), as well as other verbs such as возвраща́ться/верну́ться, повора́чивать/поверну́ть, смотре́ть/по-. All these verbs share one important thing in common: they are used with a destination that answers the question куда́?

The following directional adverbs are used with these verbs:

домо́й	[to] home
вниз	downward
наве́рх	upward
вперёд	forward
наза́д	backward
нале́во	to the left
напра́во	to the right
сюда́	[to] here
туда́	[to] there
куда́	[to] where? (interrogative pronoun)

Я обы́чно иду́ **домо́й** сра́зу по́сле рабо́ты, но сего́дня я иду́ в библиоте́ку.
I usually go home directly after work, but today I'm going to the library.

Ки́ра пошла́ **вниз** в механи́ческую лаборато́рию прове́рить, не гото́вы ли результа́ты.
Kira went down to the mechanical laboratory to check if the results are ready.

Кинотеа́тр «Росси́я»? Иди́те пря́мо, пото́м поверни́те напра́во на Тверску́ю у́лицу и он бу́дет на той стороне́ у́лицы.
The "Rossiia" Cinema? Go straight and then turn right onto Tverskaia Street and it will be on the other side of the street.

Мы вернёмся туда́ и посмо́трим, нет ли там Константи́на Миха́йловича.
We'll return there (go back there) and see if Konstantin Mikhailovich isn't there.

Упражне́ние 9.7 Fill in the blanks with the Russian equivalent of the English directional adverbs in parentheses.

1. В сове́тское вре́мя по всему́ Ленингра́ду висе́ли транспара́нты, на кото́рых бы́ли

   напи́саны ло́зунги [slogans] ти́па [such as] «(Forward) _____, к

   побе́де коммуни́зма!»

2. Ру́сские обы́чно не обраща́ли внима́ния на э́ти транспара́нты: когда́ они́ смотре́ли

   (up[ward]) _____, они́ бу́дто ничего́ осо́бенного не замеча́ли.

3. Но э́та пропага́нда броса́лась в глаза́ [stood out, were conspicuous] тури́стам, кото́рые

   приезжа́ли (here) _____ в то вре́мя.

4. К седьмо́му ноября́, дню октя́брьской револю́ции, на Зи́мнем Дворце́ висе́л большо́й

   транспара́нт с портре́тами Ма́ркса, Э́нгельса и Ле́нина. Как то́лько тури́сты проходи́ли

   Дворцо́вый мост и повора́чивали (to the left) _____, они́ ви́дели

   э́ти портре́ты революционе́ров на том до́ме, где ра́ньше жи́ли цари́.

5. По́сле распа́да СССР (there) _____ переста́ли ве́шать

   пропаганди́стские транспара́нты.

---

[1]These verbs are described in Unit 24.
[2]These verbs are described in Unit 22.

Glossary

# блю́до	*dish (type of food)*
в	*in/to (may take the accusative or prepositional case)*
вниз	*below (dir. adverb)*
вперёд	*forward (dir. adverb)*
# вари́ть/с– (I) [что?]: варю́, ва́ришь, ва́рят	*to boil or poach*
ви́деть/у– (II) [кого́? что?]: ви́жу, ви́дишь, ви́дят	*to see someone or something*
влюбля́ться (II) /влюби́ться (II) [в кого́? что?]: влюбля́юсь, влюбля́ешься, влюбля́ются; влюблю́сь, влю́бишься, влю́бятся	*to fall in love with someone or something*
# второ́е	*main course*
# го́рький	*bitter*
# горя́чее	*main course*
# гото́вить/при– (II) [что?]: гото́влю, гото́вишь, гото́вят	*to prepare (cook)*
гото́вить на пару́	*to steam*
домо́й	*[to] home (dir. adverb)*
жа́ловаться/по– (I) [на кого́? что? за что? кому́?]: жа́луюсь, жа́луешься, жа́луются	*to complain about someone or something for some reason to someone*
# жа́рить/под– (II) [что?]: жа́рю, жа́ришь, жа́рят	*to fry*
за	*for/in the place of/in exchange for/beyond/ behind [may take the accusative or instrumental case]*
# заку́ски, заку́сок (род.)	*hors d'oeuvres*
игра́ть (I) [во что?]: игра́ю, игра́ешь, игра́ют	*to play a game or sport*
# ки́слый	*sour*
крича́ть/за– (II) [на кого́? что? за что?]: кричу́, кричи́шь, крича́т	*to shout, to yell*
люби́ть/по– (II) [кого́? что?]: люблю́, лю́бишь, лю́бят	*to love, begin to love*
на	*in/to[may take the accusative or prepositional case]*

наве́рх	*above, up (dir. adverb)*
на вся́кий слу́чай	*just in case*
надея́ться (I) [на кого́? что?]: надею́сь, наде́ешься, наде́ются	*to hope for or rely on someone or something*
наза́д	*back (dir. adverb)*
нале́во	*to the left (dir. adverb)*
напра́во	*to the right (dir. adverb)*
ненави́деть/воз– (II) [кого́? что?]: ненави́жу, ненави́дишь, ненави́дят	*to hate or come to hate someone or something*
несмотря́ на что/несмотря́ на то, что…	*despite something/despite the fact that . . .*
обижа́ться (I) /оби́деться (II) [на кого́? на что? за что?]: обижа́юсь, обижа́ешься, обижа́ются; оби́жусь, оби́дишься, оби́дятся	*to take offense/to be offended at someone for something*
# о́стрый	*sharp, hot/spicy*
# пе́рвое	*first course, appetizer*
# печь/ис– (I) [что?]: пеку́, печёшь, пеку́т, пёк, пекла́, пекли́	*to bake*
под	*beneath/beyond [may take the accusative or instumental case]*
подогрева́ть (I) /подогре́ть (I) [что?]: подогрева́ю, подогрева́ешь, подогрева́ют; подогре́ю, подогре́ешь, подогре́ют	*to heat up (something previously cooked)*
понима́ть (I) /поня́ть (I) [кого́? что?]: понима́ю, понима́ешь, понима́ют; пойму́, поймёшь, пойму́т, по́нял, поняла́, по́няли	*to understand someone or something*
серди́ться/рас– (II) [на кого́? за что?]: сержу́сь, се́рдишься, се́рдятся	*to get angry at someone for something*
# сла́дкий	*sweet*
# сла́дкое	*dessert*
# солёный	*salted*
#тере́ть/по– [что?]: тру, трёшь, трут, тёр, тёрла, тёрли	*to grate something*
# тре́тье	*third course or dessert*
# туши́ть/по– (II) [что?]: тушу́, ту́шишь, ту́шат	*to roast, stew something*
уважа́ть (I) [кого́? что?]: уважа́ю, уважа́ешь, уважа́ют	*to respect someone or something*
че́рез	*in/to/across (must take the accusative)*

UNIT 10

Lexicon: Clothing

Russians use a number of expressions to describe the clothing someone is wearing. Some expressions refer to the wearing of particular clothing frequently, while others refer to the wearing of clothing on a particular day.

Wearing Something Frequently or Constantly

ходи́ть [в чём?]
  To wear something (frequently)

> Я хожу́ в чёрных свитера́х
> *I usually wear black sweaters.*

носи́ть [что?]
  To wear something (frequently)

> Америка́нские студе́нты ча́сто но́сят ста́рые джи́нсы.
> *American students often wear old jeans.*

Wearing Something on a Particular Day

быть в [чём?]
  To be wearing something on a particular day

> Он бы́л в ро́зовой руба́шке.
> *He was wearing a pink shirt.*

что [бы́ло] [на ком?]
  To be wearing or have been wearing something (on a particular day)

> На мне сего́дня ко́жаная ку́ртка.
> *I'm wearing a leather jacket today.*

быть оде́т/-а [во что?]
  To be wearing something (on a particular day)

> Она́ сего́дня оде́та в жёлтую блу́зку.
> *She's wearing a yellow blouse today.*

прийти́ [в чём?]
  To be wearing something (on a particular day)

> Он пришёл в се́ром костю́ме
> *He came in a gray suit.*

Colors

бе́лый	white	фиоле́товый	purple
бе́жевый	tan	си́ний	dark blue
жёлтый	yellow	голубо́й	light blue (sky blue)
ора́нжевый	orange	зелёный	green
ро́зовый	pink	кори́чневый	brown
кра́сный	red	чёрный	black

Это како́го цве́та? *What color is it?*
Он/-а́/-о кра́сного цве́та. *It's red.*
Он/-а́/-о кра́сный/кра́сная/кра́сное. *It's red.*

Patterns

в поло́ску	striped
в кле́тку	plaid or checked
в горо́шек	polka-dotted

Fabrics

хло́пок	cotton
шерсть	wool
шёлк	silk
синте́тика	polyester

Упражне́ние 10.1   Fill in the blanks as required by context using the following cues, though not neccessarily in this order: *blue cardigan sweater* (i.e., *a sweater with buttons*), *yellow-and-red plaid pants, red sweater, tan pants, sneakers, blue shirts, black sweaters, shoes, pink polka-dot blouse, white-and-dark-blue-striped silk shirt*, [*made of*] *wool*, [*made of*] *polyester*, *blue cotton skirt*. You may need a list of Russian items of clothing or a dictionary to complete this exercise.

Серёжа был о́чень мо́дно оде́т на ве́чере. На нём бы́ли

_____,¹ _____,²

_____³ из _____,⁴

хотя́ он обы́чно хо́дит в _____,⁵ _____

_____⁶ и _____.⁷ Мари́на то́же была́

хорошо́ оде́та. На ней бы́ли _____⁸ из

_____,⁹ _____,¹⁰

_____,¹¹ и _____

_____.¹² Она́ то́же была́ в _____¹³ на

высо́ком каблуке́, хотя́ она́ обы́чно хо́дит в _____.¹⁴

 Зада́ние 10.1   Find a color advertisement for clothing and write a paragraph describing the clothing shown in the advertisement. Bring in your description and the color advertisement to class. In class, you will put your advertisements into a pile with a partner. You will then read each others' descriptions and try to find the matching advertisement.

 Фо́то-зада́ние   Look at the photograph in the first page of this unit in the textbook. The people in the picture are buying (and selling) flowers for International Women's Day, March 8, in Moscow. Write a paragraph or prepare a presentation, as assigned by your instructor, describing what one or two of the people are wearing.

Listening Tasks

The listening text for this unit consists of a dialogue.

PRE-LISTENING TASK

Are you ever surprised by what people wear at particular occasions? How so? What do you expect someone to wear at a party thrown by your circle of friends?

LISTENING TASKS

Listen to the text and answer questions 1 through 6 in English and 7 through 9 in Russian.

1. What are the names of the two people in this dialogue?
2. It's a shame that one of them wasn't at a party at whose home?
3. Who else was at that party?
4. Describe the appearance of the woman named in the answer to question 3.
5. Describe the appearance of the man named in the answer to question 3.
6. Why is the woman in the dialogue frustrated with the man?
7. How does the man express doubt about his interest in what the woman has to say?
8. What is the Russian equivalent for the expression *in combination with what Pasha was wearing?*
9. Would you wear either of the outfits described? Why or why not?

DICTATION

Replay the tape and, as you listen, write out the dialogue in full.

PERFORMANCE

Practice reciting the dialogue.

POST-LISTENING TASK

Using the dialogue as a model, work with a classmate to create and perform your own dialogues in which you discuss the clothing worn by some of your classmates and instructors at a local nightclub or pizza joint.

CULTURAL PROBLEM

Russians often wear the same "work" outfit when they go to work every day. When they get home, they immediately wash the outfit and put on something less formal, such as a sweatsuit. Americans, on the other hand, generally wear one outfit all day long and wear a different outfit every day. Why do you think Russians might have a special "work" outfit?

Phonetics and Intonation

Review of the Five Intonation Patterns

The five intonation patterns are used in a variety of contexts, as was shown in Units 5 through 9.

Intonation pattern 1 is used for simple declarative sentences and for dependent clauses at the end of sentences. In this pattern, the pitch falls on the stressed syllable of the word that is emphasized in the sentence and does not rise again.

Intonation pattern 2 is used for questions with a question word: In this pattern, the pitch rises on the stressed syllable of the question word and then falls to the end of the sentence. The same pattern is used to indicate the semantic emphasis of a particular word in a sentence, with the pitch rising on the emphasized word. This pattern is used for imperatives, the *second* element of an either/or clause, expressions of surprise (**неужёли!**), pointing things out with the word **Вот**, and expressions with the words **ведь, же** and **однáко**.

Intonation pattern 3 is used for questions without a question word. In this pattern, the pitch rises on the stressed syllable of the word about which the question is being asked and then falls to the end of the sentence. This intonation is used for the *first* element of an either/or construction as well as for the last word in a clause interrupted by another clause (thus indicating the fact that the sentence is not completed).

Intonation pattern 4 is used for follow-up questions and for certain bureaucratic requests. The pitch rapidly rises, falls on the stressed syllable of the questioned word or requested item, and then rises on the syllable immediately following the stress.

Intonation pattern 5 is used for exclamations. A high pitch is maintaned throughout the entire utterance.

Listen to the sentences on the tape and note the intonation pattern. Boldfaced words indicate the center of the intonation pattern.

1. **Вúтя** готóвит обéд.
2. **Что** он готóвит на обéд?
3. **Вúтя** готóвит обéд?
4. **А Мáша?**
5. **Какóй вкýсный обéд!**

SELF-QUIZ

Listen to the three dialogues which you originally heard in the listening tasks in Unit 1. Follow the transcript and mark the intonation pattern for each with the number (1–5) of that pattern.

1. — Скажúте пожáлуйста, вы рабóтаете úли ýчитесь?
   — Я учýсь в Москóвском университéте. А вы?
   — Я тóже учýсь – в Вискóнсинском университéте. Я сейчáс в Москвé на стажирóвке.
   — Прáвда? Как интерéсно!
2. — На какóм факультéте вы ýчитесь?
   — На факультéте рýсской истóрии. А вы?
   — Я на факультéте рýсского языкá и литератýры, но я тáкже интересýюсь рýсским странове́дением.
3. — Какúе кýрсы вы слýшаете в э́том годý?
   — Я слýшаю кýрсы по биолóгии, по математике, по политúческим наýкам и по рýсскому языкý. А вы?
   — Я слýшаю кýрсы по экóномике, по истóрии, по психолóгии и по англúйской литератýре.

Exercises and Activities

Упражнéние 10.2   Answer the question **Где же вы бы́ли?** with the prepositional case form of each expression. Do not change the number of the adjective-noun pairs from singular to plural or vice versa.

Образе́ц: большо́й го́род
        Мы бы́ли в большо́м го́роде

1. Ле́тний сад _____

2   Крым _____

3. Калу́га _____

4. студе́нческая столо́вая _____

5. пя́тый эта́ж (на) _____

6. хоро́ший санато́рий _____

7. ле́кция по исто́рии (на) _____

8. заня́тия по ру́сскому языку́ (на) _____

9. Кремль (м.) _____

10. Кра́сная пло́щадь (на) _____

Упражне́ние 10.3   Anser the question **О чём вы говори́ли?** or **О ком вы говори́ли?** with the prepositional case form of each expression. Do not change the number of the adjective-noun pairs from singular to plural or vice versa.

Образе́ц: больши́е города́
        Мы говори́ли о больши́х города́х.

1. у́мные спортсме́нки _____

2. ру́сские _____

3. мои́ друзья́ _____

4. её сёстры _____

5. истори́ческие демонстра́ции _____

Упражне́ние 10.4   Complete the sentence **Мы ничего́ не слы́шали о(б)** with the prepositional case form of each name. Remember that names ending in **–ский/-стый/-стой, –цкий/-цкой, –ская/-стая/-цкая,** and **–ские/-стые/-цкие** are always adjectival.

1. Кири́лл Андре́ев _____

2. Татья́на Андре́ева _____

3. Кири́лл и Татья́на Андре́евы _____

4. Анато́лий Пастерна́к _____

5. Лари́са Пастерна́к _____

6. Анато́лий и Лари́са Пастерна́к _____

7. Дол Бра́ун _____

8   Па́ула Бра́ун _____

9. Пётр Чайко́вский _____

10. Бори́с и Верони́ка Верби́цкие _____

Упражнéние 10.5 Combine the phrases to form complex or compound sentences, using the word **котóрый** or a **кто/что, то/что** clause to replace repeated subjects wherever you see three dots (...). Try to make a story out of the sentences.

1. вчерá мы бы́ли у Мúши с Тáней ... мы ужé говорúли нéсколько раз о Мúше и Тáне
2. у них прекрáсная квартúра ... в их квартúре мнóго антиквариáта
3. онú большúе болтуны́: онú спокóйно говоря́т обо всём, ... (*which*) им интерéсно и обо всех, ... (*whom*) онú знáют
4. нельзя́ доверя́ть тем, ... (*who*) так легкó говорúт
5. онú дáже говорúли с нáми о лúчных проблéмах Сóни и Пéти, ... при Сóне и Пéте онú сказáли, что онú никомý ничегó никогдá не расскáжут об их проблéмах
6. я настáивала на том, ... (*that*) э́то неинтерéсная тéма
7. потóм онú нáчали говорúть об Ивáновых ... мы и так ужé достáточно знáем об Ивáновых
8. я не знáю, почемý Мúша и Тáня дрýжат с такúми людьмú, ... в такúх лю́дях я ничегó хорóшего не вúжу
9. однáко Бóря сказáл, что не хóчет проводúть врéмени с тéми людьмú, ... при (*whom*) нельзя́ говорúть свобóдно
10. и всё равнó бы́ло интерéсно слýшать истóрии Тáни и Мúши о том, как онú жúли в Лóндоне, ... в Лóндоне живýт мнóгие из их знакóмых

 Задáние 10.2 Write a story consisting of two or more paragraphs, using four of the following phrases in any order.

в, на, о, при котóром/котóрой/котóрых	*in/at/on/about which, in whose presence*
о том, что	*about the fact that*
дéло в том, что	*the thing is that*
во всех, кто	*in all those who*
во всём, что	*in all that which*
обо всех, кто	*about all those who*
обо всём, что	*about all that which*
настáивать на том, что	*to insist on*
сомневáться в том, что	*to doubt*

 Упражнéние 10.6 Translate the following passage into Russian. You may need to use locational adverbs (p. 97–98).

We are talking about the Golitsyns, whose house is on the left. They lived in St. Petersburg during the administration of Tsar Nikolas II, but now they live in France and America. Prince (**Князь**) Golitsyn had insisted on leaving Russia because of (**из-за**) the revolution. His wife and children were despairing when they left Russia: perhaps they knew that they would never return. I doubt the Golitsyns would have avoided the fate (**судьбá**) of the Romanovs.

Sergei Golitsyn is a charming young man: he was born in '60. He is married to Elena Andreeva, the daughter of my good friend. Sergei works in an institute about which I know very little. I do know that he plays the guitar and speaks four languages. His sister, Ekaterina Golitsyna, was born in '61. She is a student at the University of Texas where she insists on getting a specialization (**чтóбы получúть специáльность**) in business, despite (**вопрекú +** *dative*) her parents' wishes. When she's not in classes or at a lecture, she works in the garden.

Sergei and Ekaterina's parents, Nikolai, who works in four or five different cities, and Elizaveta, like to travel (**лю́бят путешéствовать**). They are often (**чáсто быва́ют**) in Italy, France, Greece, England, as well as in Alaska and South America. After the collapse of the Soviet Union (**распáда Совéтского Сою́за**), they also are often in Russia, especially in Moscow, St. Petersburg, Kazan' and Suzdal', the Caucasus, and Ukraine.

Задáние 10.3　Prepare a three-minute talk or write a composition, as assigned by your instructor, about when some important historical or personal events took place or will take place. Refer only to years or months.

Locational Adverbs

Russian uses special locational adverbs in constructions answering the question **где?** Constructions requiring such adverbs include those with the verbs **быть** and **находи́ться**, as well as verbs of position (such as **стоя́ть/по–, лежáть/по–, сидéть/по–,** and **висéть/по–**).[1]
The following are locational adverbs used with these verbs.

дóма	*at home*
внизý	*down, below, beneath*
наверхý	*above, up*
впереди́	*ahead*
сзáди	*in back*
слéва	*on the left*
спрáва	*on the right*
здесь, тут	*here*
там	*there*
где	*where? in what location? (interrogative pronoun)*

Note the resemblance of the locational adverbs **внизý** and **наверхý** to the special masculine nouns taking **–у/–ю** in the prepositional case for location only (**в садý, в лесý,** and so on) and the resemblance of **сзáди, слéва,** and **спрáва** to nouns in the genitive case.
The verb **быть** is implied in the first three examples below:

Макси́м? Он ещё **дóма.** Сейчáс позовý егó к телефóну.
Maksim? He's still at home. I'll call him to the phone for you.

Ки́ры здесь нет. Онá навéрно **внизý** в механи́ческой лаборатóрии проверя́ет, не готóвы ли результáты.
Kira isn't here now. She's probably down in the mechanical laboratory checking if the results are ready.

Кинотеáтр «Росси́я»? Вот он, **спрáва.**
The "Rossiia" Cinema? There it is, on the right.

Они́ бы́ли там цéлый час, надéясь, что придёт Константи́н Михáйлович.
They were there for an entire hour, hoping that Konstantin Mikhailovich would return.

Упражнéние 10.7　Fill in the blanks with the Russian equivalent of the English locational adverb in the parentheses. A Russian exchange student in the United States is showing some American friends a picture of Red Square and trying to describe the location of various famous buildings in relation to the photographer.

1. (*In front*) _____ стои́т Храм Васи́лия Блажéнного, для мнóгих

   си́мвол всей Росси́и.

2. (*On the right*) _____ стоя́т стéны Кремля́ и за ни́ми

   госудáрственные здáния и собóры.

3. Истори́ческий музéй (*behind*) _____.

---

[1]These verbs are described in Unit 22.

4. Торго́вый центр ГУМ нахо́дится (*to the left*) _____, а за ним
   —Кита́йгород.

5. (*Below*) _____, бли́же к Москве́–реке́, стои́т гости́ница «Росси́я».

Locational adverbs and directional adverbs (presented in Unit 9) can be used together as connecting phrases for constructions that require one or the other adverb.

> Ки́ра пошла́ **туда́, где** проверя́ют результа́ты.
> *Kira went to the place where the results are checked.*

> Кинотеа́тр «Росси́я»? Иди́те пря́мо, пото́м поверни́те напра́во **там, где** стои́т кио́ск пе́пси–ко́ла. Уви́дите кинотеа́тр на друго́й стороне́ у́лицы.
> *The "Rossiia" Cinema? Go straight and then turn right onto Tverskaia Street at the place where there's a big Pepsi stand. You'll see the cinema on the other side of the street.*

> Мы стоя́ли **там, куда́** приходи́ли делега́ты, но не ви́дели Константи́на Миха́йловича.
> *We were standing there where the delegates were arriving, but we didn't see Konstantin Mikhailovich.*

Упражне́ние 10.8   Fill in the blanks with the Russian equivalent of the English locational or directional adverbs in parentheses, as required by context.

1. Гали́на Петро́вна пошла́ (*to the front*) _____, (*there*)

   _____, (*where*) _____ оформля́ют биле́ты.

2. Она́ сказа́ла, что у неё уже́ есть биле́т, и спроси́ла, (*where*) _____ ей идти́.

3. Же́нщина, кото́рая стоя́ла (*behind*) _____, возмути́лась, почему́ Гали́на Петро́вна идёт без о́череди.

4. Рабо́тник «Аэрофло́та» споко́йно объясни́л Гали́не Петро́вне, что ей всё равно́

   придётся офо́рмить поса́дочный биле́т [*boarding pass*], и попроси́л её пройти́ (*back*)

   _____, (*where*) _____ она́ стоя́ла ра́ньше,

   и подожда́ть свою́ о́чередь.

5. Гали́на зна́ла, что (*below*) _____, (*where*)

   _____ уже́ пошёл её муж, больша́я толпа́, и она́ волнова́лась,

   ду́мая, что он не зна́ет, (*where*) _____ она́.

Glossary

в	*in or at (may take prepositional case)*
в виду́ того́, что…	*in light of the fact that . . .*
вещь (*ж.*)	*thing*
внизу́	*below (loc. adverb)*
впереди́	*ahead (loc. adverb)*

вокза́л (на)	*train station (not for metro or subway)*
во–пе́рвых, во–вторы́х, в–тре́тьих...	*in the first place, secondly, thirdly*
восто́рг, быть в восто́рге	*delight, to be delighted*
в тако́м слу́чае	*in that case*
год, в како́м году́	*year; in which year*
дво́р (в/на)	*courtyard*
до́ма	*[at] home (loc. adverb)*
жени́ться (II) [на ком?]: жени́сь, же́нишься, же́нятся	*to get married (said of a man)*
жить (I) [где?]: живу́, живёшь, живу́т, жи́л, жила́, жи́ли	*to live somewhere*
заня́тия, на заня́тиях	*classes (always pl.)*
здесь	*here (loc. adverb)*
игра́ть (I) [на музыка́льном инструме́нте]: игра́ю, игра́ешь, игра́ют	*to play a musical instrument*
конце́рт (на)	*concert*
ле́кция (на)	*lecture*
лес (в лесу́)	*forest*
мо́ре (на)	*sea*
на	*on or at (may take prepositional case)*
наверху́	*above (loc. adverb)*
надева́ть (I) / наде́ть (I): надева́ю, надева́ешь, надева́ют; наде́ну, наде́нешь, наде́нут	*to put on*
наста́ивать (II) [на чём?]: наста́иваю, наста́иваешь, наста́ивают	*to insist on something*
настрое́ние, быть в како́м настрое́нии	*mood, to be in what kind of mood*
# носи́ть (II) [что?]: ношу́, но́сишь, но́сят	*to wear something (frequently)*
о(б) [ком, чём?]	*about something (must take prepositional case)*
отча́яние, быть в отча́янии	*despair, to be in despair*
по́чта (на)	*post office or mail*
пол, на полу́	*floor (as opposed to ceiling)*
при [ком, чём?]	*under the auspices of, during the administration of (must take prepositional case)*

рабóта (на/в)	*work*
рот, во ртý	*mouth*
сад, в садý	*garden*
сзáди	*behind (loc. adverb)*
слéва	*the left (loc. verb)*
снег, в снегý	*snow*
сомневáться (I) [в чём?]: сомневáюсь, сомневáешься, сомневáются	*to doubt something*
состоя́ть (II) [из чегó?] (из скóльких человéк?): состои́т, состоя́т	*to consist of what (of how many people?): use-third person forms only*
спрáва	*on the right (loc. adverb)*
стадиóн (на)	*stadium*
стáнция (на)	*train station (for metro/subway)*
стол (на/в)	*table or desk*
там	*there (loc. adverb)*
ýгол (на/в)	*corner*
ýлица (на)	*street*
урóк (на/в)	*lesson (in class or book)*
# ходи́ть (II) [в чём?]: хожý, хóдишь, хóдят	*to be wearing something frequently*
час, в котóром часý?	*hour (at what hour?)*
шкáф, в шкафý	*closet, wardrobe, chest of drawers, cupboard*
этáж (на)	*floor or story (of a building)*

UNIT 11

Lexicon: Permitting and Forbidding

Russians use several different phrases and constructions to express the notions of permitting and forbidding.

Мóжно [комý? дéлать/с- что?]
Permitted, possible (комý is often implicit)

> Мóжно поговорúть с вáми?
> *May I talk with you for a little while?*

> Вам — нельзя́, а — Светлáне Андрéевне мóжно.
> *You cannot [You are forbidden], but Svetlana Andreevna may.*

> Мóжно бы́ло поéхать, но мы не поéхали.
> *We could have gone, but we didn't.*

Мóжно не [комý? дéлать что?]
Is/are not required to do something (комý is often implicit)

> Мóжно не читáть э́ту кнúгу.
> *It isn't necessary to read this book. [You] don't have to read this book.*

Нельзя́ [комý? дéлать/с- что?]
Is/are forbidden or impossible to do something (комý is often implicit)

> **нельзя́** + *imperfective* = forbidden
> **нельзя́** + *perfective* = physically impossible

> Здесь нельзя́ курúть.
> *There's no smoking here.*

> Телевúзор сломáлся: нельзя́ егó включúть.
> *The television is broken: it's impossible to turn it on.*

Возмóжно, [что?]
It's possible that . . .

> Возмóжно, что Áнна Петрóвна самá зайдёт.
> *It's possible that Anna Petrovna herself will stop by.*

Невозмóжно [дéлать/с- что?]
It's impossible

> Невозмóжно éхать сейчáс: я смогý приéхать зáвтра.
> *It's impossible for me to come now: I can come tomorrow.*

Разрешáть [комý? дéлать/с- что?]/разрешáться
To permit someone to do something (often used in passive constructions.)

> Э́ти родúтели разрешáют свойм дéтям смотрéть телевúзор.
> *These parents let their children watch television.*

Разреше́ние [на что? де́лать/с- что?]
Permission for what or permission to do something

> Мы получи́ли разреше́ние Тама́ры Васи́льевны на э́то.
> *We got permission from Tamara Vasil'evna for this.*

Про́пуск [куда́?]
Pass or permission to go somewhere

> Предъяви́те, пожа́луйста, про́пуск!
> *Please show me your pass!*

> У нас про́пуски за кули́сы к А́лле Бори́совне!
> *We have passes to go backstage to see Alla Borisovna!*

Пропуска́ть/пропусти́ть [кого́? куда́?]
To let someone through to somewhere

> Без про́пуска я не могу́ вас пропусти́ть за кули́сы.
> *Without a pass I can't let you pass backstage.*

Отпуска́ть/отпусти́ть [кого́? куда́?]
To let someone out

> За́втра профе́ссор нас отпу́стит за пятна́дцать мину́т до конца́ заня́тий.
> *Tomorrow our professor will let us go (dismiss class) fifteen minutes before the end of class.*

Впуска́ть/впусти́ть [кого́? куда́?]
To let someone in to somewhere

> Мы никого́ не впу́стим в клуб без приглаше́ния.
> *We won't let anyone into the club without an invitation.*

Выпуска́ть/вы́пустить [кого́? куда́?]
To let someone out to somewhere

> Когда́ Бо́ря просту́жен, роди́тели его́ не выпуска́ют на у́лицу.
> *When Boria has a cold, his parents don't let him out.*

Допуска́ть/допусти́ть [... , что́бы кто? де́лать/с- что?]
To let or allow someone do something, to allow something to happen

> Я не допущу́, что́бы ты э́то сде́лал!
> *I won't allow you to do this!*

> На э́тот фи́льм де́ти до шестна́дцати лет не допуска́ются.
> *Children under sixteen years of age are not admitted to this film.*

Запреща́ть/запрети́ть [кому́? де́лать/с- что?]
To forbid someone to do something (this verb is often used in passive constructions)

> Э́ти роди́тели запрети́ли свои́м де́тям смотре́ть телеви́зор.
> *These parents have forbidden their children to watch television.*

> Здесь запреща́ется фотографи́ровать.
> *It is forbidden to take pictures here.*

Запрещён, запрещена́, запрещено́, запрещены́
Is/are (was/were/will be) forbidden

> Там бы́ло запрещено́ фотографи́ровать со вспы́шкой.
> *Flash photograph was forbidden there.*

Запрёт [на что?]
Prohibition, ban (on what?)

Ра́ньше в СССР был запрёт на откры́тое обсужде́ние вы́езда евре́ев из СССР.
*There used to be a prohibition in the USSR on the open discussion of the emigration of
Jews from the USSR.*

Запре́тный
· **Prohibited, banned, forbidden**

Запре́тный плод всегда́ сла́док.
Forbidden fruit is always sweet.

В сове́тское вре́мя бы́ло мно́го запре́тных тем.
In the Soviet era there were many forbidden topics.

Упражне́ние 11.1   Fill in the blanks with the Russian equivalent of the English word or phrase in
parentheses. The conversation, between the supervisor of a Russian dormitory (Tat'iana
Sergeevna) and a dormitory student (Trofimov), takes place during the 1970s. There may be more
than one acceptable answer for each blank.

— Здра́вствуйте, Татья́на Серге́евна. (*Possible*) _____[1] зайти́?

— Пожа́луйста. (Друго́му челове́ку:) Анто́н Петро́вич, мы зако́нчили обсужде́ние э́той

проблéмы. Я вас (*let you go*) _____.[2] Так, Трофи́мов, опя́ть

потеря́ли (*pass*) _____[3]? Вы же зна́ете, без э́того вас в общежи́тие

не (*let you in/through*) _____![4]

— Нет, я не поэ́тому. Я бы хоте́л получи́ть (*permission*) _____[5]

пове́сить карти́ны [*hang up paintings*] у себя́ в ко́мнате.

— Кле́ить плака́ты [*pasting up posters*] — (*is permitted*) _____,[6] но

забива́ть гво́зди в сте́ну [*hammering nails into the walls*] —

(*is forbidden*) _____.[7]

— Но э́то о́чень краси́вые карти́ны!

— Мне уже́ жа́ловались на карти́ны, кото́рые вы хоти́те пове́сить. Мне сказа́ли, что э́то

произведе́ния [*works*] (*forbidden*) _____[8] худо́жников.

— Это непра́вда, Татья́на Серге́евна! Ра́зве Канди́нский —

(*is forbidden*) _____?[9]

— Не зна́ю. Я поду́маю и пото́м сообщу́ вам своё реше́ние [*will inform you of my decision
later*]. (Она́ начина́ет кури́ть.)

— Татья́на Серге́евна! В общежи́тии (*forbidden*) _____[10] кури́ть!

Зада́ние 11.1   Imagine that you are the parent of a sixteen-year-old. Have a discussion with your
teenager, describing what you will allow him or her to do while you and your spouse take a
weekend trip alone.

Задáние 11.2 Prepare a three-minute talk or write a composition, as assigned by your instructor, in which you explain to a Russian emigre friend who is planning to visit Russia what to bring as gifts (e.g., jeans, Bibles) and what not to bring (e.g., weapons, narcotics, pornography). Or explain what personal items to bring (e.g., comfortable shoes) and what not to bring (e.g., expensive jewelry).

 Фóто-задáние Look at the photograph on the first page of this unit in the textbook. Write a paragraph or prepare a presentation, as assigned by your instructor, describing how you would explain to the man in the picture that he is doing something good and/or that people shouldn't litter. Use words you do know to express words you don't know.

Listening Tasks

The listening text for this unit consists of a dialogue that takes place between two people concerning permission.

PRE-LISTENING TASK

Under what conditions are people forbidden to take photographs in the United States? Under what conditions do you think might photography be forbidden in Russia? Why?

 ### LISTENING TASKS

Listen to the text and answer questions 1 through 4 in English and 5 through 7 in Russian.

1. Why is the woman taking photographs if it is forbidden to do so in this place?
2. Where can she get permission?
3. What sort of place is this? Why do you think so?
4. What does the man think about the likelihood of her getting permission to take pictures on the first floor? On the second floor? On the third floor?
5. What is the Russian equivalent of *it is utterly possible*?
6. How does the woman thank the man for the information he has given her?
7. How does the man say *you're welcome*?

 ### DICTATION

Replay the tape and, as you listen, write out the dialogue in full.

 ### PERFORMANCE

Practice reciting the dialogue.

 ### POST-LISTENING TASK

Using the dialogue as a model, work with a classmate to create and perform your own dialogue in which you do one of the following: ask where smoking is allowed, ask an instructor for permission to miss a class, or ask an instructor for permission to miss an exam and take it at a later date (review the vocabulary for learning and teaching, presented in Unit 1).

CULTURAL PROBLEM

What is the role of secrecy in American society? What has been the role of secrecy in Russian society? Why might there still be a legacy of secrecy in Russia and how should foreigners respond when they confront it?

Phonetics and Intonation

The Vowels е and э

This unit presents the sound |e|, which is written with the vowels е and э.

a. Listen to the vowels е and э when stressed and preceded and followed by a hard consonant.

эс	эн	эт	эр
жес	жен	жет	жер
шес	шен	шет	шер
цес	цен	цет	цер
Бэ	Гэ	Дэ	Жэ

b. Listen to the vowels е and э when stressed and preceded by a soft consonant and followed by a hard consonant. Remember: you must pronounce the word-initial consonant as soft. Don't insert a y-glide!

вес	вен	вет	вер
нес	нен	нет	нер
тес	тен	тет	тер
зес	зен	зет	зер
дес	ден	дет	дер

c. This pronunciation is also used when soft-series vowel е is in word-initial position and is followed by a hard consonant. Note that this vowel, when in word-initial position, has a y-glide.[1] (Which other vowels also have a y-glide in word-initial position?)

ес	ен	ет	ер

d. Listen to the vowels е and э when stressed, followed by a soft consonant and preceded by a consonant that is always hard (despite the fact that it is followed by a soft-series vowel).

жей	шей	цей
жеч	шеч	цеч
жещ	шещ.	цещ
жень	шень	цень
жель	шель	цель

e. Listen to the vowels е and э when stressed and preceded and followed by a soft consonant.

сей	тей	зей
сеч	теч	зеч
сещ	тещ	зещ
сель	тель	зель
сесь	тесь	зесь

---

[1]The y-glide is also pronounced when this letter is preceded by another vowel.

f. This pronunciation is also used when soft-series vowel **e** is in word-initial position and is followed by a soft consonant.

> ей   еч   ещ

SELF-QUIZ

Listen to the numbered words and sounds and write them down as you hear them.

1. _____
2. _____
3. _____
4. _____
5. _____
6. _____
7. _____
8. _____
9. _____
10. _____

Lexicon: Belief and Faith

You already know the Russian verb **ве́рить (в кого́? во что? кому́?)**, meaning *to believe in someone or something* or *to believe someone*. This verb is used to express belief in God.

Ве́рить/по- [в кого́? во что? кому́?]
To believe in someone or something; to believe someone

> Я ве́рю в тебя́: ты всегда́ поступа́ешь пра́вильно.
> *I believe in you: you always act (behave) correctly (properly).*

> Я не ве́рю коммуни́стам.
> *I don't believe the Communists.*

Ве́ровать, (не)ве́рующий
To believe in God, a (non)believer in God

> В сове́тское вре́мя ве́рующим бы́ло тру́дно доста́ть Би́блию.
> *In the Soviet era it was difficult for believers to get a Bible.*

Ве́ра [в кого́? во что?]
Faith

> Он страда́ет, потому́ что у него́ нет ве́ры в Бо́га.
> *He's suffering because he has no faith in God.*

Вероисповедáние
Religious faith

    — Каковó вáше вероисповедáние?
    — Вся нáша семья́ — правослáвная.
    What is your religion?
    Our entire family is [Russian] Orthodox.

Моли́ться [комý? за что?]
To pray

    Роди́тели мóлятся за здорóвье больнóго ребёнка.
    The parents are praying for the health of their sick child.

The preceding words are related to a number of other words of interest:

Уверя́ть/увéрить [когó? в чём?]
To assure someone

    Я уверя́ю вас, что никогó здесь нé было.
    I assure you that no one was here.

Проверя́ть/провéрить (когó? что?)
To check for correctness

    Преподавáтель проверя́ет нáшу рабóту óчень тща́тельно.
    The teacher checks our work very thoroughly.

Доверя́ть/довéрить [комý? дéлать/с- что?]
To trust someone

    Мы не доверя́ем емý, потомý что он нас чáсто обмáнывает.
    We don't trust him because he frequently deceives (tricks) us.

Умоля́ть [когó? дéлать/с- что?]
To implore someone for something or to implore someone to do something

    Мы вас умоля́ем отпусти́ть нас за пятнáдцать минýт до концá урóка.
    We implore you to let us out fifteen minutes before the end of class.

While on the topic of faith, here are a number of terms related to the major religions of people who live on the territory of the former Soviet Union.

FAITH OR RELIGION	PEOPLE OF THIS FAITH	HOUSE OF WORSHIP	CLERGY
правослáвие	правослáвные	цéрковь, собóр	свящéнник
католици́зм, католи́чество	катóлик, католи́чка	цéрковь, костёл, собóр	свящéнник
протестáнство, протестанти́зм	протестáнт, протестáнтка	цéрковь, ки́рка, собóр	пáстор
ислáм, мусульмáнство	мусульмáнин, мусульмáнка	мечéть	имáм
иудаи́зм, иудéйство	еврéй, еврéйка	синагóга	равви́н

Упражнение 11.2   Fill in the blanks with the Russian equivalent of the English word or phrase in parentheses. The paragraph concerns religion in the former Soviet Union.

На территории бывшего Советского Союза живёт почти 300 млн. человек, у которых очень разные (*religious faiths*) _____.[1] Конечно, многие из бывших граждан Советского Союза — (*non-believers*) _____,[2] потому что Советское государство активно вело пропаганду атеизма. Тем не менее искра ([*of*] *faith*) _____[3] в Бога не угасла за 75 лет советской власти. Сегодня возрастает интерес к религии. На территории Российской Федерации, конечно, очень распространено ([*Russian*] *Orthodoxy*) _____[4] сейчас, когда русские возвращаются к своим корням. Пользуются популярностью и (*the churches*) _____[5] ([*of*] *Protestantism*) _____,[6] в которые приезжает много проповедников из Америки. На территории Балтийских республик (то есть, в Эстонии, Латвии, Литве) молодые (*Protestants and Catholics*) _____[7] ходят в (*church*) _____[8] вместе с родителями и с собственными детьми: это одно из явлений возрождения национального самознания этих народов. В Средней Азии и в Татарстане (*Moslems*) _____[9] каждый день открываются новые (*mosques*) _____,[10] в которых (*pray*) _____[11] всё больше и больше мусульман. (*Jews* [*use accusative case form*]) _____[12] (*assure* [*use* **они** *form*]) _____,[13] что в Российской Федерации не будет антисемитизма; открываются новые (*synagogues*) _____,[14] приезжают из-за границы (*rabbis*) _____,[15] и некоторые из них (*implore*) _____[16] молодых евреев не эмигрировать.

Exercises and Activities

Упражнение 11.3   Fill in the blanks with the Russian equivalent of the English phrase in parentheses.

1. Дине (*will need*) _____ машина.

2. Ему (*needed*) _____ новые материалы.

3. Гале (*needed*) _____ марки.

4. Мне (*will need*) _____ деньги.

5. Ей (*will need*) _____ поехать в Россию.

6. Кириллу (*will need*) _____ квартира.

Упражнéние 11.4   Translate the following sentences into Russian.

1. She needed help. _____

2. He needed to go to Moscow. _____

3. They need the newspaper. _____

4. We need sugar. _____

5. I will need money. _____

Упражнéние 11.5   Fill in the blanks with the Russian equivalent of the English phrase in parentheses. Use some of these words: **вéсело, грýстно, скýчно, интерéсно, хорошó, плóхо хóлодно, теплó.**

1. Áлле (*was cold*) _____ в Сибúри.

2. Им (*will be hot*) _____ в Сенегáле

3. Дмúтрию (*is cold*) _____: закрóй окнó.

4. Мне (*will be boring*) _____ в самолёте: поэтому я берý с собóй книжку.

5. Вам (*was happy/merry*) _____, когдá вы бы́ли у них в Тверú?

6. Жáнне (*was interesting*) _____ на встрéче с перевóдчиками.

Упражнéние 11.6   Fill in the blanks with the correct form of the word or phrase in parentheses.

1. Зáвтра мы расскáжем (рýсские стажёры) _____ об э́том.

2. (Нáши знакóмые) _____ óчень понрáвились нóвые технúческие словарú.

3. Мы позвонúм (декáн) _____ в университéт и спрóсим об э́том.

4. Скóлько лет (егó родúтели) _____?

5. Мы чáсто хóдим к (Кирúлл и Марúна) _____ в гóсти.

6 (Софúя Петрóвна) _____ нáдо будет купúть э́ту кнúгу.

7. (Их профéссор) _____ по (рýсский язы́к) _____ _____ нýжно купúть нóвый компью́тер.

8. Онú ужé óтдали кнúгу (бáбушка) _____.

9. Я обязáтельно передáм э́ту информáцию (Василий Анатóльевич) _____ _____.

10. Мы чáсто помогáем (отéц) _____.

Упражнёние 11.7 Fill in the blanks with the correct form of the personal pronoun in parentheses.

1. (Ты) _____ на́до бы́ло э́то сде́лать?

2. Безу́ховы о́чень симпати́чные! Мы ча́сто хо́дим к (они́) _____ в го́сти.

3. (Они́) _____ на́до бу́дет прие́хать в семь.

4. (Мы) _____ на́до э́то сде́лать.

5. Ты зна́ешь Со́ню? Мы сейча́с идём к (она́) _____. Ты не хо́чешь пойти́ с на́ми?

6. (Вы) _____ на́до бы́ло об э́том ду́мать вчера́.

Упражнёние 11.8 Complete the sentence **Они́ ча́сто помога́ют** [+ кому́] with the correct form of the names. Remember that names ending in **-ский/-стый/-стой, -цкий/-цкой, -ская/-стая/-цкая,** and **–ские/-стые/-цкие** are always adjectival.

1. Кири́лл Андре́ев _____

2. Татья́на Андре́ева _____

3. Кири́лл и Татья́на Андре́евы _____

4. Анато́лий Пастерна́к _____

5. Лари́са Пастерна́к _____

6. Анато́лий и Лари́са Пастерна́к _____

7. Пол Бра́ун _____

8. Па́ула Бра́ун _____

9. И́горь Страви́нский _____

10. Татья́на Толста́я _____

Упражнёние 11.9 One of the most common uses of the dative case is with the expression **на́до** to express *must* or *has/have to* with an infinitive. Use the names to write instructions to various individuals as indicated.

Образе́ц: Алекса́ндра Серге́ева + найти́ но́вую рабо́ту
Алекса́ндре Серге́евне на́до найти́ но́вую рабо́ту.

1. Дуби́нины + купи́ть биле́ты
2. Мари́я Васи́льевна + э́то сде́лать
3. Анато́лий + пойти́ в магази́н за молоко́м
4. На́ша знако́мая + прочита́ть э́ту кни́гу
5. Э́тот учёный + купи́ть но́вый костю́м

Упражне́ние 11.10   Fill in the blanks with the Russian equivalent of the English phrase in parentheses. Use constructions such as **не́когда, у него́ есть когда́**... and so forth.

1.   В общежи́тии о́чень шу́мно: ей (*has no place*) _____ занима́ться.

2.   Он живёт с роди́телями и поэ́тому ему́ у него́ (*has a place*) _____ занима́ться.

3.   Ему́ (*has no reason*) _____ звони́ть: он не зна́ет, что нам нужна́ его́ по́мощь.

4.   Она́ зна́ет, что мы ждём её звоно́к, поэ́тому ей у неё (*has a reason*) _____ позвони́ть.

5.   В Аме́рике нам (*have no one with whom*) _____ говори́ть по–ру́сски.

6.   В Аме́рике вам у вас (*people with whom*) _____ говори́ть по–ру́сски: в ка́ждом го́роде мно́го эмигра́нтов из бы́вшего СССР!

Упражне́ние 11.11   Fill in the blanks with the Russian equivalent of the English phrase in parentheses. Use **хоте́ть/за–, хоте́ться/за–,** and **хоте́л/-а/-и бы.**

1.   (*I really want*) _____ пое́хать в Росси́ю в сле́дующем году́.

2.   (*I don't feel like*) _____ идти́ на ле́кцию по фи́зике сего́дня.

3.   (*I would like*) _____ спроси́ть вас об э́том, но бою́сь, что у вас не бу́дет вре́мени отвеча́ть на мой вопро́с.

4.   (*She suddenly came to want*) _____ получа́ть сто́лько же, ско́лько получа́ет Ивано́в.

5.   (*They wanted*) _____ всё уви́деть сра́зу, но э́то бы́ло невозмо́жно.

6.   (*He felt like*) _____ поговори́ть об э́том со мной, но я не могла́ ему́ сове́товать.

7.   (*We suddenly felt like*) _____ вы́бежать из авто́буса, на кото́ром мы весь день е́здили по го́роду, но у нас не хвати́ло сме́лости.

8.   Е́сли (*you suddenly [will] feel like*) _____ поговори́ть об э́том, пожа́луйста, ра́ди Бо́га, вот моя́ визи́тная ка́рточка: позвони́те!

9.   (*He would have liked*) _____ зае́хать к вам, но не смог: за́втра бу́дет экза́мен.

10.   (*We would like*) _____, что́бы вы объясни́ли нам ра́зницу ме́жду э́тими двумя́ выраже́ниями.

Упражнéние 11.12   Combine the clauses to form complex or compound sentences, using the word **котóрый**, or a **кто/что, то/что** clause to replace a repeated subject wherever you see three dots (...). Try to make a story out of the sentences.

1. зáвтра у Жóры бýдет контрóльная по геогрáфии ... об э́той контрóльной емý рассказáла Ди́на
2. все студéнты, ... студéнтам скýчно на занятиях по геогрáфии, не хóдят на э́ти заня́тия
3. Жóра, ... Жóре тóже скýчно на э́тих заня́тиях, тóже не хóдит на них
4. профéссор по геогрáфии считáет, что все студéнты ... (*who*) не хóдят на заня́тия, бýдут озадáчены контрóльной
5. Ди́на предупреди́ла Жóру, ... Жóре нýжно мнóго готóвиться к контрóльной
6. Ди́на звони́ла всем, (*who*) нé было на заня́тиях в тот день, когдá профéссор объяви́л, что бýдет контрóльная
7. Жóра взял всё, (*that*) емý нýжно бы́ло, и пошёл в библиотéку
8. он взял все учéбники, ... по э́тим учéбникам рабóтает профéссор
9. в библиотéке он нашёл ребя́т, ... ребя́там помогáла Óльга Николáевна, чáстный репети́тор по геогрáфии
10. Жóре помогáли все, (*who*) ходи́л на урóки Óльги Николáевны
11. Жóра хотéл позвони́ть Ди́ме и попроси́ть и его́ пóмощи, но знал, что Ди́ма не согласи́тся: Ди́ма навéрно скáжет, что не помогáет тем, (*who*) нéкогда бы́ло ходи́ть на заня́тия
12. Слáва Бóгу, Жóра написáл контрóльную... контрóльная былá не óчень трýдной

Упражнéние 11.13   Translate the following passage into Russian.

Yesterday I visited the Romanovs and I was surprised at the fact that Olia Romanova turned 17. I thought that she was only 12! It seemed that Olia was bored at the party (although it was interesting for me there). I liked Olia's friend, Nikita, a lot: I think that he likes Olia. He gave her a nice (**ми́лый**) present and talked about her all evening. I remember that Olia had no interest in boys (**ей бы́ло не до мáльчиков**) and she had no one with whom to be friends (**дружи́ть**), but, thank God, now she has someone to be friends with.

It's time (**порá**) for Olia [*dat.*] to think about university. By '97 she'll have her high school diploma (**аттестáт зрéлости**). Judging from what her parents say, she's a smart girl. She got [received] an "A" (**пятёрку**) in physics without a tutor (**репети́тор**). Previously her parents thought that they needed money for (**на** + *acc.*) tutors, but now that isn't necessary for them.

Tomorrow I'll call Boris Romanov at work and ask him about Olia's plans. He, probably, will say that Olia has nothing to fear for two reasons: first, she's rather bright; second, she works [studies] a lot. She probably will manage to get into [be admitted into] a good institute.

Задáние 11.3   Write a story consisting of two or more paragraphs, using four of the following phrases in any order

к котóрому/котóрой/котóрым	*to which/whom*
котóрому рассказáли	*who was told*
котóрой подари́ли	*who was given*
котóрому/котóрой/котóрым скýчно	*who are bored*
котóрому онá помогáет	*whom she helps*
котóрым нéгде	*who have nowhere to . . .*
удивля́ются томý, что	*are surprised by the fact that*
всё, что нýжно	*all that which is necessary*
котóрым позвони́ли	*whom we/you/they called*
котóрым написáли	*whom we/you/they wrote*

Задáние 11.4   Write a paragraph describing when you have to complete homework assignments for three different classes, using the dative construction to express the notion of deadlines. Use the words **закóнчить задáние**, and **написáть рабóту**.

Glossary

# вѐра [в кого? во что?]	*faith in someone or something*
# вѐрить/по– (II) [в кого? во что? комỳ?]: вѐрю, вѐришь, вѐрят	*to believe in someone or something, to believe someone*
# вѐровать (I), вѐрующий/не–	*to believe in God, believer (nonbeliever in God)*
# вероисповедáние	*religious faith*
вѐсело [комỳ?]	*merry, fun*
возмóжно/не– [дѐлать что?]	*possible, impossible*
# впускáть (I) /впустѝть (II) [когó? кудá?]: впускáю, впускáешь, впускáют; впущỳ, впýстишь, впýстят	*to let someone in somewhere*
# выпускáть (I) /вы́пустить (II) [когó? кудá?]: выпускáю, выпускáешь, выпускáют; вы́пущу, вы́пустишь, вы́пустят	*to let someone out somewhere*
говорѝть (II) /сказáть (I) [комỳ? что?]: говорю́, говорѝшь, говорят; скажỳ, скáжешь, скáжут	*to tell something to someone*
грỳстно [комỳ?]	*sad*
давáть (I) /дать (*) [комỳ? что?]: даю́, даёшь, даю́т, давáй(те)!; дам, дашь, даст, дадѝм, дадѝте, дадýт, дáй(те)! дал, далá, дáли	*to give someone something*
# доверя́ть (I)/доверить (II) (комỳ? дѐлать что?): доверя́ю, доверя́ешь, доверя́ют; довѐрю, довѐришь, довѐрят	*to trust someone to do something*
дóлжен, должнá, должны́ (+ инфинитѝв)	*must (used with nominative case of person who must)*
# допускáть (I) /допустѝть (II) [когó? кудá?]: допускáю, допускáешь, допускáют; допущỳ, допýстишь, допýстят	*to let someone do something*
# еврѐй, еврѐйка	*Jew*
# запрещáть (I) /запретѝть (II) [когó? дѐлать что?] : запрещáю, запрещáешь, запрещáют; запрещỳ, запретѝшь, запретя́т	*to forbid someone from doing something*
# запрещён, запрещенá, запрещенó, запрещены́	*forbidden, prohibited*
# запрѐт	*prohibition, ban*
# запрѐтный	*prohibited, banned*
звонѝть/по– (II) [комỳ? кудá?]: звоню́, звонѝшь, звоня́т	*to call someone somewhere*
# имáм	*Imam (Moslem cleric)*
интерѐсно [комỳ?]	*interested*
# ислáм	*Islam*

исполниться (II) [кому́? ско́лько лет?]:
кому́ испо́лнится 21 год, испо́лнился 21 год,
испо́лнилось 22 го́да

to become a certain age
who will become 21 years
old, who became 21 years
old, who became 22 years
old

иудаи́зм, иуде́йство

Judaism

к [кому́? чему́?]

to, by, toward (plus the
dative)

като́лик, католи́чка

Catholic

католици́зм, католи́чество

Catholicism

ки́рка

Protestant church

костёл

Catholic Cathedral

мече́ть (ж.)

mosque

мо́жно [кому́? чему́? де́лать что?]

may, possible, permitted

мо́жно не [кому́? чему́? де́лать что?]

it is possible to not . . .

моли́ться (II) [кому́? за что?]:
молю́сь, мо́лишься, мо́лятся

to pray to someone for
something

мусульма́нин, мусульма́нка

Moslem (m; f.)

мусульма́нство

Islam

на́до [кому́? + инфинити́в]

must (used with the dative
case of the person who
must)

не́где [кому́? де́лать что?]

there is nowhere for . . . to . . .

не́зачем [кому́? де́лать что?]

there is no reason for . . .
to . . .

не́когда [кому́? де́лать что?]

there is no time for . . . to . . .

не́кому [кому́? де́лать что?]

there is no one for . . . to . . .

не́куда [кому́? де́лать что?]

there is nowhere for . . . to . . .

нельзя́ [кому́? де́лать что?]

forbidden or impossible (plus
the dative of the person
who is forbidden)

не́чего [кому́? + инфинити́в]

there is nothing for . . . to . . . .

не́чем [кому́? де́лать что?]

there is nothing for . . . with
which to . . .

нра́виться/по– (II) [кому́? что?]:
нра́влюсь, нра́вишься, нра́вятся

to like (used with the dative
case of the person who
likes and the nominative
case of the person or thing
which is liked)

ну́жен, нужна́, ну́жно, нужны́

necessary, needed (used with
the dative case of the
person who needs)

отпускáть (I) /отпустúть (II) [когó? кудá?]:   *to let someone go*
   отпускáю, отпускáешь, отпускáют; отпущý, отпýстишь,
   отпýстят

пáмятник [комý?]   *monument to someone*

пáстор   *pastor, minister*

по [комý? чемý?]   *by, in (used with the dative case)*

подóбен, подóбна, подóбно, подóбны [чемý?]   *similar to (used with the dative case)*

помогáть (I) /помóчь (I) [комý? дéлать что?]:   *to help, give assistance to (used with the dative case)*
   помогáю, помогáешь, помогáют; помогý, помóжешь,
   помóгут, помóг, помоглá, помоглú

по мéре тогó, как   *inasmuch as . . .*

по слéдующей причúне/по слéдующим причúнам . . .   *for the following reason(s)*

правослáвие, правослáвный   *[Russian] Orthodox*

привыкáть (I) /привы́кнуть (I) [к комý? к чемý?]:   *to get used to someone or something*
   привыкáю, привыкáешь, привыкáют; привы́кну,
   привы́кнешь, привы́кнут, привы́к, привы́кла, привы́кли

приходúться (I) /прийтúсь (I) [комý? дéлать что?]:   *to have to do something, to be compelled to do something*
   нам прихóдится/приходúлось; нам придётся/пришлóсь

прия́тно [комý?]   *pleased*

проверя́ть (I) /провéрить (II) [когó? что?]:   *to check someone or something*
   проверя́ю, проверя́ешь, проверя́ют; провéрю, провéришь,
   провéрят

прóпуск   *pass (a document) to go somewhere*

пропускáть (I) /пропустúть (II) [когó? кудá?]:   *to let someone through to somewhere*
   пропускáю, пропускáешь, пропускáют; пропущý,
   пропýстишь, пропýстят

протестáнство, протестантúзм   *Protestantism*

протестáнт, протестáнтка   *Protestant*

раввúн   *rabbi*

расскáзывать (I) /рассказáть (I) [комý? о чём?]:   *to tell someone a story*
   расскáзываю, расскáзываешь, расскáзывают; расскажý,
   расскáжешь, расскáжут

разрешáть (-ся) (I) [комý? дéлать что?]:   *to permit someone to do something*
   разрешáю (-сь), разрешáешь (-ся), разрешáют (-ся)

разрешéние   *permission (may be written or oral)*

свящéнник   *priest (Russian Orthodox or Catholic)*

синагóга   *synagogue*

скýчно [комý?]   *bored*

слáва Бóгу

собóр

сýдя по чемý/сýдя по томý, что . . .

теплó [комý?]

уверя́ть (I)/увéрить (II) [когó? в чём?]:
уверя́ю, уверя́ешь, уверя́ют; увéрю, увéришь, увéрят

удавáться (I) /удáться (*) [комý? дéлать/с- что?]:
нам удаётся/удавáлось; нам удáстся/удалóсь

удивля́ться (I) /удиви́ться (II) [комý? чемý?]:
удивля́юсь, удивля́ешься, удивля́ются; удивлю́сь,
удиви́шься, удивя́тся

умоля́ть (I) [когó? дéлать что?]:
умоля́ю, умоля́ешь, умоля́ют

цéрковь (ж.), цéркви (род.)

хóлодно [комý?]

glory (thanks) to God

cathedral (of any Christian
faith)

judging by something,
judging by the fact that . . .

warm

to assure someone of
something

to be able to do something, to
be able to get something
done

to be surprised at someone or
something

to implore someone to do
something

church (of any Christian
faith)

cold

UNIT 12

Lexicon: Jobs and Professions

Russians use a number of expressions to describe choosing and entering a profession and looking for a job.

Учи́ться [на кого́?]
To study to become something (colloquial)

> Она́ у́чится на врача́.
> *She's studying to be a doctor.*

Станови́ться/стать [кем?]
To become something

> О́льга, наве́рно, ста́нет лингви́стом.
> *Ol'ga will probably become a linguist.*

Выбира́ть/вы́брать профе́ссию
To choose a profession

> Ру́сские выбира́ют профе́ссию ра́ньше, чем её выбира́ют америка́нцы.
> *Russians choose a profession earlier than Americans do.*

> Я вы́брал профе́ссию учи́теля и о́чень люблю́ свою́ профе́ссию.
> *I chose the profession of a teacher and I like my profession very much.*

Кто вы по профе́ссии? (Кто вы по специа́льности?)
What is your profession? What is your specialty?

> Татья́на Влади́мировна по профе́ссии врач–онко́лог.
> *Tat'iana Vladimirovna is an oncologist.*

Рабо́тать/по– [кем?]
To work in a certain job (not necessarily one's actual profession)

> По профе́ссии я актёр, но рабо́таю официа́нтом.
> *I'm an actor by training, but I work as a waiter.*

Быть [кем?]
To work a certain job

> Де́душка был пло́тником.
> *My grandfather was a carpenter.*

Увольня́ть/уво́лить [кого́?] с рабо́ты, увольня́ться/уво́литься с рабо́ты
To lose a job

> Он уво́лился с рабо́ты и на́чал за́ново писа́ть автобиогра́фию.
> *He lost his job and began to write a new resumé.*

119

Искáть/по– рабóту, мéсто
To look for a job, position

> Я ищý рабóту с рýсским языкóм.
> *I'm looking for a job connected with Russian.*

Находи́ть/найти́ рабóту, мéсто
To find a job, position, or vacancy

> Он кáждый год ухóдит с однóй рабóты, и нахóдит себé нóвую.
> *Every year he leaves one job and finds himself another.*

Поступáть/поступи́ть на рабóту
To begin a new job, to take up a position

> Зи́на поступи́ла на эту рабóту в апрéле.
> *Zina started this job in April.*

Упражнéние 12.1   Fill in the blanks with the correct word or words, using the following cues, though not necessarily in this order: *will become, to become, are looking for work, translator, translators, were choosing, veterinarian (twice), to study (twice), chose.* Read the whole paragraph before completing the first blank.

Серёжа и Лéна óчень дóлго _____¹ профéссию. Наконéц Лéна

реши́ла поступи́ть в институ́т и _____² на

_____.³ Серёжа реши́л _____ ⁴

_____,⁵ потомý что мнóгие из его друзéй

_____.⁶ Лéна сказáла, что онá _____ ⁷

_____⁸ потомý что онá óчень лю́бит живóтных, а Серёжа

_____⁹ свою́ профéссию тóлько потомý, что он бои́тся сам

принимáть решéния. Лéна тóже сказáла, что хотя́ нéкоторые друзья́ Серёжи ужé стáли

перевóдчиками, они́ всё ещё _____,¹⁰ и поэтому лýчше вы́брать

другу́ю профéссию.

Задáние 12.1   Continue the story begun in **Упражнéние 12.1**.

Задáние 12.2   Prepare a three-minute talk or write a composition, as assigned by your instructor, beginning with the phrase **Когдá я закóнчу университéт, я хочý стáть** + *profession in the instrumental case,* **по слéдующим причи́нам...** (*When I finish school I want to become . . . because . . .*). Cite at least three reasons and provide details supporting your reasons.

Фóто-задáние   Look at the photograph on the first page of this unit in the textbook. Pretend that you are a fortune-teller and write a paragraph or prepare a presentation, as assigned by your instructor, describing what two or three of the children in the picture will grow up to become.

Listening Tasks

The listening text for this unit consists of a dialogue in which two people try to arrange for a "professions night" at a local school to expose schoolchildren to a variety of professions.

PRE-LISTENING TASK

What kinds of professions might be represented at such an event?

LISTENING TASKS

Listen to the text and answer questions 1 through 4 in English and 5 through 7 in Russian.

1. What are the names of the two people participating in the dialogue?
2. As you listen to the dialogue, list the names of the people mentioned and their professions.
3. What can Tania bring along to show the kids?
4. What's the problem with inviting Vitia?
5. Find the Russian equivalent of *whom else can we invite*?
6. How does one of the speakers express disdain for Vitia's professional success?
7. Find the Russian equivalent for *in that case, let's invite Vera*.

DICTATION

Replay the tape and, as you listen, write out the dialogue in full.

PERFORMANCE

Practice reciting the dialogue.

POST-LISTENING TASK

Ask your classmates what professions they aspire to. Then, using the dialogue as a model, work with a classmate to create and perform your own dialogue in which you discuss setting up a "professions night" at a local school with members of your class role-playing the professions they would like to take up upon graduation.

CULTURAL PROBLEM

One of the professions mentioned in the dialogue is a relatively recent addition to the Russian business world. What American professions or jobs might be new to Russia since the collapse of the USSR?

Phonetics and Intonation

Hard and Soft л

This unit presents hard and soft л. For hard л, place the tip of your tongue at the place where your front upper teeth meet your hard palate (the front of the roof of your mouth). For soft л, place the tip of your tongue at the place where your front lower teeth meet the gum and puff the middle of your tongue up towards the roof of your mouth. Pronounce soft л with the middle of your tongue, not the tip of your tongue. (American pronunciation of many sounds is focused on the very tip of the tongue, but Russian pronunciation is usually not "off the tip of one's tongue"!)

Listen to the hard л and the soft л on the tape.

	INITIAL HARD л	INITIAL SOFT л		FINAL HARD л	FINAL SOFT л
1.	лак	ляк	11.	вал	валь
2.	лам	лям	12.	мял	мяль
3.	лон	лён	13.	вол	воль
4.	лоб	лёб	14	бол	боль
5	лун	люн	15.	нул	нуль
6.	лут	лют	16.	тюл	тюль
7.	лэс	лес	17.	сел	сель
8.	лэш	леш	18.	шел	шель
9.	лык	лик	19.	сыл	сыль
10.	лыс	лис	20.	кил	киль

SELF-QUIZ

Listen to the tape and circle the letters that best represent each numbered sound.

1.	лак	ляк	11.	вал	валь
2.	лам	лям	12.	мял	мяль
3.	лоб	лёб	13.	вол	воль
4.	лон	лён	14.	бол	боль
5.	лун	люн	15.	нул	нуль
6.	лут	лют	16.	тюл	тюль
7.	лэс	лес	17.	сел	сель
8.	лык	лик	18.	шел	шель
9.	лыс	лис	19.	сил	силь
10.	лыт	лит	20.	кил	киль

Lexicon: Holiday Greetings

Russians use two key expressions to greet one another on secular and religious holidays.

Поздравля́ть/поздра́вить [кого́? с каки́м пра́здником?]
To congratulate someone on what holiday, to wish someone a happy holiday

> Я вас поздравля́ю с Но́вым го́дом!
> *I wish you a happy New Year!*

> За́втра мы поздра́вим Петро́вых с Рождество́м.
> *Tomorrow we'll wish the Petrovs a Merry Christmas.*

Жела́ть [кому́? чего́?]
To wish something for someone

> Мы жела́ем вам всего́ наилу́чшего.
> *We wish you all the best.*

These greetings can be used for most major secular and religious holidays, except for Russian Orthodox Easter and Passover for which there are special greetings.

HOLIDAY	DATE OR TIME OF YEAR	GREETING: Поздравляю Вас...
Нóвый год	1 января́	С Нóвым гóдом!
Рождествó [правослáвное]	6 января́	С Рождествóм Христóвым!
Междунарóдный жéнский день	8 мáрта	С жéнским днём!
День Побéды	9 мáя	С днём Побéды!
Пáсха	весно́й	Христóс воскрéсе! Во-и́стину воскрéсе!
Еврéйская Пáсха	весно́й	В Слéдующем году́ в Иерусали́ме!
Еврéйский Нóвый год, Рош-ха-шáна	óсенью	С Нóвым гóдом!
Рождествó [зáпадное]	25 декабря́	С Рождествóм Христóвым!
Хáнука	óсенью/зимóй	С Хáнукой!

Задáние 12.3 Write short notes congratulating friends on three of the holidays in the preceding chart.

Exercises and Activities

Упражнéние 12.2 Answer the question **Кем (чем) студéнты недовóльны?** with the cue.

1. э́та стáрая лóшадь _____

2. жизнь в университéте _____

3. э́тот музéй _____

4. большáя шкóла _____

5. гости́ница _____

6. э́ти лю́ди _____

7 вáши дéти _____

8. э́та лаборатóрия _____

Упражнéние 12.3 Fill in the blanks with the instrumental case form of the personal pronoun in parentheses.

1. Мари́на Сергéевна óчень довóльна (они́) _____.

2. Мы чáсто хóдим в кинó с (он) _____.

3. Они́ тáкже óчень довóльны (онá) _____.

4. Мы все óчень довóльны (он) _____.

5. Михаи́л óчень недовóлен (вы) _____.

6. Они́ ужé говори́ли со (я) _____ об э́том.

Упражне́ние 12.4   Complete the sentence **Мы говори́ли с...** with the instrumental case form of each name. Remember that names ending in **–ский/-стый/-стой, –цкий/-цкой, –ская/-стая/-цкая,** and **–ские/-стые/-цкие** are always adjectival.

1.   Кири́лл Андре́ев _____

2.   Татья́на Андре́ева _____

3.   Кири́лл и Татья́на Андре́евы _____

4.   Анато́лий Пастерна́к _____

5.   Лари́са Пастерна́к _____

6.   Анато́лий и Лари́са Пастерна́к_____

7.   Пол Бра́ун _____

8.   Па́ула Бра́ун _____

9.   Бори́с и Верони́ка Вербицкие _____

10. Лев Тро́цкий _____

 Зада́ние 12.4   Prepare a three-minute talk or write a composition, as assigned by your instructor, explaining with what or whom you are dissatisfied.

 Упражне́ние 12.5   Following the model, complete the sentences with the cues.

Образе́ц: Я счита́ю ... Ми́ша ... плохо́й бизнесме́н
Я счита́ю Ми́шу плохи́м бизнесме́ном.

1.   Татья́на Анато́льевна ... спосо́бный архите́ктор
2.   Ди́ма ... краси́вый ма́льчик
3.   Ки́ра Васи́льевна ... гениа́льный фи́зик
4.   Арка́дий и Гали́на ... хоро́шие роди́тели
5.   Ири́на Петро́вна ... ужа́сный поэ́т
6.   Анато́лий Миха́йлович ... безда́рный драмату́рг

 Упражне́ние 12.6   Following the model, complete the sentence with the cues.

Образец: Михаи́л ... плохо́й бизнесме́н
Михаи́л оказа́лся плохи́м бизнесме́ном.

1.   Мари́я Дми́триевна ... тала́нтливый хи́мик
2.   Серге́й Па́влович ... гениа́льный пиани́ст
3.   Ле́на ... чувстви́тельная тётя
4.   Верони́ка и Анато́лий ... хоро́шие роди́тели
5.   Кири́лл Бори́сович ... ужа́сный инжене́р
6.   Вале́рия Серге́евна ... безда́рный ску́льптор

 Зада́ние 12.5   Prepare a three-minute talk or write a composition, as assigned by your instructor, about someone who turned out to be different from what you expected. Use the constructions **счита́ть кого́ кем/каки́м/како́й, оказа́ться кем.**

 Упражне́ние 12.7   Rewrite the sentences in **Упражне́ние 12.6** in the future tense, adding the words **Я ду́мал /-а, что.**

Образе́ц: *Я ду́мал/-а, что Андре́й Матве́евич ока́жется спосо́бным архите́ктором.*

Упражне́ние 12.8   Combine the phrases to form complex or compound sentences, using the word **кото́рый**, or а кто/что, то/что clause to replace repeated subject wherever you see three dots (...). Try to make a story out of the sentences.

1. Вале́рия Петро́вна не зна́ла, что де́лать с те́ми, (who) пришёл ра́ньше восьми́ часо́в
2. в конце́ концо́в она́ пригласи́ла их посмотре́ть альбо́мы по иску́сству, ... они́ залюбова́лись альбо́мами
3. пока́ они́ бы́ли за́няты альбо́мами, Вале́рия вы́тащила из духо́вки пече́нье, ... она́ была́ о́чень дово́льна пече́ньем
4. в во́семь часо́в пришли́ все други́е го́сти, ... за э́тими гостя́ми она́ бе́гала туда́ сюда́, что́бы им помо́чь
5. наконе́ц все пришли́, и Вале́рия заме́тила, что То́ля сиде́л ря́дом с Кузнецо́выми, ... с Кузнецо́выми он говори́т ка́ждый ве́чер
6. Вале́рия реши́ла посади́ть Ле́ночку ря́дом с То́лей, ... с Ле́ночкой у него́ мно́го о́бщего.
7. Всем бы́ло о́чень ве́село: И́нна Серге́евна да́же смея́лась над те́ми, (who) реши́л не приходи́ть к Вале́рии Петро́вне
8. И́горь Васи́льевич заме́тил репроду́кцию Ренуа́ра... над репроду́кцией Ренуа́ра висе́ла оригина́льная рабо́та малоизве́стного худо́жника
9. Все, (who) сиде́л ря́дом с И́горем Васи́льевичем, обрати́ли его́ внима́ние на э́ту необы́чную рабо́ту
10. Наконе́ц, Вале́рия Петро́вна объяви́ла то, (for which) она́ всех их пригласи́ла: она́...

Зада́ние 12.6   Finish the story begun in **Упражне́ние 12.8** using as many instrumental case constructions as you can.

Зада́ние 12.7   Write a story consisting of two or more paragraphs, using five of the following phrases in any order

под кото́рым/кото́рой/кото́рыми	*under which*
ме́жду кото́рыми	*between which or whom*
за кото́рым/кото́рой/кото́рыми	*beyond/behind which or whom*
все, с кем	*all those with whom*
всё, над чем	*everything under which*
кото́рыми руково́дит	*who are supervised*
дово́льна те́ми, кто	*pleased with those who*
дово́лен всем, что	*pleased with everything that*
кото́рыми любу́ются	*which are the object of fascination of*
кото́рым/кото́рой занима́ется/занима́ются	*in which she, he, or they are involved*
кото́рыми интересу́ются	*in which they are interested*
с кото́рым/кото́рой/кото́рыми	*with which/whom*

Упражне́ние 12.9   Translate the following passage into Russian.

Once [одна́жды] in the winter of last year, I was walking along at a rapid pace when I saw Pasha and Nika. Nika noticed me and said, "Masha, is that you?"

It turned out that they lived in one of the buildings between the movie theater and Haymarket [Се́нная] Square. I hadn't seen them in years. When I last saw them, several years ago, Pasha was working as a waiter and Nika was working as a secretary. They told me that they were satisfied with their life then when they weren't so busy [occupied] with problems. Pasha became a doctor and Nika became a manager and a writer. She showed me a book about business, which is very popular [enjoys great popularity] in Moscow and St. Petersburg now. She said that she had worked on the book for two years and that in comparison with the other book written by her this one was much better.

"With your two books, Pasha must be very proud of you, Nika!" I said.

"Well, yes, and I'm proud of Pasha. He is interested in very important medical problems and supervises twelve other doctors in the hospital where he works. I consider him to be a very talented doctor."

We talked for a while and when I told them that I am rarely [**ре́дко быва́ю**] outside [**за**] the city, they invited me to visit them at their dacha outside [**под**] St. Petersburg. Pasha wrote down their phone number in green pencil.

Of course I went to visit them at the dacha and there I became acquainted with Dima Skvortsov, with whom I now own [**име́ю**] a small restaurant. We became partners! We laugh at how we met, because at the time he seemed to me so silly.

 Зада́ние 12.8 Prepare a three-minute talk or write a composition, as assigned by your instructor, beginning with the phrase **Де́ти иногда́ смею́тся над други́ми детьми́,…** (*Children sometimes laugh at other children . . .*).

Glossary

быть [кем?]: бу́ду, бу́дешь, бу́дут, бы́л, была́, бы́ли	*to be of a certain profession*
времена́ го́да: весна́, весно́й ле́то, ле́том о́сень, о́сенью зима́, зимо́й	*seasons of the year* *spring, in the spring* *summer, in the summer* *fall, in the fall* *winter, in the winter*
времена́ су́ток: у́тро, у́тром день, днём ве́чер, ве́чером ночь, но́чью	*parts (times) of the day:* *morning, in the morning* *afternoon, in the afternoon* *evening, in the evening* *night, in the night*
в связи́ с чем/в связи́ с тем, что…	*in connection with what/in connection with the fact that . . .*
в соотве́тствии с чем/в соотве́тсвии с тем, что ..	*in connection with what/in connection with the fact that . . .*
# вступа́ть (I) /вступи́ть (II) [в до́лжность]: вступа́ю, вступа́ешь, вступа́ют; вступлю́, всту́пишь, всту́пят	*to take up a position (at work)*
# выбира́ть (I)/вы́брать (I) профе́ссию: выбира́ю, выбира́ешь, выбира́ют; вы́беру, вы́берешь, вы́берут, вы́бери(те)! вы́брал, вы́брала, вы́брали	*to choose a profession*
горди́ться (II) [кем? чем?]: горжу́сь, горди́шься, горди́тся	*to be proud of someone or something*
дово́лен (дово́льна, дово́льны) [кем? чем?]	*to be satisfied with someone or something*
за [кем? чем?]	*behind or beyond someone or something (this preposition may take the accusative in other contexts)*

занима́ться (I) [чем?]:
   занима́юсь, занима́ешься, занима́ются

to be busy or occupied with something (e.g., to do homework in a particular subject)

интересова́ться/за– (I) [чем?]:
   интересу́юсь, интересу́ешься, интересу́ются

to be interested in something

иска́ть/по– (I) [рабо́ту]:
   ищу́, и́щешь, и́щут

to search or look for (work)

Кто вы по профе́ссии?

What do you do?

ме́жду [кем? чем?]

between some people or some things (must take the instrumental case)

над [кем? чем?]

above some people or things (must take the instrumental case)

находи́ть (II) /найти́ (I) [рабо́ту]:
   нахожу́, нахо́дишь, нахо́дят; найду́, найдёшь, найду́т, нашёл, нашла́, нашли́

to find a job

ока́зываться (I) /оказа́ться (I) [кем? чем? каки́м?]:
   ока́зываюсь, ока́зываешься, ока́зываются; окажу́сь, ока́жешься, ока́жутся

to turn out to be someone or something

пе́ред [кем? чем?]

in front of or before something (in a physical sense, not temporal) (must take the instrumental case)

под [кем? чем?]

under or beneath (this preposition may take the accusative case in some contexts)

поздравля́ть (I) /поздра́вить (II) [кого́? с чем?]:
   поздравля́ю, поздравля́ешь, поздравля́ют; поздра́влю, поздра́вишь, поздра́вят

to congratulate someone on a particular holiday

по́льзоваться/вос– (I) [чем?]:
   по́льзуюсь, по́льзуешься, по́льзуются

to use something or enjoy something (may not be used in the sense of "using a person" or "taking advantage of a person")

по сравне́нию с чем/по сравне́нию с тем, что...

in comparison with what/in comparison with the fact that

поступа́ть (I) /поступи́ть (II) [на рабо́ту]:
   поступа́ю, поступа́ешь, поступа́ют; поступлю́, посту́пишь, посту́пят

to begin a job, to enter into a position at work

рабо́тать (I) [кем? над чем?]:
   рабо́таю, рабо́таешь, рабо́тают

to work in a certain job or to work on something

руководи́ть (II) [кем? чем?]:
   руковожу́, руководи́шь, руководя́т

to supervise or run someone or something

с(о) [кем? чем?]

with someone or something (this preposition may take the genitive case in other contexts)

считáть (I) [когó? что? кем? каки́м/какóй?]:
считáю, считáешь, считáют

to consider someone or something to be some way

смея́ться (I) [над кем? над чем?]:
смеюсь, смеёшься, смеются

to laugh at someone or something

станов́иться (II) /стать (I) [кем? чем?]:
становлю́сь, стано́вишься, стано́вятся; стáну, стáнешь, стáнут

to become someone or something (to become a practitioner of a certain profession)

увольня́ть(I)/увóлить(II) [когó?] с рабóты:
увольня́ю,увольня́ешь, увольня́ют; увóлю, увóлишь, увóлят, увóль(те)!

to fire someone

увольня́ться (I) /увóлиться (II) с рабóты:
уволня́юсь, увольня́ешься, уволня́ются; увóлюсь, увóлишься, увóлятся

to lose a job

учи́ться (II) [на когó?]: (*colloquial*)
учу́сь, у́чишься, у́чатся

to study to become something

UNIT 13

Lexicon: Health and Illness

Russians use several key expressions to complain about ill health.

Болеть/за-: у меня болит (болят) _____.
To be in pain: my _____ hurts.

> Вдруг у меня заболели глаза: до сих пор у меня болят глаза.
> *Suddenly my eyes began to hurt: my eyes still hurt now.*

[Кто?] Болен/больна/больны [чем?]
To be sick with something

> Они уже две недели больны гриппом.
> *They have been sick with the flu for two weeks already.*

Болеть/за–, заболевать/заболеть [чем?]
To get sick, to come down with something

> Дети, которые ходят в ясли, часто заболевают.
> *Children who go to day care often come down with something (often get sick).*

> В прошлом году Танечка болела менингитом.
> *Last year Tanechka had meningitis.[1]*

> На прошлой неделе Боря заболел воспалением лёгких: он сейчас лежит в больнице.
> *Last week Boria came down with pneumonia: he's in the hospital now.*

Простужаться/простудиться
To catch a cold

> Люди, которые не делают зарядки, часто простужаются.
> *People who don't exercise often get colds*

Поправляться/поправиться
To get better, gain weight

> Как только Боря поправится, он выпишется и пойдёт домой.
> *As soon as Borya gets better, he'll be discharged (from the hospital) and go home.*

> Борис Николаевич, поправляйтесь!
> *Get better soon, Boris Nikolaevich!*

Вызывать/вызвать врача или скорую помощь
To call (summon) a doctor or an ambulance

> Они — очень мнительные: они раз в неделю вызывают врача!
> *They are hypochondriacs: they call for a doctor at least once a week!*

---

[1]The use of the imperfective indicates that this condition no longer holds, that is, that Tanechka is better.

Принима́ть/приня́ть (пить/вы́ –) лека́рство
To take medicine

Со́ня принима́ет аспири́н три ра́за в день.
Sonia takes aspirin three times a day.

Измеря́ть/изме́рить [кому́?] температу́ру
To take someone's temperature

Ко́ля изме́рил до́чери температу́ру и по́нял, что дочь попра́вилась.
Kolia took his daughter's temperature and realized that she had recovered.

Ре́зать/по– себе́ [что?], ушиба́ть/ушиби́ть себе́ [что?]
To cut, bruise or hurt oneself

Я поре́зал себе́ па́лец, когда́ ре́зал ку́рицу.
I cut my finger while cutting some chicken.

Она́ уши́бла себе́ го́лову, когда́ упа́ла.
She hurt (bruised) herself in the head when she fell.

Ложи́ться/лечь в больни́цу, класть/положи́ть [кого́] в больни́цу
To go/to be admitted to the hospital, to put someone in the hospital

У него́ был инсу́льт: его́ положи́ли в больни́цу.
He had a stroke and was put in the hospital.

Её больны́е ложа́тся в хоро́шую больни́цу.
Her patients go to a good hospital.

Лежа́ть/по– в больни́це
To be in the hospital

Я лежа́ла в больни́це три дня, но пото́м вы́писалась.
I was in the hospital for three days, but then I was discharged.

Лома́ть/с– но́гу/но́ги, ру́ку/ру́ки
To break one's leg or arm

Я слома́л но́гу, когда́ ката́лся на лы́жах в Каре́лии.
I broke my leg while skiing in Karelia.

Чиха́ть, ка́шлять, поно́с, запо́р, тошнота́ [кого́ тошни́т], рво́та [кого́ рвало́/вы́-], у кого́ кру́-жится голова́
To sneeze, to cough, diarrhea, constipation, nauseous [who is nauseous], vomitting [who was vomitting/who vomited], whose head is spinning

У меня́ ужа́сный грипп: я весь день ка́шляю и чиха́ю; то у меня́ поно́с, то запо́р, а всё вре́мя — тошнота́ . У меня́ весь день кру́жится голова́; меня́ уже́ два ра́за сего́дня вы́рвало.
I have a horrible flu: I have been coughing and sneezing all day; first I have diarrhea, then constipation (I'm constipated), and I'm nauseous all the time. I've been dizzy (my head has been spinning) and I've already vomitted twice today.

Упражне́ние 13.1 Fill in the blanks with the Russian equivalent of the English phrase in parentheses. The sentences are comments made by nurses and doctors attending people who were unlucky enough to have eaten a bowl of bad soup at a university cafeteria.

1. У него́ (*head is dizzy*) _____.

2. У неё (*eyes hurt*) _____.

3. Он говорит, что у него вдруг (*stomach began to hurt*) _____

_____.

4. Они думали, что (*sick with the flu*) _____, или что

они (*caught a cold*) _____, но они отравились [*got*

food poisoning].

5. Я им сказала, что они скоро (*will feel better*) _____.

6. Хорошо, что они (*called an ambulance*) _____.

7. Эта женщина уже (*takes medicine*) _____ от

головной боли: я боюсь, что могут смешаться лекарства.

8. Врач уже (*took the temperature*) _____ этим

мужчинам.

9. Эта девочка очень больна: она должна (*be admitted to the hospital*) _____

_____.

10. У этого мальчика сильно (*stomach and chest hurt*) _____

_____.

Упражнение 13.1   Translate the following passage into Russian.

I seldom get ill, but yesterday I felt poorly all day. When I got up in the morning, I felt fine, but by the time I got out of the shower, it seemed to me that I had a not very high temperature. My head ached. When I got to work, my stomach ached. I began to cough and sneeze and felt dizzy. My throat was sore and my ears ached. I went home early, had a cup of tea and some aspirin, and laid down. Soon I felt nauseous and the vomiting began. I called the ambulance and the medics (**медики**) said that I had come down with the flu. They told me to stay in bed for a couple of days and that I would feel better. This morning I felt much better as soon as I woke up.

Фото-задание   Look at the photograph on the first page of this unit in the textbook. Write a paragraph or prepare a presentation, as assigned by your instructor, from the perspective of either the doctor or the patient, describing the patient's visit to the doctor.

Listening Tasks

The listening text for this unit consists of a dialogue between two people about issues of illness and health.

PRE-LISTENING TASK

When was the last time you talked about your health? Under what circumstances did this conversation take place?

LISTENING TASKS

Listen to the text and then answer questions 1 through 5 in English and 6 through 9 in Russian.

1. What is the name of the person who was sick?
2. Who do you think might be talking with this person and why?
3. What were the symptoms?
4. What did the sick person do when he became sick?
5. What is the sick person told to do and why?
6. How does the sick person say that his temperature was elevated?
7. How does the sick person explain that all his symptoms passed?
8. What are the two expressions that mean *recovered*?
9. What is the expression that means *or else we'll all come down with . . .* ?

DICTATION

Replay the tape, and, as you listen, write out the dialogue in full.

PERFORMANCE

Practice reciting of the dialogue.

POST-LISTENING TASK

Using the dialogue as a model, work with a classmate to create and perform your own dialogue in which you interact about a health crisis.

CULTURAL PROBLEM

What are some of the differences between typical Russian and American attitudes toward health, doctors, and medicine? Consider the importance of geography and climate, socialized medicine and private insurance, and homeopathic care (herb therapy) and scientific/medicinal care.

Phonetics and Intonation

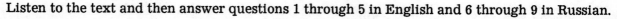

Hard and Soft н

This unit reviews the pronunciation of hard and soft н. For hard н, place the front third of your tongue on your hard upper palate. For soft н, place the middle third of your tongue on your soft upper palate.

Listen to the hard н and the soft н on the tape.

1.	нак	няк	9.	нуж	нюж
2.	нат	нят	10.	ныл	нил
3.	нал	нял	11.	ныр	нир
4.	ном	нём	12.	нылв	нив
5.	нос	нёс	13.	вон	вонь
6.	нор	нёр	14.	чин	чинь
7.	нук	нюк	15.	сан	сань
8.	нуб	нюб			

SELF-QUIZ

Circle the letters that best represent the sounds you hear on the tape.

1.	нак	няк	9.	нуж	нюж
2.	нат	нят	10.	ныл	нил
3.	нал	нял	11.	ныр	нир
4.	ном	нём	12.	ныв	нив
5.	нос	нёс	13.	вон	вонь
6.	нор	нёр	14.	чин	чинь
7.	нук	нюк	15.	сан	сань
8.	нуб	нюб			

Exercises and Activities

Упражне́ние 13.3   Make a chart of the complete declension (all cases, singular and plural) for the following words: **типи́чный студе́нт, типи́чная студе́нтка, интере́сное поня́тие, шика́рный санато́рий, больша́я организа́ция, интере́сная по́весть, большо́й слова́рь.**

Зада́ние 13.1   Write a paragraph about typical students, using the words in as many different cases as you can.

Зада́ние 13.2   Write a paragraph about an interesting concept or a big organization, using the words in as many different cases as you can.

Зада́ние 13.3   Write a paragraph about an interesting novella or a big dictionary, using the words in as many different cases as you can.

Упражне́ние 13.4   Write out the complete declension for all the personal pronouns (**я, ты,** etc.) and for **кто, что, тот, то, та, те.**

Упражне́ние 13.5   Write out the complete declension for **оди́н, одна́, одно́, одни́, э́тот, э́та, э́то, э́ти, чей, чья, чьё, чьи,** and **кото́рый.**

Упражне́ние 13.6   Fill in the blanks with the Russian equivalent of the English word in parentheses.

1. Мы уже́ поговори́ли обо (*everyone*) _____*всех*_____.

2. — Вы случа́йно не ви́дели журна́лы, (*which*) _____*которые*_____ то́лько что лежа́ли здесь на столе́?

   — Вы име́ете в виду́ журна́лы, о (*which*) _____*которых*_____ *prepositional* мы вчера́ говори́ли?

3. Они́ хоро́шие студе́нты. Они́ уже́ прочита́ли (*everything*) _____*всё*_____, (*which*) _____*что*_____ бы́ло за́дано [*was assigned*] преподава́телем на понеде́льник.

4. Где́ же Са́ша? (*He*) _____*Его́*_____ и вчера́ не́ было на заня́тиях!

5. (*We*) _____*Нам*_____ о́чень нра́вятся на́ши но́вые профессора́. Мы о́чень ча́сто разгова́риваем с (*them*) _____*ними*_____ на ра́зные те́мы.

6. Это моя́ ста́ршая сестра́ Ли́за. Вы, наве́рно, уже́ слы́шали о (her)
___ *ней* ___.

7. Вот писа́тели, с (whom) ___ *кото́рыми* ___ мы познако́мились вчера́ на конфере́нции!

8. — Вы всё вре́мя говори́те обо (everything) ___ *всём* ___, (about which)
___ *о чём* ___ не ну́жно говори́ть.

9. — Да, а вы всё вре́мя жа́луетесь на (I) ___ *мина* ___!

Упражне́ние 13.7 Fill in the blanks with the correct form of **чей, чья, чьё, чьи**.

Образе́ц: _____ бра́та ты ви́дела в общежи́тии?
Я ви́дела бра́та Ве́ры в общежи́тии.
Чьего́ бра́та ты ви́дела в общежи́тии?

1. О _____ кни́гах говори́ли на ле́кции?

На ле́кции говори́ли о мои́х кни́гах.

2. Ты _____ кни́гу нашёл?

Я нашёл кни́гу Ва́си.

3. _____ отцу́ помога́ет Андре́й?

Андре́й помога́ет отцу́ Ви́ктора Матве́евича.

4. У _____ роди́телей была́ Ва́ря в гостя́х?

Ва́ря была́ в гостя́х у мои́х роди́телей.

5. Профе́ссор был недово́лен _____ докла́дами?

Он был недово́лен докла́дами Вита́лия.

6. К _____ друзья́м ходи́ли Со́ня и Бо́ря?

Они́ ходи́ли к друзья́м Пе́ти Петухо́ва.

Упражне́ние 13.8 Fill in the blanks with the Russian equivalent of the English word or phrase in parentheses. Some blanks require a form of **свой**, and some require no possessive modifier at all!

1. К сожале́нию, у Мари́ны о́чень боля́т (her) _____ глаза́ и ча́сто боли́т (her) _____ голова́.

2. Она́ ча́сто хо́дит к офтальмо́логу и жа́луется на (her) _____ очки́.

3. Вади́м бои́тся, что (his) _____ сестра́ осле́пнет [become blind].

4. У Мари́ны есть (her) _____ маши́на.

5. Мари́на не то́лько фи́зик, но ещё и автомеха́ник–люби́тель. Она́ о́чень хорошо́ чи́нит [repairs] и (her own) _____ маши́ну и маши́ны (her) _____ друзе́й.

6. Вади́му не нра́вится, что Мари́на так ча́сто во́зится с маши́нами. Он говори́т, что (her) _____ кварти́ра па́хнет бензи́ном!

7. Мари́на живёт вме́сте с(о) (her) _____ роди́телями.

8. Она́ наде́ется, что ско́ро полу́чит (*her own*) _____ кварти́ру.

9. У Вади́ма уже́ есть (*his own*) _____ кварти́ра, где он живёт с(о) (*his*)
_____ жено́й, Лари́сой.

10. У Вади́ма с Лари́сой тро́е дете́й: Са́ша, Ма́ша и Па́ша. (*Their*) _____ де́ти о́чень
лю́бят (*their*) _____ отца́ и ма́ть.

Упражне́ние 13.9   Fill in the blanks with the correct form of the phrase **не тот**. Remember that a preposition, if necessary, is placed between these two words.

Вчера́ у меня́ был о́чень неуда́чный день. Я наде́л _____[1] руба́шку:
я взял руба́шку сосе́да. По́сле того́, как я пришёл на заня́тия, я заме́тил, что наде́л и
_____[2] носки́: оди́н чёрный, а друго́й — кори́чневый. Зате́м у меня́
был ужа́сный сюрпри́з: я гото́вился _____[3] к
_____[4] контро́льной. Ду́мал, что бу́дет экза́мен по грамма́тике, а
оказа́лось, что контро́льная рабо́та — по перево́ду. По́сле контро́льной я был в ужа́сном
состоя́нии и реши́л пойти́ в кафе́ вы́пить ко́фе. Когда́ пришёл в кафе́, по́нял, что взял с
собо́й _____[5] бума́жник: у меня́ не́ было де́нег. К сча́стью, меня́
уви́дел прия́тель, кото́рый мне одолжи́л де́нег. Мы вме́сте вы́пили ко́фе и пошли́ на
сле́дующую ле́кцию, где мне сказа́ли, что я занима́лся _____[6]
вопро́сами. Сплошна́я неуда́ча. Я реши́л пое́хать домо́й — хва́тит, уже́, ду́мал я. Прие́хал
домо́й, доста́л ключи́ из карма́на и … О у́жас!, у́тром я взял _____[7]
ключи́. Или, мо́жет быть, я живу́ _____[8] кварти́ре!

Упражне́ние 13.10   Fill in the blanks with the correct form of the phrases **тот же, тако́й же**.

Ди́ма си́льно подража́ет Ва́ле. На про́шлой неде́ле он мне сказа́л, что купи́л
_____[1] футбо́лку, как купи́ла Ва́ля. Неуже́ли э́то ну́жно? У него́ уже́
есть _____[2] футбо́лки. Ра́зве нужна́ ещё одна́? Пото́м он на́чал
говори́ть _____[3] слова́ми и фра́зами, кото́рыми говори́т Ва́ля,
наприме́р, «во класс» и «кла́ссно». Э́ти клише́ давно́ устаре́ли, но Ди́ма их лю́бит, потому́
что так говори́т Ва́ля. Ди́ма на́чал слу́шать _____[4] му́зыку, кото́рую
слу́шает Ва́ля. Мне никогда́ не нра́вилась му́зыка в сти́ле «ди́ско» семидеся́тых годо́в, и не
хо́чется слу́шать э́ту му́зыку до́ма. Но Ва́ля лю́бит э́ту му́зыку, и поэ́тому лю́бит её и
Ди́ма. Я спроси́ла Ди́му, е́сли Ва́ля пры́гнет с высо́кого зда́ния, пры́гнет ли и он? Ди́ма
сказа́л, что наве́рно пры́гнет, но не с _____[5] зда́ния, а с ме́ньшего!
Надо что–то приду́мать, что́бы поко́нчить с э́тим бессмы́сленным подража́нием!

Упражне́ние 13.11 Fill in the blanks with the correct form of the word **сам**.

1. О́ля вчера́ была́ в гостя́х у _____ Ивано́вых.

2. Па́вловы _____ захоте́ли э́то сде́лать.

3. Ни́на сказа́ла, что она́ вчера́ ходи́ла в кино́ с Пе́тей, и они́ уви́дели

   _____ Жирино́вского в зри́тельном за́ле.

4. Па́ша хо́чет пригласи́ть _____ Та́ню Бори́сову на ве́чер.

5. Мы ходи́ли к _____ Ивано́вой, и она́ сказа́ла, что мы должны́

   пойти́ на э́ту ле́кцию.

6. Кири́лл говори́л об э́том с _____ Тури́цыным.

Упражне́ние 13.12 Fill in the blanks with the correct form of the word **друг**.

1. Они́ друг _____ о́чень понра́вились.

2. К сожале́нию, Анто́н и Ле́на избега́ют друг _____.

3. Они́ ча́сто жа́луются друг на _____.

4. Бо́ря и Бе́лла говоря́т то́лько друг о _____.

5. Где же вы друг _____ нашли́?

6. Они́ ча́сто звоня́т друг _____.

Упражне́ние 13.13 The following chart gives the purchase prices of apartments in buildings from the Stalin period, in five- and nine-floor prefabicated buildings (typically five to forty years old), and in newer buildings (less than 5 years old). Practice your numbers by reading aloud the cost of these different apartments in each region of Moscow: **ц = центр, с = се́вер, ю = юг, в = восто́к, з = за́пад**. Note that prices are give in American dollars.

Cost = $ per square meter of living space as of October 1994.

Упражне́ние 13.14   Many Russians rent rather than own their apartments. Complete the sentences with what you think might be appropriate figures in dollars. Write out numbers as words.

1. Я смогу́ плати́ть до _____ в ме́сяц.

2. Они́ говоря́т о _____, кото́рые они́ пла́тят за кварти́ру ка́ждый ме́сяц.

3. Я не бу́ду плати́ть бо́льше _____ в ме́сяц.

4. За _____, кото́рые мы пла́тим в ме́сяц за кварти́ру, мы смогли́ бы съе́здить в Аме́рику на две неде́ли!

5. Они́ пла́тят _____ за кварти́ру в ме́сяц.

6. В отноше́нии _____, кото́рые они́ пла́тят за кварти́ру, они́ должны́ поговори́ть с дире́ктором инотде́ла.

7. Таки́е кварти́ры сто́ят _____ в ме́сяц.

Зада́ние 13.5   Prepare a three-minute talk or write a short composition, as assigned by your instructor, about a famous couple who have a very bad day, doing all the wrong things. At the end of the day, they compare notes and find that they did the same wrong things (separately). Use the word **сам** and the expressions **не тот** and **тот же/тако́й же** in as many different cases as you can.

Glossary

а́дский	*hellish*
бельё	*underwear*
# бо́лен, больна́, больны́ [чем?]	*sick with something (fleeting bug)*
# боле́ть /за– (II) [чем?]: боле́ю, боле́ешь, боле́ют;	*to be sick with something (longer lasting illness)*
#боле́ть: [у кого́? что?] боли́т/боля́т У меня́ боли́т пра́вый гла́з. У меня́ боля́т глаза́.	*to hurt somewhere: My right eye hurts. My eyes hurt.*
бра́ть (I) /взять (I) [что?] с собо́й: беру́, берёшь, беру́т, брал, брала́, бра́ли; возьму́, возьмёшь, возьму́т, взял, взяла́, взя́ли	*to take something along*
вести́/по– (I) себя́ (хорошо́ и́ли пло́хо): веду́, ведёшь, веду́т, вёл, вела́, вели́	*to behave oneself (well or poorly)*
вождь (*м.*)	*leader*
# вызыва́ть (I) /вы́звать (I) врача́, ско́рую по́мощь: вызыва́ю, вызыва́ешь, вызыва́ют; вы́зову, вы́зовешь, вы́зовут	*to call for a doctor or an ambulance*
друг дру́га	*one another*
дверь (*ж.*)	*door (f.)*

двóе	*a couple of (with genitive plural)*
жизнь (ж.)	*life*
жирáф	*giraffe*
# заболевáть (I) /заболéть (I) [чем?]: заболевáю, заболевáешь, заболевáют; заболéю, заболéешь, заболéют	*to come down with something, become ill*
здáние	*building*
# измерять (I) /измéрить (II) [комý?] температýру: измеряю, измеряешь, измеряют; измéрю, измéришь, измéрят	*to take someone's temperature*
# класть (I) /положить (II) [когó?] в больницу: кладý, кладёшь, кладýт; положý, полóжишь, полóжат	*to put someone in the hospital*
компьютер	*computer*
кремль (м.)	*kremlin (Russian fortress)*
#кружиться: крýжится головá, кружилась головá	*to spin*
кýхня	*kitchen*
лаборатóрия	*laboratory*
# лежáть/по– (II) в больнице: лежý, лежишь, лежáт	*to be in the hospital*
# ложиться (II) /лечь (I) в больницу: ложýсь, ложишься, ложáтся; лягу, ляжешь, лягут, ляг(те)! лёг, леглá, легли	*to go to the hospital (to be admitted to the hospital)*
# ломáть/с– (I) нóгу, рýку: ломáю, ломáешь, ломáют	*to break one's leg or arm*
лóшадь (ж.)	*horse*
мáмин, пáпин	*mom's, dad's*
мóре	*sea*
#кáшлять: кáшляю, кáшляешь, кáшляют	*to cough*
óба/óбе	*both*
óзеро, озёра	*lake, lakes*
описáние	*description*
письмó, письма	*letter, letters*
# пить/вы– (I) лекáрство: пью, пьёшь, пьют, пей(те)! пил, пилá, пили	*to take medicine*
# поправляться (I) /попрáвиться (II): поправляюсь, поправляешься, поправляются; попрáвлюсь, попрáвишься, попрáвятся	*to get better*

представля́ть (I) /предста́вить (II) себе́: представля́ю, представля́ешь, представля́ют; предста́влю, предста́вишь, предста́вят	to *imagine*
# принима́ть (I) /приня́ть (I) лека́рство: принима́ю, принима́ешь, принима́ют; приму́, при́мешь, при́мут, прими́(те)! при́нял, приняла́, при́няли	to *take medicine*
# простужа́ться (I) /простуди́ться (II): простужа́юсь, простужа́ешься, простужа́ются; простужу́сь, просту́дишься, просту́дятся	to *catch a cold*
#рвать/вы-: рвёт, вы́рвет, рвало́, вы́рвало	to *throw up, use only third* *person singular form with* *the accusative case of the* *person who is vomitting*
# ре́зать/по- (I) (себе́) [что?]: ре́жу, ре́жешь, ре́жут, режь(те)!	to *cut oneself where*
сам/-а́/-и	*self*
санато́рий	*sanitarium*
сло́во, слова́	*word, words*
стена́, сте́ны	*wall, walls*
тот, та, то, те	*that (one), those*
#тошни́ть	to *be nauseous, use only third* *person singular form with* *the accusative case of the* *person who is nauseous*
тро́е	*three of a . . . (with genitive* *plural)*
# ушиба́ть (I) /ушиби́ть (II) (себе́) [что?]: ушиба́ю, ушиба́ешь, ушиба́ют; ушибу́, ушибёшь, ушибу́т, уши́б, уши́бла, уши́бли	to *hurt oneself (where?)*
чей/чья/чьё/чьи	*whose*
че́тверо	*a foursome (with genitive* *plural)*
#чиха́ть: чиха́ю, чиха́ешь, чиха́ют	to *sneeze*
чу́вствовать (I) себя́: чу́вствую, чу́вствуешь, чу́вствуют	to *feel*
э́тот, э́та, э́то, э́ти	*this (one), these*

UNIT 14

Lexicon: Dormitory Life and Cleaning

Russian students often live in dormitories, especially when they study at institutions located far away from their hometown. If they study at an institution in their hometown, Russians are most likely to live at home.

Общежи́тие
Dormitory

> Мне не о́чень нра́вится общежи́тие, в кото́ром я живу́.
> *I'm not fond of the dormitory in which I live.*

Отде́льная ко́мната
Private room

> В э́том году́ я получи́ла отде́льную ко́мнату.
> *This year I got a private room.*

Блок
Suite in a dormitory: usually two or more bedrooms with a common bathroom

> В про́шлом году́ я жил в бло́ке с двумя́ па́рнями.
> *Last year I lived in a suite with two other guys.*

Сосе́д/-ка по ко́мнате, сосе́д/-ка по бло́ку
Roommate, suite mate

> У меня́ три сосе́дки по бло́ку.
> *I have three suite mates (female).*

Грязь/гря́зный, чистота́/чи́стый
Filth or dirt/dirty, order or cleanliness/clean

> У них в ко́мнате — така́я невыноси́мая грязь!
> *Their room is unbearably filthy!*

> Пе́тя о́чень лю́бит чистоту́: у него́ всегда́ о́чень чи́сто.
> *Petia really loves cleanliness: his room is always very clean.*

Убира́ть/убра́ть [что? где?]
To clean or straighten something up

> На́шу ко́мнату ча́сто убира́ет Анто́н.
> *Frequently it's Anton who cleans up our room.*

> Та́ня, убери́ на ку́хне: ско́ро приду́т го́сти!
> *Tania, please clean up in the kitchen: our guests will be here soon!*

Мыть/по– [что?]

To wash something (except clothing) or to mop

Вчера́ я помы́л пол на ку́хне шва́брой.
I mopped the kitchen floor yesterday.

У нас гото́вит Па́ша, а я мо́ю посу́ду.
At our place Pasha cooks and I wash the dishes.

Стира́ть/по– [что?]
To do the laundry

С тремя́ ма́ленькими детьми́ мне ка́жется, что я то́лько и стира́ю кру́глые су́тки!
With three little kids it seems to me that all I do is laundry round the clock!

Стира́ть пыль
To dust

Мы стира́ем пыль два ра́за в неде́лю, и всё равно́, у нас всё покры́то пы́лью!
We dust twice a week, but all the same everything is covered with dust in our home!

Протира́ть тря́пкой [что]?
To wipe something clean (with a rag)

Мы протира́ем тря́пкой шкафы́ на ку́хне два ра́за в ме́сяц.
We wipe clean all the cupboards in the kitchen twice a month.

Мести́/под– [что? где?]
To sweep

Подмети́ [пол] на ку́хне, пожа́луйста.
Please sweep up [the floor] in the kitchen.

Пылесо́сить
To vacuum

У нас три ко́шки, и поэ́тому мы постоя́нно пылесо́сим.
We have three cats and so we are always vacuuming.

Мы́ло (туале́тное для лица́ и рук, и́ли хозя́йственное для посу́ды)
Soap (for the face and hands or for dishes)

Вчера́ я купи́л но́вое мы́ло для посу́ды.
Yesterday I bought a new kind of dish soap.

Стира́льный порошо́к, отбе́ливатель
Laundry detergent, bleach

На́до купи́ть стира́льный порошо́к!
We have to buy more laundry detergent!

Дезинфици́рующее сре́дство
Disinfectant

У Скворцо́вых всегда па́хнет дезинфици́рующим сре́дством.
The Skvortsovs' place always smells of disinfectant.

Упражне́ние 14.1   Fill in the blanks with the correct word, using the following cues, though not necessarily in this order: *filthy, cleanliness, wash, does laundry, vacuum cleaner, roommate (female), suite, cleans up, clean room, with soap (use the instrumental case without a preposition), single or private room, wash, dormitory.*

К сожалению, у меня нет _____¹ в _____.² Я

живу в одном _____³ с тремя девушками. Наша комната в ужасном

состоянии: она совершенно _____,⁴ потому что одной

_____⁵ никогда не хочется соблюдать _____.⁶

Её зовут Инна: она никогда не _____.⁷ Сегодня, например, мне

пришлось _____⁸ посуду, которую она оставила грязной на кухне.

Инна не _____⁹ свою одежду, а отдаёт её в химчистку раз в две

недели. Её грязная одежда валяется по всему блоку: нужно постоянно

_____¹⁰ шкафы _____,¹¹ чтобы не воняло! В

следующем году, надеюсь, что я не буду жить вместе с Инной. У Веры есть свой

_____.¹² Надеюсь жить вместе с ней в

_____!¹³

Задание 14.1 Prepare a skit in which two or more roommates argue about cleaning up their suite, the "dirtiest" suite in the dormitory. Some of the roommates should say that the others never clean up certain parts of the suite, while others should argue that no matter how much they clean. . . .

Фото-задание Look at the photograph on the first page of this unit in the textbook. Write a paragraph or prepare a presentation, as assigned by your instructor, describing how this room should be straightened up.

Listening Tasks

The listening text for this unit consists of a dialogue about cleaning up a dormitory room.

PRE-LISTENING TASK

What do you have to do when you clean up your dorm room, apartment, or house? If you have roommates, do you split up the tasks? How is the work divided up?

LISTENING TASK

Listen to the text and then answer questions 1 through 4 in English and 5 through 7 in Russian.

1. What's wrong with the room in the dormitory?
2. Make a list of all the problems reported about the situation.
3. What are the two possible solutions suggested to help the situation?
4. Why can't the first possible solution be implemented?
5. Find the Russian equivalent of the expressions *in what sense?* and *in the literal sense.*
6. Find the Russian equivalent of the expression *ask to be moved into another room.*
7. One of the speakers responds sarcastically to the solution proposed by the other speaker. Find the sarcastic expression and translate it into English.

DICTATION

Replay the tape and, as you listen, write out the dialogue in full.

PERFORMANCE

Practice reciting the dialogue.

POST-LISTENING TASK

Using the dialogue as a model, work with a classmate to create and perform your own dialogue in which you discuss how to divide up the responsibility of cleaning a very messy dormitory suite or an apartment from which you are moving at the end of your lease.

CULTURAL PROBLEM

What public spaces are kept clean in North America? What public spaces are not kept as clean as they should be? How do you think Russians might react when they see the streets (or public restrooms) of Philadelphia or Detroit or when they see Yellowstone National Park? What are your expectations of the cleanliness of streets, parks, public restrooms, and other public spaces in Russia?

Phonetics and Intonation

Hard and Soft т and д

This unit reviews the pronunciation of hard and soft т and д. For hard т and д, place the front third of your tongue on your hard upper palate. For soft т and д, place the middle third of your tongue on your soft upper palate (in the middle of the roof of your mouth) and pronounce these sounds with the middle of your tongue.

Listen to the hard т and д and the soft т and д on the tape and repeat.

1.	так	тяк	6.	дал	дял
2.	тор	тёр	7.	дон	дён
3.	тут	тют	8.	дут	дют
4.	жат	жать	9.	вод	водь
5.	сут	суть	10.	вед	ведь

SELF-QUIZ

Circle the letters that best represent the sounds you hear.

1.	так	тяк	6.	съест	съесть
2.	тор	тёр	7.	дам	дям
3.	тыл	тил	8.	дул	дюл
4.	тэп	теп	9.	дык	дик
5.	колот	колоть	10.	вод	водь

Lexicon: To Change

Russian uses a variety of constructions and verbs to convey the English verb *to change*.

Переодеваться/переодеться
To change clothes, to take off one outfit or item of clothing and put on another

> Я вся мокрая: подождите одну минуту, и я переоденусь.
> *I'm all wet: wait a minute and I'll change.*

Передумывать/передумать
To change one's mind

> Мы передумали и решили не ехать в Новгород.
> *We changed our minds and decided not to go to Novgorod.*

Пересаживаться/пересесть, делать/с- пересадку
To change buses, trains, or planes, to make a transfer

> Когда я езжу в Москву, я обычно пересаживаюсь в Париже.
> *When I go to Moscow I usually make a transfer in Paris.*

> Оттуда мы летим без пересадок в Москву.
> *From there we fly nonstop to Moscow.*

Изменять(-ся)/изменить(-ся); изменение
To change, alter, or modify something; a change or alteration

> Ольга Петровна хитрый бизнесмен: она опять изменила тактику.
> *Olga Petrovna is a clever businesswoman: she's changed her tactics again.*

> После операции он сильно изменился.
> *After the operation he was a changed man (he seriously changed).*

> Большие изменения в расписании самолётов.
> *There are big changes in the flight schedule.*

Заменять/заменить
To change in the sense of to replace, even if only temporarily

> Наш профессор был болен, и его заменила Мария Антоновна.
> *Our professor was ill and he was replaced by Maria Antonovna.*

Сменять/сменить
To change or relieve as in a work shift, or to replace

> Мы проработаем три часа, и потом вы нас смените.
> *We'll work for three hours and then you'll relieve us (take our place).*

Менять/по–, менять/переменить; перемена
To change, to switch; a changeover

> Я поменяла работу.
> *I changed jobs.*

> После перемены системы работы мы сможем лучше работать.
> *After the work system changes we'll be able to work better.*

Разме́нивать/разменя́ть

To change something into an equivalent of the same kind, to break a large bill of currency into smaller units

> Разменя́йте, пожа́луйста, сто ты́сяч рубле́й.
> *Please give me change for one hundred thousand rubles.*

Обме́нивать/обменя́ть

To change something into an equivalent of a different kind, to change currencies

> Я обы́чно обме́ниваю де́ньги в ба́нке, а не в пу́нктах обме́на.
> *I usually change money (from rubles to dollars or vice versa) at the bank, not at the exchange points.*

Отменя́ть(-ся)/отмени́ть(-ся)

To cancel something

> Рейс № 217 Москва́— Петербу́рг отменя́ется из–за нелётной пого́ды.
> *Flight No. 217 from Moscow to Petersburg is canceled due to poor weather.*

Превраща́ть(-ся)/преврати́ть(-ся) [во что? в кого́?]

To change or turn into something (a physical or emotional transformation of an object or person into another)

> При по́лной луне́ он превраща́ется в ужа́сное чудо́вище!
> *When the moon is full he turns into an awful monster!*

> Вода́ превраща́ется в лёд при температу́ре три́дцать два гра́дуса по Фаренге́йту, что равня́ется нулю́ гра́дусов по Це́льсию.
> *Water turns into ice at a temperature of 32 degrees Farenheight, which is equivalent to 0 degrees Celsius.*

Текст 14.1   This poem by Pushkin is about the relationship between two people and the use of the pronouns **вы** and **ты**.

PRE-READING TASK

What is the importance of the proper pronouns (**ты** and **вы**) in Russian social life? How might a mistake in usage complicate social relations? What sort of mistake in English might produce a similar effect?

Пусто́е[1] *вы* серде́чным[2] *ты*
Она́, обмо́лвясь,[3] замени́ла,
И все счастли́вые мечты́[4]
В душе́ влюблённой[5] возбуди́ла.[6]
Пред[7] ней заду́мчиво[8] стою́,
Свести́ оче́й[9] с неё нет си́лы;[10]
И говорю́ ей, как *вы* ми́лы!
И мы́слю:[11] как *тебя́* люблю́!

А.С. Пу́шкин, 1828

[1] *empty*
[2] *arduous*
[3] *misspeaking*
[4] все... *all the happy dreams*
[5] в... *in a soul in love*
[6] [she] *aroused*
[7] *перед*
[8] *pensively*
[9] *take my eyes*
[10] *strength*
[11] *think*

POST-READING TASK

1. Write a one- or two-sentence summary of the poem.
2. What is the meaning of the verb **заменить** in the second line of the poem?
3. The Russian word for *eye* in the sixth line is archaic: **óко** (nom. sing.), **óчи** (nom. pl.). Do you know any words similar to the singular form of this word? How might they be related?
4. What is the root of the Russian verb meaning *to think* in the last line? Do you know any other words with the same root?
5. Assume the role of the woman who misspoke and write a response to this poem.

Упражнéние 14.2 Fill in the blanks with the Russian equivalent of the English word or phrase in parentheses.

1. Нина Сергéевна (*changed her mind*) _____ и решила поéхать в

   Тýлу.

2. Всё–таки онá понялá, что никтó не мóжет её (*replace, take her place*)

   _____.

3. Ей придётся (*change planes*) _____ во Фрáнкфурте, а потóм ещё

   раз в Москвé.

4. Пóсле длинного полёта во Фрáнкфурт онá смóжет (*change clothes*)

   _____ до вылета слéдующего самолёта в Москвý.

5. Онá говорит, что ей не нрáвится эта рабóта, потомý что онá слишком чáсто éздит в

   командирóвки. Онá считáет, что óчень (*changed*) _____ на этой

   рабóте и хóчет (*change*) _____ рабóту.

6. Онá дýмает: Пусть меня (*relieve, succeed*) _____ Сергéй

   Ивáнович: он спосóбный инженéр.

Exercises and Activities

Упражнéние 14.3 Fill in the blanks with the Russian equivalent of the English word or phrase in parentheses to complete the story about a shy young man, Vasia. Use the correct form of the negative adverbial or pronominal expression and insert prepositions as necessary.

1. Все студéнты избегáют Вáсю, но он (*no one*) _____ *Никого* _____ не избегáет.

2. Другие студéнты бывáют в рáзных кафé и ресторáнах, но Вáся (*nowhere*)

   _____ *Нигде* _____ не бывáет.

3. Он скýчный человéк. Он (*about nothing, about no one*) _____ *Ни о ком* _____,

   _____ *Ни о чем* _____ не говорит.

4. Он (*nothing*) _____ *Ничем* _____ интерéсным не занимáется.

5. Нет, это неправда. Вася, всё-таки, очень умный парень. Он (*nothing*) ___*ничему*___ не удивляется.

6. Да Вася и очень симпатичный: он всем помогает, а Света, наоборот, (*no one*) ___*никому*___ не помогает.

7. Может быть, Вася очень стесняется, он (*with no one*) ___*ни с кем*___ не разговаривает.

8. Наверно, надо его пригласить пойти вместе с нами в кафе: тогда, может быть, он научится общаться, а то ведь он (*to no one*) ___*ни к кому*___ (*never*) ___*никогда*___ не ходит в гости.

Задание 14.2   Using the story in **Упражнение 14.3** as a model, write a story about an unlucky woman named Tania. Use as many of the constructions presented in this unit as you can.

Упражнение 14.4   Translate the following sentences into Russian.

1. They're not afraid of anything.
2. I'm not avoiding anyone.
3. I'm not doing anything now.
4. They won't tell about anything tonight.
5. She isn't surprised at (by) anything.
6. He doesn't help anyone.
7. We never go anywhere.
8. We never get (**получать**) letters from anyone.
9. They don't love anyone.
10. She isn't working on anything right now.

Упражнение 14.5   Fill in the blanks with the correct particle, –**то** or –**нибудь**.

1. — Мы видели Тамару в метро. Она читала какую-_____ книгу по химии.

   — Она чему-_____ удивилась, когда вы нашли её?

   — Да, она чему-_____ удивилась, но не хотела сказать, чему именно.

2. — Боря и Вера сказали, что не могут прийти в субботу. Они кому-_____ помогают?

   — Да, они кому-_____ помогают красить квартиру.

3. — Его родители кому-_____ понравились?

   — Да, они точно кому-_____ понравились.

4. — Лена чего-_____ испугалась, когда она была там?

   — Да, она чего-_____ испугалась.

5. — Кто-_____ приходил, когда меня не было?

   — Да, приходила какая-_____ женщина, которая хотела поговорить с тобой.

6. — Ксения всегда что-_____ интересное рассказывает, когда возвращается из Самары.

Упражнéние 14.6   Translate the following sentences into Russian.

1. Did anyone call while I was out (was not here)?
2. Yes, someone called.
3. Was Tania surprised at anything?
4. Yes, she was surprised at something.
5. Read (to) me something interesting.
6. I always read (to) you something interesting.
7. Will Vadim tell (**рассказáть**) about some American student tonight?
8. He already told about some American student yesterday evening.

Упражнéние 14.7   Translate the following dialogue (an argument between two roommates) into Russian.

"Did anyone call while I was out?"
"Someone called, but I forgot her name."
"You always forget everything!"
"That's not true. Sometimes I forget, but I never forget anything important."
"You don't have any time to remember that which is important for me."
"And you never help me."
"I have no reason to help you: you don't help anyone."
"There's no one here for me to help."
"I often need your help."
"You always need someone's help!"
"Let's forget about this and watch a film on television."
"You always want to watch something or other on television."
"And you never want to watch anything."
"There's never anything to watch on television and I have no one to watch with, anyway."
"I'm surprised at what you're saying."
"You have nothing to be surprised at!"
"I am going to complain to the commandant (**комендáнт**) about you."
"You have nothing to complain about!"
"I certainly have something to complain about!"

Задáние 14.3   With a classmate, prepare a short skit (or write a short script) of a conversation between two irascible roommates who disagree about everything. Try to use the following particles, words, and expressions as frequently as possible: **–то, –нибудь, всегдá, иногдá, никогдá, нéкогда, есть когдá, вездé, нигдé, нéгде, всю́ду, никудá, нéкуда, нéзачем, есть зачéм, нé с кем, есть с кем, нéкому, есть комý,** and so forth.

Glossary

блок	*suite*
бы...ни + *past tense of verb*	*no matter . . . or . . . ever (for example: no matter where you look, wherever you look)*
# дезинфицúрующее срéдство	*disinfectant*
# грязь (*ж.*), гря́зный	*filth, filthy*

# заменя́ть (I) /замени́ть (II) [кого́? что?]: заменя́ю, заменя́ешь, заменя́ют; заменю́, заме́нишь, заме́нят	*to change, to replace, or to fill in for*
# изменя́ть(-ся) (I) /измени́ть(-ся) (II): изменя́ю(-сь), изменя́ешь(-ся), изменя́ют(-ся); изменю́(сь), изме́нишь(-ся), изме́нят(-ся)	*to change, to alter, to modify or to be changed, altered, modified*
# меня́ть /по– (I) [что?]: меня́ю, меня́ешь, меня́ют	*to change, to switch*
# мести́/под– (I) [что?]: мету́, метёшь, мету́т, мёл, мела́, мели́	*to sweep up*
# мы́ло	*soap*
# мы́ть/по– (I) [что?]: мо́ю, мо́ешь, мо́ют, мо́й(те)!	*to wash something*
не́где + инфинити́в [кому́?]	*there's nowhere to + infinitive (for whom?)*
не́чего + инфинити́в [кому́?]	*there's nothing to + infinitive (for whom?)*
не́когда + инфинити́в [кому́?]	*there's no time to + infinitive (for whom?)*
не́куда + инфинити́в [кому́?]	*there's no where to + infinitive (for whom?)*
– нибудь	*indefinite particle: neither known nor identified (often used in the future tense or in questions)*
нигде́ не	*nowhere/anywhere (depending on context)*
ничего́ не	*nothing/anything (depending on context)*
никогда́ не	*never/ever (depending on context)*
никто́ не	*no one*
никуда́ не	*nowhere/anywhere (depending on context)*
# обме́нивать (I) /обменя́ть (I) [что?]: обме́ниваю, обме́ниваешь, обме́нивают; обменя́ю, обменя́ешь, обменя́ют	*to change, to exchange, i.e., to change rubles for dollars or vice versa*
# общежи́тие	*dormitory*
# отде́льная ко́мната	*private room*
# отменя́ть (I) /отмени́ть (II) [что?]: отменя́ю, отменя́ешь, отменя́ют; отменю́, отме́нишь, отме́нят	*to cancel something*

передýмывать (I) /передýмать (I):
передýмываю, передýмываешь, передýмывают; передýмаю,
передýмаешь, передýмают

to change one's mind

меня́ть (I) /перемени́ть (II) [что?]:
меня́ю, меня́ешь, меня́ют; переменю́, переме́нишь,
переме́нят

to change, to replace

переодева́ться (I) /переоде́ться (I):
переодева́юсь, переодева́ешься, переодева́ются;
переоде́нусь, переоде́нешься, переоде́нутся

to change an item of clothing or an outfit

переса́живаться/пересе́сть [где? на что?]:
переса́живаюсь, переса́живаешься, переса́живаются;
переся́ду, переся́дешь, переся́дут

to change buses, trains or planes, to make a transfer (where, onto what?)

#превраща́ться (I) /преврати́ться (II) [во что? в кого?]:
превраща́юсь, превраща́ешься, превраща́ются;
превращу́сь, преврати́шься, преврати́тся

to change, to metamorphose into something

пылесо́сить [что? где?]:
пылесо́шу, пылесо́сишь, пылесо́сят, пылесо́сь(те)!

to vacuum something, somewhere

протира́ть тря́пкой [что?]:
протира́ю, протира́ешь, протира́ют

to wipe something down with a rag

разме́нивать (I) /разменя́ть (I):
разме́ниваю, разме́ниваешь, разме́нивают; разменя́ю,
разменя́ешь, разменя́ют

to change something into something equivalent, i.e., to break a larger bill into smaller units of the same currency

сосе́д/-ка (по ко́мнате, по бло́ку)

roommate, suite mate

сменя́ть (I) /смени́ть (II) [что?]:
сменя́ю, сменя́ешь, сменя́ют; сменю́, сме́нишь, сме́нят

to change, to relieve, to replace (succeeding in time)

стира́льный порошо́к

laundry detergent

стира́ть пыль:
стира́ю, стира́ешь, стира́ют

to dust

стира́ть/по– (I):
стира́ю, стира́ешь, стира́ют

to do laundry

–то

indefinite particle: known, but not identified. often used in the past tense

убира́ть (I) /убра́ть (I) [что? где?]:
убира́ю, убира́ешь, убира́ют; уберу́, уберёшь, уберу́т, убра́л,
убрала́, убра́ли

to clean something up, to straighten something up

чистота́, чи́стый

cleanliness, clean

UNIT 15

Lexicon: Describing People's Appearances

Here is a list of expressions used to describe people's appearances.

Ма́ленького ро́ста, сре́днего ро́ста, высо́кого ро́ста
Short, average height, tall

> Она́ – высо́кого ро́ста, а он – сре́днего ро́ста.
> *She's tall, and he's of average height.*

То́лстый, худо́й
Plump, slender

> Он дово́льно то́лстый, хотя́ в де́тстве был худы́м.
> *He's rather plump (fat), but as a child he was slender.*

Мускули́стого сложе́ния, спорти́вная фигу́ра
Muscular build, trim or good shape

> Па́вел – мускули́стого сложе́ния.
> *Pavel has a muscular build.*

> У Та́ни спорти́вная фигу́ра.
> *Tania is in good shape.*

Во́лосы: тёмные (чёрные, кашта́новые), све́тлые (белоку́рые, ры́жие), седы́е; лю́ди с таки́ми во́лосами: шате́н/-ка, брюне́т/ка, блонди́н/-ка
Hair: dark (black, brown), light (blond, red), gray; people with this hair color: brunet/te, blond/e.

> У него́ кашта́новые во́лосы.
> *He has brown hair.*

Во́лосы: прямы́е, кудря́вые, вью́щиеся; густы́е, ре́дкие; коро́ткие, дли́нные
Hair: straight, curly, wavy; thick, thinning; short, long

> Мои́ роди́тели пло́хо отно́сятся к ма́льчикам с дли́нными волоса́ми.
> *My parents don't like boys with long hair.*

Лы́сый, лы́сина, лысе́ть
Bald, a bald spot, to grow bald

> У Вади́ма больша́я лы́сина: он уже́ давно́ на́чал лысе́ть. Де́душка по ма́тери был совсе́м лы́сым в 35 лет.
> *Vadim has a big bald spot: he started to go bald a long time ago. His grandfather on his mother's side was completely bald by the time he was 35 years old.*

Усы́, борода́
Mustache, beard

> Серге́й тепе́рь отпуска́ет бо́роду, так как его́ оте́ц сбрил свои́ усы́ и бо́роду.
> *Sergei is growing a beard now that his father has shaved off his beard and mustache.*

Глазá: сéрые, голубы́е, зелёные, кáрие
Eyes: gray, blue, green, brown

> У негó блестя́щие голубы́е глазá.
> *He has sparkling blue eyes.*

Быть в очкáх/носи́ть очки́, в серéбряной, золотóй, роговóй опрáве
To wear glasses on a particular occasion/to wear glasses generally, with a silver, gold, tortoise-shell frame

> Онá былá в очкáх в серéбряной опрáве.
> *She was wearing glasses with a silver frame* (*that night*).

Упражнéние 15.1 Fill in the blanks with the Russian equivalent of the English word or phrase in parentheses.

1. Наполеóн был (*short*) _____.

2. У Клеопáтры бы́ли (*long, straight hair*) _____.

3. К концý своéй жи́зни Мáлкольм Икс носи́л (*glasses*) _____.

4. Актёры Тéлли Савáлас и Юл Бри́ннер бы́ли (*bald*) _____.

5. Конéчно, Майкл Джóрдан – óчень (*tall*) _____.

6. У Альбéрта Эйнштéйна бы́ли (*mustache and beard*) _____.

7. В э́том фи́льме актри́са игрáла мнóго рáзных ролéй: у неё бы́ли то (*wavy hair*) _____, то (*curly hair*) _____.

8. Э́тот молодóй человéк чáсто крáсит свои́ вóлосы: иногдá он (*redhead*) _____, иногдá (*blond*) _____, иногдá (*brunet*) _____.

 Фóто-задáние Look at the photograph on the first page of this unit in the textbook. Write a paragraph or prepare a presentation, as assigned by your instructor, describing the teacher from the viewpoint of one of the children (who are going to school for the first time) or describing the grandparents from the viewpoint of the teacher (holding the sign).

Задáние 15.1 Bring a photograph of some friends to class. You should not be depicted in the photo you select. Your instructor will collect all the photos. Working with a classmate, describe the appearance of your friends and listen to the description of your classmate's friends. Then see if you can pick out your classmate's photo from all of those brought in by your other classmates.

Listening Tasks

The listening text for this unit consists of a series of brief physical descriptions.

PRE-LISTENING TASK

How would you describe your physical appearance? Your parents' appearance? Your siblings' and friends' appearance? Think of the words you would need or want to use.

LISTENING TASK

1. Match the Russian description you hear with the English descriptions.

   SOME ELEMENTS OF THE DESCRIPTION   NUMBER
                                                                    ON TAPE

   a. a tall, muscular blond man with a big nose   _____

   b. a woman with red hair and blue eyes   _____

   c. a bald man with a gray beard   _____

   d. a woman of average height with brown eyes   _____

   e. a woman who wears glasses   _____

   f. a man of average height with curly blond hair   _____

2. Add as many details as you can in English to each of the preceding descriptions. Replay the tape if necessary.

3. Make a list of all the synonymous expressions you can find in the Russian descriptions.

DICTATION

Replay the tape and, as you listen, write out the text in full.

PERFORMANCE

Practice reciting the text.

POST-LISTENING TASK

Using the text as a model, describe the physical appearance of members of your family to a classmate so that he or she could recognize them at an airport, train station, or bus station.

CULTURAL PROBLEM

What is the role of weight and build in one's personal appearance in North America? How and why might Russians have a different attitude toward weight and build?

Phonetics and Intonation

Hard and Soft с and з

This unit reviews the pronunciation of hard and soft с and з. To pronounce hard с and з, place the front third of your tongue on your hard upper palate. To pronounce soft с and з, place the middle third of your tongue on your soft upper palate (in the middle of the roof of your mouth) and pronounce these sounds with the middle of your tongue. This unit also reviews the devoicing of voiced consonant з when in word-final position or when followed by a voiceless consonant, and the voicing of voiceless consonant с when followed by a voiced consonant.

Listen to the hard с and з and then the soft с and з on the tape and repeat.

1.	сок	сёк		6.	зон	зён
2.	сут	сют		7.	зут	зют
3.	ас	ась		8.	зыб	зип
4.	ис	ись		9.	оз	озь
5.	зал	зял		10.	ез	езь

SELF-QUIZ #1

Circle the letters that best represent the sounds you hear.

1.	сам	сям		6.	зал	зял
2.	сум	сюм		7.	зум	зюм
3.	сыв	сив		8.	зыб	зиб
4.	ос	ось		9.	оз	озь
5.	ес	есь		10.	ез	езь

Voiced and Voiceless с and з

Listen to the voiced and the voiceless с and з on the tape.

1.	база	баз	бас
2.	доза	доз	дос
3.	везла	вез	вес
4.	роза	роз	рос
5.	безо	без	бес
6.	туза	туз	тус
7.	вызов	выз	выс
8.	миза	миз	мис
9.	феза	фез	фес
10.	юза	юз	юс
11.	без Бори	с Борей	без Пети	с Петей
12.	без Димы	с Димой	без Тани	с Таней
13.	без Гали	с Галей	без Кости	с Костей
14.	без Зины	с Зиной	без Сони	с Соней
15.	без Жоры	с Жорой	без Шуры	с Шурой

SELF-QUIZ #2

Write one or, if possible, two spellings for each sound you hear.

1. _____ _____

2. _____ _____

3. _____ _____

4. _____ _____

5. _____ _____

6. _____ _____

7. _____ _____

8. _____ _____

9. _____ _____

10. _____ _____

Lexicon: Only

There are two important ways to express the concept of *only* in Russian, but English uses only one word for both contexts. Consider the following English examples.

> She *only* works in the evenings. (*only* = adverb modifying the verb *works*)
> This is the *only* copy of this book. (*only* = adjective modifying the noun *copy*)

English uses the same word as an adverb and an adjective. Russian, however, has two different words for these contexts. Consider the translation of the English sentences into Russian.

> Она работает **только** вечером.
> Это **единственный** экземпляр книги.

Russian uses **только** to express the English adverb *only* and a form of **единственный** to express the English adjective *only*. **Единственный** must agree in gender, case and number with the noun it modifies.

There are other possible meanings for the word *only* in English: *alone, only one,* or *nothing but.*

> *Only* he was home.
> The child was in *only* his diapers.
> There are *nothing but* hooligans there.

Russian would translate these sentences either with **только** or, more often, with a form of **один**.

> Он **один** был дома
> Ребёнок был в **одинх** пелёнках. (Ребёнок был **только** в пелёнках.)
> Там **одни** хулиганы. (Там **только** хулиганы.)

Упражнéние 15.2   Review the declension of the word **один** in Unit 13 and the appendix of your textbook (p. 174 and p. 354).

Упражнéние 15.3   Fill in the blanks with **только, единственный (–ая, –ое, –ые)**, or **один (одна, одно, одни)**.

1. Вéра и Витя рабóтают в _____ вьетнáмском ресторáне,

   ресторáне «Ханóй», в Москвé.

2. Вéра рабóтает _____ вéчером, а Витя — утром и днём.

3. Они видятся _____ тогдá, когдá Витя собирáется уходить, а Вéра

   прихóдит.

4. В этом ресторáне готóвят _____ вьетнáмские блюда: всё очень

   вкусно.

5. _____ в райóне пиццерия нахóдится рядом, и поэтому в

   ресторáне «Ханóй» всё время пáхнет пиццей.

6. В пиццерии предлагáется _____ пицца.

7. Там обéдают _____ молодые.

8. В ресторáне «Ханóй» обéдают _____ бизнесмéны, потому что

   цéны — довóльно высóкие.

Упражне́ние 15.4   Translate the following sentences into Russian, using то́лько, еди́нственный (–ая, –ое, –ые), or оди́н (одна́, одно́, одни́).

1. Viktor sometimes works in the only library in this region (райо́н) of the city.
2. There is a skating rink (като́к) in front of the library and there are nothing but children there and in the library.
3. Viktor only goes (хо́дит) to the library when his wife visits with her friends because he does not want to be home alone.
4. When he is home alone, he sits in nothing but his pajamas and watches television.
5. Viktor is often the only adult reader (чита́тель) in the library.

Exercises and Activities

Упражне́ние 15.5   Referring to the definitions in your textbook (p.187), mark each Russian sentence with the English letter A or P to denote whether the boldfaced adjective is attributive or predicative. A — описатель

1. _A_ **Вели́кий** князь так и сказа́л.
2. _A_ В э́том магази́не продаю́тся **интере́сные** кни́ги.
3. _A_ Я люблю́ таки́х **краси́вых** соба́к.
4. _P_ Они́ о́чень **бога́тые**.

A — определение

5. _P_ Э́та страна́ **бога́та** не́фтью.
6. _A_ Э́то — **дли́нные** пи́сьма.
7. _A_ Э́то **сумасше́дшие** лю́ди.
8. _P_ Э́ти лю́ди — **сумасше́дшие**.

Упражне́ние 15.6   Practice using some of the most common short-form adjectives by filling in the blanks. Choose from among the following words and supply the appropriate ending (masculine, feminine, neuter, or plural): **винова́т, гото́в, до́лжен, похо́ж, прав, рад, разочаро́ван, серди́т, согла́сен.**

1. Мы (*should*) ___должны́___ э́то сде́лать сейча́с, а то они́ рассе́рдятся на нас.
2. Он был (*ready*) ___гото́в___ провали́ться сквозь зе́млю.
3. Она́ (*should*) ___должна́___ написа́ть письмо́ ма́тери.
4. Он ужа́сно (*guilty*) ___винова́т___ пе́ред на́ми.
5. Они́ о́чень (*look like*) ___похо́жи___ на ба́бушку.
6. Они́ (*at fault*) ___винова́ты___ в э́том; и э́то их оши́бка!
7. Он соверше́нно (*in agreement*) ___согла́сен___ с ней.
8. Мы о́чень (*glad*) ___ра́ды___, что всё хорошо́ получи́лось.
9. Они́ о́чень (*angry*) ___серди́ты___ на свои́х роди́телей.
10. Она́ была́ не (*wrong*) ___права́___, но все молча́ли.

очировах кем

11.   Они́ бы́ли о́чень (*disappointed*) _разочірованы_ в нём.

12.   Ко́ля был (*right*) _прав_, когда́ сказа́л, что Ви́ка всё сде́лает.

Зада́ние 15.3   Prepare a three-minute talk or write a composition, as assigned by your instructor, describing the physical resemblances of either your own family or a famous family (factual or fictitious).

Упражне́ние 15.7   Translate the following passage into Russian. (Review or preview rules on reported speech as explained in your textbook on pp. 233–235 before completing this assignment.)

I am very angry at her and disappointed in her. She asked, "Are you free on Thursday evening?" I told her I was busy on Thursday, but free on Saturday. I told her I would be happy to meet her at the restaurant. I went to the restaurant, but she didn't come. I was ready to drop through the earth. The Belovs were right: I cannot rely on her. On Sunday, she said she was terribly guilty before me and I told her that I agreed with that. Then she told me that my pants were too big, my shirt too small, but that my tie was just right. I told her she was crazy.

Glossary

Short-form adjectives are provided in the masculine form only if there are no stress shifts in the feminine or plural forms. Short-form adjectives with shifting stress are listed in masculine, feminine, and plural forms.

# борода́	*beard*
бо́лен/больна́/больны́	*sick*
# быть в очка́х	*to be wearing glasses on a particular occassion*
вели́к/велика́/велики́ [что? кому́?]	*too big [what is too big for whom?]*
винова́т	*guilty, at fault*
# во́лосы: тёмные, све́тлые, прямы́е, вью́щиеся, кудря́вые, коро́ткие, дли́нные, густы́е, ре́дкие	*hair: dark, light, straight, wavy, curly, short, long, thick, thinning*
# глаза́: се́рые, голубы́е, зелёные, ка́рие	*eyes: gray, blue, green, brown*
гото́в	*ready*
до́лжен/должна́/должны́ [+ инфинити́в]	*obligated, ought to do something*
жив/жива́/жи́вы	*lively, vibrant*
как раз	*just the right size*
како́в/какова́/каково́/каковы́	*what kind of*
# лы́сый, лы́сина, лысе́ть (I): лысе́ю, лысе́ешь, лысе́ют	*bald, bald spot, to go bald*
мал/мала́/мало́/малы́ [что? кому́?]	*too small [what? for whom?]*

# мускули́стого сложе́ния	*muscular build (for either males or females)*
# носи́ть (II) очки́: ношу́, но́сишь, но́сят	*to wear glasses generally*
ну́жен/нужна́/нужны́	*needed, necessary*
# опра́ва: сере́бряная, золота́я, рогова́я	*glasses frame: silver, gold, tortoise shell*
похо́ж [на кого́? что?]	*similar to in appearance*
прав/права́/пра́вы	*right, correct*
рад [де́лать/с- что? чему́?]	*happy, glad to do something or happy, glad at something*
разочаро́ван [в ко́м? в чём?]	*disappointed in someone or something*
# рост: ма́ленького ро́ста, сре́днего ро́ста, высо́кого ро́ста	*height: short, average, tall*
серди́т [на кого́?]	*angry at someone*
согла́сен [с кем? с чем?]	*agreed with whom on what point*
# спорти́вная фигу́ра	*good shape (for males or females)*
тако́в/такова́/таково́/таковы́	*such*
# то́лстый	*plump, fat*
# усы́, усо́в (*род.*)	*mustache*
# худо́й	*thin, slender*

UNIT 16

Lexicon: Describing People's Personalities

The Russian word **хара́ктер** is used to describe someone's personality. (Note that this word is not used to mean a "character" in a novel, play, or movie; the term **геро́й/герои́ня** or **де́йствующее лицо́** is used in that context.) Here is a list of adjectives to describe someone's personality.

у́мный/не-, глу́пый	*smart/stupid*
спосо́бный/не-	*talented/untalented*
интеллиге́нтный/не-, культу́рный/не-	*cultured/uncultured*
общи́тельный/ро́бкий	*outgoing/timid*
дружелю́бный/неприя́зненный	*friendly/antagonistic*
разгово́рчивый/молчали́вый	*talkative/reticent*
ла́сковый/не-	*affectionate/unaffectionate*
трудолюби́вый/лени́вый	*hardworking/lazy*
ще́дрый/жа́дный, скупо́й	*generous/greedy, stingy*
добросо́вестный/не-	*conscientious/not conscientious*
серьёзный/не-	*serious/not serious*
непредубеждённый/предубеждённый	*open-minded/closed-minded*
ги́бкий/упря́мый	*flexible/stubborn*
эмоциона́льный/сде́ржанный	*emotional/reserved*
ве́рный/не-	*loyal/disloyal*
надёжный/не-	*reliable/unreliable*
че́стный/не-	*honest/dishonest*
ве́жливый/не-, гру́бый	*courteous/rude*
лёгкий хара́ктер/тяжёлый хара́ктер	*gentle disposition/difficult disposition*

Упражне́ние 16.1   Fill in the blanks with the Russian equivalent of the English word or phrase in parentheses.

1. — Ле́на о́чень (*talented*) _____, о́чень (*cultured*)

   _____: она́ тебе́ понра́вится.

2. — Э́то не са́мое ва́жное: (*outgoing*) _____ ли она́? Она́ (*reserved*)

   _____ и́ли (*talkative*) _____?

3. И са́мое гла́вное, мне ну́жно познако́миться с (*serious*) _____,

   (*reliable*) _____, (*honest*) _____ де́вушкой с

   (*gentle disposition/easy to get along with*) _____.

4. — Интере́сно, что ну́жно Ле́не? Ду́мает ли она́, что ей ну́жен молодо́й челове́к, кото́рый

   (*closed-minded*) _____, (*stubborn*) _____

   и (*dishonest*) _____?

   — Ну, ты даёшь!

Зада́ние 16.1 Using the preceding vocabulary, describe the personalities and physical traits of three famous people. Bring your descriptions to class and, without revealing names, see if your classmates can guess whom you are describing.

 Фо́то-зада́ние Look at the photograph on the first page of this unit in the textbook. Write a paragraph or prepare a presentation, as assigned by your instructor, describing the personalities of the men in the picture based on their facial expressions.

Listening Tasks

The listening text for this unit consists of a dialogue in which we hear how Ira breaks up with Grisha.

PRE-LISTENING TASK

How would you describe the personality of your best friend? What kind of personality do you think this friend would look for in a mate?

 ## LISTENING TASKS

Listen to the text and then answer questions 1 and 2 in English and 3 through 6 in Russian.

1. How does Ira describe Grisha?
2. What is Grisha's main complaint about Ira?
3. How does Ira say that she is fed up with Grisha?
4. How does Grisha complain of her unfair judgment?
5. How does Grisha say that Ira is not perfect? (He uses the word *present* or *gift* in doing so.)
6. How does Ira tell Grisha to do as he pleases, but that she is leaving?

 ## DICTATION

Replay the tape and, as you listen, write out the dialogue in full.

PERFORMANCE

Practice reciting the dialogue.

POST-LISTENING TASK

Using the dialogue as a model, work with a classmate to create and perform your own dialogue in which you do some matchmaking for two famous individuals.

CULTURAL PROBLEM

What is a "friend" in North American society? How often do North Americans move from one city to another? When North Americans move, do they remain close to friends they left behind? How often do you think Russians move from one city to another? What is a "friend" in Russian society?

Phonetics and Intonation

ш and щ

This unit reviews the distinction between **ш** and **щ**. To pronounce **ш**, place the tip of your tongue into the hollow of your mouth near where your hard and soft palates meet. If you are pronouncing the sound correctly, and try to add the vowel sound **и** after **ш**, it will sound like **ы** (which is correct). To pronounce **щ**, place the middle third of your tongue against your soft palate and pronounce the sound with the middle of your tongue. If you are pronouncing the sound correctly, you should be able to make the sound **и** after **щ**.

Listen to the distinction between **ш** and **щ** on the tape.

1.	шат	щат		6.	наш	нащ
2.	шок	щёк		7.	кош	кощ
3.	шум	щум		8.	муш	мущ
4.	шел	щел		9.	леш	лещ
5.	шит	щит		10.	тиш	тищ

SELF-QUIZ

Circle the letters that best represent the sounds you hear.

1.	шат	щат		6.	тиш	тищ
2.	шёс	щёс		7.	шурь	щурь
3.	шел	щел		8.	шить	щить
4.	наш	нащ		9.	леш	лещ
5.	муш	мущ		10.	рюш	рющ

Lexicon: To Use

Russian has several verbs meaning *to use*.

Употреблять/употребить [что?]
  To use a word, phrase, or an ingredient in food

> Элла редко употребляет иностранные слова.
> *Ella rarely uses foreign words.*

Употребляться/употребиться
  To be used, especially in explaining grammatical constructions

> После этого глагола употребляется родительный падеж.
> *The genitive case is used after this verb.*

Пользоваться/вос– [чем?]
  To use, to take advantage, to use something up, to enjoy

> Я пользуюсь Машиным словарём, когда занимаюсь русским языком.
> *I use Masha's dictionary when I'm doing my Russian homework.*

> Эта артистка пользуется большой популярностью у молодёжи.
> *This performer enjoys great popularity among young people.*

Использовать, применять/применить [что?]
To use or apply something

> Она использует свой метод в этой работе.
> *She uses (applies) her own method in this work.*

> Я боюсь, что он применит силу в этой ситуации.
> *I'm afraid he'll use force in this situation.*

Потреблять, расходовать, тратить [что?]
To use, to consume, to waste

> Автомобиль «Кадиллак» расходует много бензина.
> *The Cadillac uses a lot of gas.*

Злоупотреблять [чьим + чем? чем?] эксплуатировать [кого? что?]
To use someone or something, to take advantage of or exploit someone or something

> Говорят, что Михаил эксплуатирует своих подчинённых и злоупотребляет моим доверием.
> *It's said that Mikhail exploits his subordinates and abuses my trust.*

Упражнение 16.2   Fill in the blanks with the Russian equivalent of the English word or phrase in parentheses.

1. — Наша преподавательница всегда (*uses*) _____ зелёным

   карандашом, когда проверяет наши контрольные.

2. — Может быть она не хочет (*waste*) _____ чернила.

3. — Ты напрасно так говоришь. Она просто (*uses*) _____ эту

   тактику в проверке: не хочет нас обижать красными чернилами. Ведь чернила —

   это навсегда! А красный цвет говорит: стоп!

4. — А когда она пишет зелёным карандашом, что после этого предлога (*is used*)

   _____ дательный падеж, это как будто не очень серьёзная

   ошибка.

Exercises and Activities

Упражнение 16.3   Read the dialogue between Boris Yeltsin and Lee Iacocca. Substitute the numbered expressions for the boldfaced expressions to create different versions of the dialouge.

Ельцин понимает, что если Россия будет покупать американские машины, то она должна будет что–нибудь продавать американцам. Ельцин говорит с мистером Аякокой и хочет уговорить его покупать русскую водку.

Е: По сравнению с американской водкой русская водка — **крепче**.
А: Да, она **намного (гораздо, значительно) крепче** американской водки.
Е: Да, с каждым годом наша водка **всё крепче и крепче**.
А: Ну, американцы хотят водку **как можно более крепкую**. В Детройте, например, говорят, **чем крепче, тем лучше!**

1. сладкая
2. дешёвая

3. мягкая
4. вкусная

Упражне́ние 16.4   Read the next dialogue between Boris Yeltsin and Lee Iacocca. Substitute the numbered expressions for the boldfaced expressions to create different versions of the dialogue.

Аяко́ка не хо́чет покупа́ть во́дку и поэ́тому Е́льцин начина́ет говори́ть с ним о ру́сской бума́ге. Ведь в Росси́и са́мые больши́е запа́сы ле́са в ми́ре. Ита́к, Е́льцин угова́ривает ми́стера Аяко́ку купи́ть ру́сскую бума́гу.

Е. По сравне́нию с америка́нской бума́гой ру́сская бума́га — **чи́ще**.
А. Да, она́ **намно́ю (гора́здо, значи́тельно) чи́ще** америка́нской бума́ги.
Е. Да, с ка́ждым го́дом на́ша бума́га **всё чи́ще и чи́ще**.
А. Ну, америка́нцы хотя́т бума́гу **как мо́жно бо́лее чи́стую**. В Детро́йте, наприме́р, говоря́т, **чем чи́ще, тем лу́чше!**

1. бе́лая
2. то́нкая
3. твёрдая

4. дешёвая
5. лёгкая
6. проста́я

Упражне́ние 16.5   Read the dialogue between Yeltsin and some representatives of Japanese automobile manufacturers who disagree with Iacocca. Create a new dialogue, using the numbered expressions.

Е́льцин та́кже говори́т с представи́телями япо́нских автомоби́льных фирм. Япо́нцы не согла́сны с ми́стером Аяко́кой.

Я. По сравне́нию с води́телями америка́нских маши́н, води́телям япо́нских маши́н о́чень ве́село.
Е. Да, им намно́го веселе́е, чем води́телям америка́нских маши́н.
Я. Да, и ка́ждый год на́шим води́телям всё веселе́е и веселе́е.
Е. Ну, мы хоти́м покупа́ть маши́ны, води́телям кото́рых бу́дет как мо́жно веселе́е. В Москве́ говоря́т: чем веселе́е, тем лу́чше!

1. В япо́нских маши́нах пассажи́рам о́чень тепло́.
2. Япо́нские маши́ны о́чень ма́ленькие и ую́тные.
3. Япо́нские маши́ны о́чень до́лго рабо́тают.
4. Япо́нские маши́ны о́чень ти́хо рабо́тают.

Упражне́ние 16.6   Read the dialogue in which the representatives of Japanese automobile manufacturers complain about American cars. Create a new dialogue using the numbered expressions.

Япо́нцы жа́луются на америка́нские маши́ны.

Я1: Америка́нские маши́ны о́чень дороги́е.
Я2: Ка́ждый год они́ всё доро́же и доро́же.
Я1: Мы ду́маем, что в Детро́йте говоря́т: «Как мо́жно доро́же! Чем доро́же, тем лу́чше!»

1. Америка́нские маши́ны о́чень больши́е и громо́здкие.
2. Покупа́тели америка́нских маши́н должны́ быть о́чень бога́тыми.
3. Хоро́шие америка́нские маши́ны очень ре́дки.

Упражне́ние 16.7   Fill in the blanks with the Russian equivalent of the English word or phrase in parentheses.

Жизнь америка́нского и росси́йского президе́нтов

1. Жизнь америка́нского президе́нта — тяжела́, но жизнь росси́йского президе́нта —

   (*much harder*) _____.

2. Америка́нский президе́нт занима́ется о́чень сло́жными пробле́мами, но росси́йский президе́нт занима́ется ещё (*much more complicated*) _____*бо́лее*_____ _____ пробле́мами.

3. Америка́нский президе́нт живёт в хоро́ших усло́виях, а росси́йский президе́нт живёт в (*less pleasant*) _____ усло́виях.

4. Избира́тельные кампа́нии в Росси́и стано́вятся (*more expensive all the time*) _____, но избира́тельные кампа́нии в Аме́рике давно́ ста́ли (*much more expensive*) _____, чем в Росси́и.

5. Америка́нский президе́нт реша́ет серьёзные экономи́ческие пробле́мы, но росси́йский президе́нт до́лжен реша́ть ещё (*more serious economic problems*) _____ _____, име́я (*fewer*) _____ де́нежных ресу́рсов.

6. Америка́нский президе́нт име́ет нема́ло пробле́м с америка́нскими коммуни́стами и фаши́стами, но росси́йский президе́нт име́ет (*many more problems*) _____ _____ с росси́йскими коммуни́стами и фаши́стами.

7. Америка́нский президе́нт — президе́нт одно́й из (*the wealthiest*) _____ стран ми́ра.

8. Росси́йский и америка́нский президе́нты – президе́нты (*of the strongest*) _____ стран ми́ра.

9. Америка́нскому президе́нту предстои́т (*the longest*) _____ избира́тельная кампа́ния.

10. Росси́йскому президе́нту в избира́тельной кампа́нии предстоя́т бесконе́чные пое́здки по (*the largest*) _____ стране́ ми́ра, по оди́ннадцати часовы́м поя́сам.

Упражне́ние 16.8 Fill in the blanks with the Russian equivalent of the English word or phrase in parentheses.

Е́льцин возвраща́ется домо́й и реша́ет не покупа́ть ни америка́нских маши́н, ни япо́нских. Он счита́ет, что ([*it's*] *more important*) _____*бо́лее ва́жно*_____[1] покупа́ть росси́йские маши́ны, хотя́ они́ сейча́с, наве́рно, (*worse*) _____*ху́же*_____[2] америка́нских и япо́нских маши́н и (*not as/less pretty than them*) _*не таки́е краси́вые как*_[3] Он большо́й патрио́т Росси́и. Он ду́мает, что, когда́ слома́ется росси́йская маши́на, росси́йский автозаво́д бу́дет намно́го (*closer*) ___*бли́же*___,[4] чем япо́нский и́ли америка́нский. Е́льцин зна́ет, что ([*there are*] *more Russians than Japanese*) ___*бо́лее ру́сских*___,[5] но что ([*there are*] *fewer Russians than Americans*) ___*ме́нее америка́нцев*___ [6] Он счита́ет, что ру́сские хотя́т е́здить на свои́х маши́нах. (Прав он, и́ли нет?) Ра́ньше ру́сские не относи́лись стро́го к свои́м ли́дерам, но тепе́рь они́ относя́тся (*more and more severely*) ___*стро́же и стро́же*___,[7] и наве́рно, счита́ет Е́льцин, (*the more severely, the better*) ___*чем стро́же, тем лу́чше*___,[8] потому́ что ли́деры должны́ учи́тывать жела́ния и интере́сы наро́да.

Упражне́ние 16.9   Translate the following passage into Russian.

Anna is looking for an apartment in Tver' today. In the morning she found an apartment bigger in size (**по площади**) than the one in Moscow where she lived previously, but she wants an apartment nearer to the institute where she works. She found another apartment, but it was on the second floor, and she wants to be on a higher floor. The third apartment that she found was too expensive: 500,000 rubles a month. She wants an apartment cheaper than that, but she doesn't want an apartment that is as cheap as possible, because such apartments are generally not clean. She wants an apartment cleaner than the one she lived in previously. Later she found a fourth apartment that was smaller than the first three apartments, but less expensive and nearer to the institute. It seemed quieter than the first two apartments, but not as quiet as the third apartment, and not as beautiful, either. She knew she would not live in the apartment longer than a year, so she decided to rent (**снять**) that apartment.

Зада́ние 16.2   Consider the questions raised in **Упражне́ние 16.7** and respond to the following questions about the lives and responsibilities of the American and Russian presidents: **Чья жизнь трудне́е? Чья жизнь сложне́е? Как вы ду́маете?**

Зада́ние 16.3   Prepare a sixty-second radio advertisement to sell a product of your choice. Use as many comparatives as possible to demonstrate that your product is better than its competition.

Зада́ние 16.4   Prepare a three-minute talk or write a composition, as assigned by your instructor, describing and comparing the various places (dorm room, fraternity or sorority house, apartment, room in a house, and so on) you have lived in while a student at your college or university.

Фо́то-зада́ние   Look at the photograph on the first page of this unit in the textbook (or on the first page of Unit 1, Unit 8, or Unit 12) and prepare a presentation or write a composition, as assigned by your instructor, comparing the people depicted.

Glossary

Adverbs and adjectives are alphabetized according to the adverb; comparative forms are provided only when they are irregular simple forms. Regular simple forms, such as **краси́вый/краси́вее**, are *not* listed.

блю́до   *dish* (*type of food*)

в	*in/to (may take the accusative or prepositional case)*
# вари́ть/с– (I) [что?]: варю́, ва́ришь, ва́рят	*to boil or poach*
бли́зко, бли́зкий, бли́же	*near, near, nearer*
бога́то, бога́тый, бога́че	*richly, rich/wealthy, richer/wealthier*
большо́й, бо́льше	*big, bigger*
бо́лее	*more [+ adjective or adverb]*
бы́стро	*quickly*
# ве́рный/не–	*faithful, loyal/unfaithful, disloyal*
# ве́жливый/не–	*courteous/dis-*
ве́село, весёлый, веселе́е	*merrily/happily, merry/happy, merrier/happier*
всё ____ и ____	*____er and ____er [+ comparative]*
высоко́, высо́кий, вы́ше	*high, high, higher*
далеко́, далёкий, да́льше	*far, distant, farther*
до́рого, дорого́й, доро́же	*expensively, expensive, more expensive*
до́лго, до́лгий, до́льше	*for a long time, long, longer*
дёшево, дешёвый, деше́вле	*inexpensively, inexpensive, more inexpensive (less expensive)*
ги́бкий	*flexible*
глубоко́, глубо́кий, глу́бже	*deeply, deep, deeper*
гора́здо	*much more [+ comparative]*
гро́мко, гро́мкий, гро́мче	*loudly, loud, louder*
# гру́бый	*coarse, rude*
# добросо́вестный/не–	*conscientious/not*
# дружелю́бный	*friendly*
# жа́дный	*stingy, greedy*
# злоупотребля́ть (I) [чьим+чем? чем?]: злоупотребля́ю, злоупотребля́ешь, злоупотребля́ют	*to misuse someone's or something, to take advantage of or exploit someone's or something*
значи́тельно	*significantly [+ comparative]*

# интеллигéнтный/не—	*cultured/uncultured*
# испóльзовать (I) [что?]: испóльзую, испóльзуешь, испóльзуют	*to use, make use of something*
интерéсный	*interesting*
как мóжно ____	*as ____ as possible [+ comparative]*
кóротко, корóткий, корóче	*shortly/briefly, short/brief, shorter/briefer*
# культýрный/не—	*cultured/uncultured*
лáсковый/не—	*affectionate/not*
легкó, лёгкий, лéгче	*easily, easy, easier*
# ленúвый	*lazy*
мáленький, мéньше	*small, smaller*
мéнее	*less [+ adjective or adverb]*
молодóй, молóже, млáдший	*young, younger, younger*
# молчалúвый	*reserved, reticent*
мя́гкий, мя́гче	*soft, softer*
# надёжный/не—	*reliable/unreliable*
намнóго	*much more [+ comparative]*
неинтерéсный	*uninteresting*
некрасúвый	*ugly, not handsome/ beautiful*
# неприя́зненный	*antagonistic, hostile*
неýмный	*stupid, not smart*
плóхо, плохóй, хýже	*badly, bad, worse*
пóздно, пóздний, позже, позднéе	*late, late, later, later*
# пóльзоваться/вос— (I) [чем?]: пóльзуюсь, пóльзуешься, пóльзуются	*to use, to take advantage of something, to enjoy something*
# потребля́ть (I) [что?]: потребля́ю, потребля́ешь, потребля́ют	*to use, to consume or waste something*
# предубеждённый/не—	*closed-minded/open- minded*
# применя́ть (I) /применúть (II) [что?]: применя́ю, применя́ешь, применя́ют; применю́, примéнишь, примéнят	*to use, to apply*
прóсто, простóй, прóще	*simply, simple, simpler*
# привéтливый	*outgoing*
рáно, рáнний, рáньше, рáнее	*early, early, earlier, earlier*
# расхóдовать (I) [что?]: расхóдую, расхóдуешь, расхóдуют	*to use, to consume or waste something*
# разговóрчивый	*talkative*

рéдко, рéдкий, рéже	*rarely, rare, rarer*
рóбкий	*timid, shy*
сáмый	*the most [+ adjective]*
# сдéржанный	*reticent, reserved*
# серьёзный/не–	*serious/not serious*
скóлько…стóлько	*as much as*
# скупóй	*miserly*
спосóбный/не–	*capable/not capable, talented/not talented*
стáрый, стáрше	*old, older*
# стоúческий	*stoic*
стрóго, стрóгий, стрóже	*strictly, strict, stricter*
так…как…	*as . . . as . . .*
тúхо, тúхий, тúше	*quietly, quiet, quieter*
твёрдый, твёрже	*hard, harder*
# трáтить /ис- [что?]: трáчу, трáтишь, трáтят	*to use, to consume or waste something*
# трудолюбúвый	*hardworking*
умный/не–	*smart/stupid*
# употреблять (I) /употребúть (II) [что?]: употребляю, употребляешь, употребляют; употреблю, употребúшь, употребят	*to use a word, phrase, or ingredient in food*
# употребляться (I) /употребúться (II): употребляется, употребляются; употребится, употребятся	*to be used, especially in explaining grammatical constructions*
# упрямый	*stubborn*
# харáктер: мягкий, тяжёлый	*character, personality: easygoing, not easygoing*
хорошó, хорóший, лучше	*well, good, better*
чáсто, чáстый, чáще	*frequently, frequent, more frequently*
чем ____, … тем ____	*the ____er, the ____er [+ comparatives]*
# чéстный/не–	*honest/dishonest*
чúсто, чúстый, чúще	*cleanly, clean, cleaner (more clean)*
# щéдрый	*generous*
# эксплуатúровать (I) [что? когó?]: эксплуатúрую, эксплуатúруешь, эксплуатúруют	*to exploit, to use*
# эмоционáльный	*emotional*

UNIT 17

Lexicon: Weather

Russians use several constructions to talk about the weather.

Погóда, прогнóз погóды на суббóту, зáвтра
Weather, forecast for Saturday, tomorrow

> — Какáя зáвтра бýдет погóда?
> *What will the weather be like tomorrow?*

> — Я не слы́шала прогнóз на зáвтра.
> *I haven't heard the forecast for tomorrow.*

Ожидáется/ожидáются…
Is/are expected

> В Петербýрге ожидáются дожди́ и грóзы.
> *Petersburg is expecting rain showers and thunderstorms today.*

Погóда: сóлнечная, óблачная, дождли́вая, хорóшая, плохáя
Weather: sunny, cloudy, rainy, good, bad

> Какáя сегóдня хорóшая погóда!
> *What great weather we've got today! What a great day!*

Свéтит сóлнце, свети́ло сóлнце
The sun is shining, the sun was shining

> Стоя́ла прекрáсная погóда: свети́ло сóлнце, дул лёгкий вéтер.
> *It was a beautiful day: the sun was shining and there was a gentle breeze.*

Идёт дождь/снег, пойдёт дождь/снег, бýдет идти́ дождь/снег
It's raining/snowing, it will start to rain or snow, it will be raining or snowing

> Éсли пойдёт дождь, мы поéдем домóй на такси́.
> *If it starts to rain we'll go home in a taxi.*

> Говоря́т, что сегóдня весь день бýдет идти́ снег.
> *They say it's going to snow all day.*

В такýю погóду
In such weather

> Нельзя́ éхать в такýю погóду!
> *We can't go in such weather!*

Дуть (дýет вéтер) и́ли сквозня́к
To blow (it's windy, there's a draft)

> Опя́ть дýет си́льный вéтер с мóря.
> *There's a strong ocean wind today again.*

Бу́ря, гроза́, мо́лния, мете́ль, урага́н, смерч
Storm, thunderstorm/thunder, lightning, blizzard, hurricane, tornado

В Росси́и ре́дко быва́ют сме́рчи.
Tornadoes seldom occur in Russia.

О́блако/облака́, ту́ча/ту́чи
Cloud(s), storm cloud(s)

Вчера́ бы́ло мно́го облако́в, но сего́дня нет.
Yesterday there were a lot of clouds, but there aren't any today.

Вла́жность, давле́ние
Humidity, (barometric) pressure

За́втра бу́дет высо́кая вла́жность.
The humidity will be high tomorrow.

Упражне́ние 17.1 Fill in the blanks with the Russian equivalent of the English word or phrase in parentheses.

1. — Вчера́ весь день (*rained*) _____.

2. — Куда́ же ты ходи́л в (*in such weather*) _____!

3. — Ле́том здесь обы́чно о́чень (*hot and humid*) _жарко_ _влажно_ _____.

4. — Но за́втра (*snow is expected*) _____.

5. — Да, по ра́дио сказа́ли, что за́втра (*it will snow*) _____.

6. — Сейча́с опя́ть (*the wind is blowing*) _____ с мо́ря.

7. — Кака́я (*awful weather*) _____!

8. — Смотри́те на э́ти (*storm clouds*) _____: ско́ро бу́дет

   (*thunderstorm*) _____гроза_____.

9. — Я наде́юсь, что не бу́дет (*tornado*) _____!

10. — Да, сейча́с о́чень высо́кое (*pressure*) _____.

Зада́ние 17.1 Prepare a description of this week's weather in some region of the world, without revealing the name of the place. See if your classmates can guess the name of the place you have in mind.

 Фо́то-зада́ние Look at the photograph on the first page of this unit in the textbook. Write a paragraph or prepare a presentation, as assigned by your instructor, from the point of view of a Russian man or woman your age: What kinds of things do you like to do in the winter? In the summer?

Listening Tasks

Note: Listening tasks for this unit are based on time expressions (date and clock time).

The listening texts for this unit consist of excerpts from two radio reports. The first concerns some of the changes in the Soviet border during and after World War II. The second provides a time line for some of the events in Moscow during the night of the failed coup of August 1991.

PRE-LISTENING TASK FOR TEXT 1

What do you know about border changes in the Soviet Union during World War II? Make a list of some of the changes you know about. Then look at maps of Russia and the world in your textbook and make a list of all the countries that border on Russia including those countries that were once republics of the former Soviet Union.

LISTENING TASK FOR TEXT 1

Listen to the text and then answer questions 1 through 9 in English and 10 through 14 in Russian.

1. When did the Red Army cross the border with Poland?
2. When were the parts of Poland the Red Army occupied incorporated into the Soviet Union?
3. Were any of these lands returned to Poland and if so on what date?
4. When did the war with Finland end?
5. Romania annexed Bessarabia in what year?
6. Did the Soviet government recognize this annexation?
7. When did the Soviet Union reacquire this land?
8. When were the republics of Lithuania, Latvia and Estonia incorporated into the Soviet Union?
9. When was Tuva incorporated into the Soviet Union? When did it become an autonomous republic?
10. Find the Russian equivalent of the expression *the border with Poland at that time*. (Hint: *at that time* is expressed in Russian in one word.)
11. Find the Russian equivalent of the expression *take under its defense the life and property*.
12. Find the Russian equivalent of the expression *incorporated into the USSR*. (Hint: the Russian expression is literally translated as *included in the makeup of the USSR*.)
13. Find the Russian equivalent of the word *turn* (used in reference to the fate of Bessarabia).
14. Find the Russian equivalent of the words *annexation* and *to concede or yield something to someone*.

DICTATION

Replay the tape and, as you listen, write out the text in full.

PERFORMANCE

Practice reciting the text.

POST-LISTENING TASK

Write out a time line, in Russian, listing all Soviet border changes.

CULTURAL PROBLEM

Does anything surprise or interest you about the border changes in the Soviet Union during this period?

LISTENING TASK FOR TEXT 2

Listen to the text and then answer questions 1 through 10 in English and 11 through 15 in Russian.

1. When was the first round of automatic gunfire heard?
2. When was the second round heard?
3. When were short rounds heard in the area of Pushkin Square?
4. At what time did the Tamanskaia division leave Moscow on Lenin Prospect?
5. When did Burbulis make his appeal?
6. When did the people inside the "White House" first get instructions to lower the blinds, stay away from the windows, and keep the lights off whenever possible?
7. When were more gunfire and shouting heard on the square?
8. When were the deputies called to the Council of Nationalities Chamber?
9. When was the first casualty thought to have happened?
10. When was shooting heard in the city?
11. Find the Russian equivalent of the expression *automatic round(s)*.
12. Find the Russian equivalent of the expression *at the same time*.
13. Find the Russian equivalent of the expression *from the direction of* [*Taganka Square*].
14. Find the Russian equivalent of the expression *there are no casualties*.
15. Find the Russian equivalent of the expression *to appeal to all those inside and near the "White House."*

DICTATION

Replay the tape and, as you listen, write out the text in full.

PERFORMANCE

Practice reciting the text.

POST-LISTENING TASK

Using the timeline, as a model, describe what might have happened minute by minute on a famous night in history anywhere in the world.

CULTURAL PROBLEM

What is the perspective of the author of this text on the events of August 1991? What is your perspective on these events?

Phonetics and Intonation

This unit reviews the pronunciation of **ц** and **-тся** and the sound produced when **с** is followed by **ч**.

ц and -тся

When **-тся** occurs at the end of a verb it is pronounced like **ца** (with the final vowel pronounced as unstressed).

Listen to **ц** and **-тся** on the tape and repeat.

1. цап   сап   сяп
2. цок   сок   сёк
3. цум   сум   сюм
4. цел   сэл   сел
5. цен   сэн   сен
6. цирк   сыр   сир
7. цын   сын   син
8. улыбáется
9. открывáется
10. занимáется

SELF-QUIZ #1

Circle the letters that best represent the sounds you hear.

1. цап   сап   сяп
2. цок   сок   сёк
3. цум   сум   сюм
4. цел   сэл   сел
5. цен   сэн   сен
6. цыр   сыр   сир
7. цын   сын   син

с + ч = щ

Listen to **с** and **ч** on the tape and repeat. Note the standard and colloquial pronunciation of two common words, **тысяча** and **сейчáс**.

ч	щ
1. часть	счáстье
2. честь	счéсть
3. читáть	считáть
4. читáю	считáю
5. читáешь	считáешь
6. чи́танные	счи́танные
7. тысяча	[тыща]
8. сейчáс	[щас]

SELF-QUIZ #2

Circle the letters that best represent the sounds you hear.

1. часть	счáстье
2. честь	счесть
3. читáть	считáть
4. читáю	считáю
5. читáешь	считáешь
6. чи́танные	счи́танные
7. тысяча	[тыща]
8. сейчáс	[щас]

Exercises and Activities

Упражнéние 17.2   Fill in the blanks with the Russian equivalent of the English word or phrase in parentheses. Write out all numbers as words.

1. (*Last year*) _____ мы éздили в Россию.

2. (*Before*) _____, как мы уéхали из Амéрики, мы офóрмили

    пáспорт и россѝйскую вѝзу.

3. Мы приéхали в Петербýрг (*tenth of July*) _____ и провелѝ там (*a*

    week) _____.

4. (*On the first day*) _____ в Петербýрге мы éздили по гóроду (*for*

    three hours) _____.

5. Мы óчень устáли и наконéц остановѝлись пообéдать (*at 2:30*) _____ .

6. (*In the evening*) _____ мы ходѝли по Нéвскому проспéкту и по

    нáбережным: какáя красотá!

7. Нам сказáли, что ([*at*] *nights*) _____ развóдятся мостýı, чтóбы

    пропустѝть кораблѝ.

8. (*Two days before*) _____, как мы уéхали из

    Петербýрга, я познакóмилась с рýсской медсестрóй.

9. Онá пригласѝла меня́ к себé домóй, и я провелá у неё (*the entire evening*)

    _____.

10. Онá спросѝла меня́, (*when*) _____ я уезжáю.

11. Когдá я сказáла, что уезжáю (*in two days, on Wednesday*) _____

    _____, в Москвý (*for five days*) _____, ей

    стáло óчень грýстно.

12. Онá спросѝла, (*at what time*) _____ я уезжáю.

13. Я объяснѝла, что нам нýжно собрáться на Москóвском вокзáле (*by evelen in the*

    evening on Wednesday) _____ .

14. Онá сказáла, что онá заéдет за мной в гостѝницу (*at 9:45*) _____

    _____ , чтóбы помóчь мне добрáться до вокзáла.

15. Мне бы́ло óчень грýстно, когдá я уезжáла из Петербýрга, но я обещáла своéй нóвой

    подрýге, что вернýсь (*next year*) _____ , (*in the spring*)

    _____, навéрно (*in April*) _____.

Упражне́ние 17.3   A Russian manager of a multinational project in Russia is concerned about meeting deadlines. Fill in the blanks with the Russian equivalent of the English word or phrase in parentheses. Write out all numbers as words.

Как мы попа́ли в э́ту ситуа́цию? Мы должны́ зако́нчить на́шу рабо́ту (*within four weeks*)

_____,¹ (*before*) _____ ²

начнём но́вый прое́кт. Америка́нцы в пе́рвый раз заговори́ли об э́том прое́кте (*three years*

ago) _____,³ (*in July of '93*) _____

_____,⁴ но пригласи́ли нас рабо́тать с ни́ми то́лько (*last year*)

_____,⁵ (*on the 12th of April of '94*) _____

_____.⁶ (*In the summer of last year*) _____

_____⁷ к нам прие́хали представи́тели америка́нской стороны́ с тем,

что́бы посмотре́ть объе́кты в Москве́.

Упражне́ние 17.4   The story continues. Fill in the blanks with the Russian equivalent of the English word or phrase in parentheses. Write out all numbers as words.

Они́ прие́хали (*for one week*) _____,¹ но перегово́ры

шли (*for two weeks*) _____.² Пото́м, (*a month later*)

_____,³ прие́хал дире́ктор америка́нской фи́рмы

подписа́ть догово́р. Когда́ э́то бы́ло? Ка́жется, (*last fall*) _____

_____.⁴ (*On that evening*) _____, ⁵

когда́ мы подписа́ли догово́р, родила́сь моя́ вну́чка: э́то случи́лось (*on the fourth of*

November) _____.⁶ (*In the morning*) _____

_____,⁷ (*on the next day*) _____ ⁸

мы с жено́й е́здили к до́чери в роди́льный дом. (*Since the time that*)

_____⁹ уе́хала америка́нская делега́ция, на́ши дела́ пошли́ пло́хо.

Упражне́ние 17.5   The manager continues to fret. Fill in the blanks with the Russian equivalent of the English word or phrase in parentheses. Write out all numbers as words.

Что тепе́рь де́лать? Мы зако́нчим пе́рвую часть на́шей рабо́ты (*next week*)

_____,¹ но втору́ю часть зако́нчим то́лько (*next month*)

_____,² а после́днюю часть, наве́рно, зако́нчим то́лько (*next year*)

_____.³ Éсли че́стно сказа́ть, то мо́жно наде́яться, что зако́нчится

рабо́та то́лько (*by February of '99*) _____

_____,⁴ (*two months before*) _____ ⁵

конца́ пе́рвого кварта́ла, (*but four months after*) _____

_____⁶ сро́ка контра́кта. Бу́дут ли америка́нцы дово́льны тако́й ситуа́цией?

Наве́рно, нет. Они́ же хоте́ли, чтобы мы всё зако́нчили (*before*) _____

_____[7] у них откро́ется но́вый заво́д в Теха́се. Всё-таки, (*until we

receive*) _____[8] материа́лы от партнёров в Си́этле, у

нас не мо́жет быть никако́го улучше́ния.

Упражне́ние 17.6   The manager continues to fret. Fill in the blanks with the Russian equivalent
of the English word or phrase in parentheses. Write out all numbers as words.

Госпожа́ Ро́джерс приезжа́ет за́втра (*at 9:20*) _____

_____.[1] Мы ся́дем и хорошо́ поговори́м обо всём. (*At 11:00*) _____

_____[2] прие́дет Господи́н Яшимо́то, с япо́нской

стороны́, а (*at 12:50*) _____[3] прие́дет Госпожа́ Ба́уэр, с

неме́цкой стороны́. Когда́ прие́дет Ба́уэр, мы пока́жем им всем образцы́ на́шей проду́кции,

вы́пущенной (*from the twenty-eighth of March to the thirtieth of April*) _____

_____.[4] (*After*) _____

_____,[5] как образцы́ бу́дут пока́заны, предста́вим гра́фик

потенциа́льной проду́кции (*from 1997 to 2001*) _____

_____.[6] Мо́жет быть, они́ успоко́ятся?

Упражне́ние 17.7   Translate the following passage into Russian.

Kira and Petia went (**пое́хали**) to Omsk for a month and will return next week, but Tania is
coming on Saturday the seventeenth. I'm sure we'll be talking about this all next month. Next
year, in (*fill in the next calendar year here*), they should not stay in Omsk for a month. Kira
and Petia know Tania always comes in February. Maybe Kira and Petia can come back two
days before Tania comes? I don't think Tania can stay two days later than she had planned
because she is going to Cheliabinsk for three weeks on the twenty-first. The last time we saw
Tania was in the fall, when she used to work in the library on Wednesdays. We haven't seen
her since she had the baby! I hope Kira and Petia can return a little earlier.

Упражне́ние 17.8   Translate the following passage into Russian.

Sergei is waiting (**сиди́т** [*sitting*]) in the café until Dina returns: she said she would return
(**вернётся**) in two hours. Dina is studying (**занима́ться**) in the library because she will have a
mathematics test in three days. Sergei knows that Dina has to study because she got sick
(**заболе́ла**) the day before the previous (**предыду́щий**) test and did poorly on it (**пло́хо её
написа́ла**). Dina is a good student (**хорошо́ у́чится**), but she has been worried about this
exam since she took (**сдава́ла**) the last one. Until now Sergei hasn't worried about Dina, but
now he's nervous. He will drink (**вы́пьет**) three cups of coffee before Dina returns. After she
takes her test they will calm down (**успоко́ятся**)!

Зада́ние 17.3   Describe your annual schedule, explaining how it differs during the school year
and the summer.

Зада́ние 17.4   Describe your schedule, describing how weekends are different from school or
work days.

Зада́ние 17.5 Describe your schedule, explaining how Mondays, Wednesdays, and Fridays are different from Tuesdays and Thursdays.

Зада́ние 17.6 Describe your family's annual cycle of holidays, including family birthdays and anniversaries.

Зада́ние 17.7 Describe what happened on the day or days preceding a recent family event, such as a wedding, baptism, circumcision or naming, bar or bat mitzvah, communion or confirmation, Christmas, Rosh Ha-Shanah, Thanksgiving, Fourth of July, picnic, Easter, or Passover. Use clock time to describe the process of preparation for the event.

Glossary

# бу́ря	*storm*
# вла́жность	*humidity*
вчера́шний	*yesterday's*
Во ско́лько вре́мени?	*At what time?*

вре́мя го́да:
  весна́, весно́й
  ле́то, ле́том
  о́сень, о́сенью
  зима́, зимо́й
	season of the year:
	  spring, in the spring
	  summer, in the summer
	  fall, in the fall
	  winter, in the winter

вре́мя су́ток:
  у́тро, всё у́тро, у́тром
 	
  день, весь день, днём
 	
  ве́чер, весь ве́чер, ве́чером
 	
  ночь, всю ночь, но́чью
	time of day:
	  morning, all morning, in the morning
	  afternoon, all afternoon, in the afternoon
	  evening, all evening, in the evening
	  night, all night, in the night

# в таку́ю пого́ду	*in such weather*
год, в како́м году́?	*year, in what year?*
# гроза́	*thunderstorm*
# давле́ние	*pressure (barometric)*

дни неде́ли:
  понеде́льник, в...
  вто́рник, во...
  среда́, в сре́ду
 	
  четве́рг, в...
  пя́тница, в пя́тницу
  суббо́та, в суббо́ту
  воскресе́нье, в...
	day of the week:
	  Monday, on Monday
	  Tuesday, on Tuesday
	  Wednesday, on Wednesday
	  Thursday, on Thursday
	  Friday, on Friday
	  Saturday, on Saturday
	  Sunday, on Sunday

до тех пор, как...; пока́ не...	*until*

до того́, как...	*before*
# до́ждь: идёт, пойдёт, бу́дет идти́	*rain: it is raining, it will start to rain, it will be raining*
# ду́ет ве́тер, ду́ет сла́бый ве́тер	*it's windy, there's a gentle breeze*
за [како́е вре́мя?] (до того́, как...)	*[time] before [some event]*
зака́зывать (I) /заказа́ть (I) но́мер: зака́зываю, зака́зываешь, зака́зывают; закажу́, зака́жешь, зака́жут	*to order a hotel room*
за́втрашний	*tomorrow's*
к [како́му вре́мени?]	*by [a certain time]*
Како́е сего́дня число́?	*What's today's date?*
Како́го числа́...?	*On what date (did or will something happen?)*
ме́сяцы: янва́рь, февра́ль, ма́рт, апре́ль, ма́й, ию́нь, ию́ль, а́вгуст, сентя́брь, октя́брь, ноя́брь, дека́брь	*months of the year*
# мете́ль (ж.)	*snowstorm, blizzard*
мину́та	*minute*
на [како́е вре́мя?]	*for [a certain time period; duration of time follows completion of the action, the results of the action in effect for the duration of the time period]*
наза́д [како́е вре́мя?]	*ago [time]*
неде́ля	*week*
но́мер (в гости́нице)	*hotel room*
# о́блако, облака́	*cloud, clouds*
# ожида́ется, ожида́ются	*are expected (used with weather events)*
по утра́м, по вечера́м, по понеде́льникам, по сре́дам	*in the mornings, in the evenings, on Mondays, on Wednesdays*
# пого́да: со́лнечная, о́блачная, дождли́вая, хоро́шая, плоха́я	*weather: sunny, cloudy, rainy, good, bad*
полови́на	*half (used with clock time expressions with the genitive case of the number adjective of the next hour)*
по́сле того́, как...	*after*
# прогно́з	*weather forecast*

про́шлый	last (*as in last week, last year*)
раз в неде́лю, два ра́за, пять раз в неде́лю	once, twice, five times a week
ро́вно	sharp (*in time expressions*)
с [како́го вре́мени?]...до [како́го вре́мени?]	from [*time*] to [*time*]
сего́дняшний	today's
секу́нда	second (*as a unit of time*)
Ско́лько сейча́с вре́мени?	What time is it now?
сле́дующий	next
# смерч	tornado
# со́лнце све́тит, свети́ло	the sun shines, was shining
# снег: идёт, пойдёт, бу́дет идти́	snow: it's snowing, it will start to snow, it will be snowing
с тех пор, как...	since the time that
# ту́ча	storm cloud
# урага́н	hurricane
час	hour
че́рез [како́е вре́мя?] (по́сле того́, как...)	in/after [*time: the action occurs only after the time has elapsed*]

UNIT 18

Lexicon: Sports

Sports are as popular in Russia as they are in the United States. In general, Russians are more interested in their traditionally favorite sports, such as hockey and soccer, than they are in foreign sports, such as golf or baseball, though the latter are growing in popularity.

Игра́ть/по– [во что?]
To play something/to play for a while

> Мы с друзья́ми ча́сто игра́ем в волейбо́л.
> *My friends and I often play volleyball.*

> Мы поигра́ли в баскетбо́л и пото́м разошли́сь.
> *We played basketball for a while and then went our separate ways.*

Сыгра́ть матч
To play a game or round

> Дава́йте сыгра́ем матч.
> *Let's play a game.*

Про́игрывать/проигра́ть [кому́?]
To lose

> «Дина́мо» ча́сто про́игрывает «Спартаку́».
> *The "Dynamo" team usually loses to the "Spartacus" team.*

Вы́игрывать/вы́играть [у кого́? что?]
To win

> Я наде́юсь, что «Спарта́к» вы́играет ку́бок у «Дина́мо».
> *I hope "Spartacus" wins the cup against "Dynamo."*

Де́лать заря́дку
To do calisthenics

> Мы де́лаем заря́дку три ра́за в неде́лю.
> *We do calisthenics three times a week.*

Боле́ть [за что? кого́?], боле́льщик
To root for something or someone, fan

> Я всегда́ боле́ю за сбо́рную Росси́и в Олимпи́йских и́грах.
> *I always root for the Russian team in the Olympic Games.*

Занима́ться спо́ртом, занима́ться каки́м ви́дом спо́рта?
To engage in sports, to engage in what kind of sports?

> Когда́ я была́ моло́же, я занима́лась спо́ртом ка́ждый день.
> *When I was younger I engaged in sports every day.*

> Каки́м ви́дом (Каки́ми ви́дами) спо́рта вы занима́лись?
> *What kind of sports were you involved in?*

Упражне́ние 18.1 Create a list of sports according to some criteria of your own selection (e.g., sports that can be violent or dangerous vs. sports that are not violent; team sports vs. individual sports; outdoor vs. indoor sports).

 Зада́ние 18.2 Prepare a presentation or a paragraph, as assigned by your instructor, describing your involvement in sports or the involvement of someone you know.

 Фо́то-зада́ние Look at the photograph on the first page of this unit in the textbook. Write a paragraph or prepare a presentation, as assigned by your instructor, describing how kids entertained themselves during the summer in your neighborhood when you were growing up.

Listening Tasks

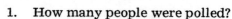

Note: Listening tasks in this unit are based on the grammar of Unit 18 in the textbook, not the lexicon.

The listening text for this unit is a radio report about a poll on the question "In what era would you like to have lived?" Although the journalists use the construction, «**В како́й эпо́хе вы хоте́ли бы жить?**», the preferred time expression is actually «**В каку́ю эпо́ху...**»

PRE-LISTENING TASK

In what eras and places would you like to have lived? In what eras and places do you think some of your friends and family would like to have lived? How do you think Russians might answer this question?

 ## LISTENING TASK

Listen to the text and answer questions 1 through 7 in English and 8 through 14 in Russian.

1. How many people were polled?
2. When and where would Andrei, Stas, Mikhail, and Vera like to have lived and why?
3. Does the majority of people polled like current life in Russia or not?
4. Would the majority of people polled like to have lived in some other time on the territory of Russia or somewhere else?
5. For those who would like to have lived somewhere else, what places were mentioned?
6. Three quarters of those who would like to have lived somewhere else and/or in another time want something special in their lives: what is that?
7. How many people express a wish to live in the future? Why or why not?
8. Find the Russian equivalent for *one doesn't get to choose the time* [*in which one lives*].
9. Find the Russian equivalent for the expression [*if*] *it was your lot to be born in the Stone Age, you would chase after mammoths your whole life.*
10. Find the Russian equivalent for the noun that means *majority age* (i.e., of an adult age, not a minor). What are the roots of this word?
11. Find the Russian adjective meaning *now* or *current*.
12. Find the Russian equivalent for *to touch, to come into contact with a new reality.*
13. Find the Russian equivalent for the expression *regardless of their geographic coordinates.* What are the two Russian words meaning *regardless* and what is the root of the second of these words?
14. Find the Russian expression meaning *no one wanted to be a Russian serf.*

DICTATION

Replay the tape and, as you listen, write out the text in full.

PERFORMANCE

Practice reciting the text.

POST-LISTENING TASK

Poll twenty people (in English) in a dining hall, dormitory, library, pizzeria or other campus hangout about when and where they would like to have lived. Prepare a brief report in Russian of the results.

CULTURAL PROBLEM

Several important cultural figures are mentioned in this text: **Егóр Гайдáр** (a prominent politician), **Лёня Голубкóв** (a fictional character from a TV ad campaign), and **Владúмир Высóцкий** and **Алексáндр Гáлич** (famous bards). In addition, one woman specifically mentions performances at the **Теáтр на Тагáнке** and **Вечерá в Политехнúческом музéе**. Select one of these cultural figures or events and prepare a brief presentation on the importance of the figure or event in Russian culture in the 1970s, 1980s, or 1990s.

Phonetics and Intonation

Russian ч and English *ch*

This unit presents the Russian sounds **ч** and **р**, distinguishing them from the English sounds with which they may be confused. In order to pronounce Russian **ч** correctly, place the middle third of your tongue on the soft upper palate of your mouth. Listen to the following pairs of words on the tape and repeat; the first word in each pair is Russian, the second is English.

1.	чап	chop		5.	чип	cheap
2.	чу	chew		6.	чит	cheat
3.	чек	check		7.	скач	scotch
4.	чес	chess		8.	эч	etch

SELF-QUIZ #1

Circle the letters that best represents the sounds you hear (i.e., whether the sounds are Russian or English).

1.	чап	chop		5.	чип	cheap
2.	чу	chew		6.	чит	cheat
3.	чек	check		7.	скач	scotch
4.	чес	chess		8.	эч	etch

Hard and Soft **р**

As you pronounce **р**, be sure to let your tongue vibrate with a stream of air. The vibration is long and vigorous for hard **р**, but is less noticeable for soft **р** because of the placement of the middle part of the tongue on the soft upper palate. Note that in American English pronunciation of *r*, the tip of the tongue is raised toward the hard palate and the entire tongue is held rigid and tense. This is not at all the case with Russian **р**. Furthermore, when American English *r* is preceded by *t* or *d*, the resulting diphthong is sometimes pronounced like "chr" or "jr"; try pronouncing these words to see if your pronunciation follows this pattern: *tree, train, try, drive, drill, drain.* In Russian, when **р** is preceded by either **т** or **д**, there is never a diphthong, as illustrated in the sounds on the tape.

Listen to the hard **р** and soft **р** and repeat.

1.	рат	рят	6.	драк	дряк
2.	руб	рюб	7.	друб	дрюб
3.	рыб	риб	8.	ар	арь
4.	трак	тряк	9.	ур	урь
5.	труб	трюб	10.	ер	ерь

SELF-QUIZ #2

Circle the letters that best represent the sounds you hear.

1.	руб	рюб	6.	друб	дрюб
2.	рыб	риб	7.	дрыж	дриж
3.	трак	тряк	8.	ор	орь
4.	трыж	триж	9.	ур	урь
5.	драк	дряк	10.	ер	ерь

Exercises and Activities

Упражне́ние 18.2   Read the Russian sentences and write a question that asks about the boldfaced word. Use the particle **ли** in each question.

Образе́ц: Ви́тя **сказа́л**, что он придёт в семь часо́в.
Сказа́л ли Ви́тя, что он придёт в семь часо́в?

1. Кири́лл игра́ет в **ре́гби**.
2. Кирилл **хорошо́** игра́ет в ре́гби.
3. **Кири́лл** игра́ет в ре́гби.
4. И́ра рабо́тает в **э́той** лаборато́рии.
5. И́ра **рабо́тает** в э́той лаборато́рии.
6. Ири́на и О́льга уе́хали в **командиро́вку** в Волгогра́д.
7. Ири́на и О́льга уе́хали в командиро́вку в **Волгогра́д**.

Упражне́ние 18.3   Read the Russian sentences and write a statement that you don't know whether or not the boldfaced item is true. Use the particle **ли** in each statement.

Образе́ц: А́ня была́ вчера́ **на рабо́те**.
Я не зна́ю, на рабо́те ли была́ А́ня вчера́.

1. **Ма́ша** пригото́вила докла́д.
2. Ма́ша **пригото́вила** докла́д.

3. Máша пригото́вила **докла́д**.
4. То́ля гото́вит **вку́сный** борщ.
5. **То́ля** гото́вит вку́сный борщ.
6. Та́ня придёт **с Анто́ном** ро́вно в шесть часо́в.
7. Та́ня придёт с Анто́ном ро́вно в **шесть** часо́в.
8. Та́ня **придёт** с Анто́ном ро́вно в шесть часо́в.

Упражне́ние 18.4   Translate the following sentences into Russian with the particle **ли**. Do not translate information in brackets; use that information to help define context. Boldfaced words should be the focus of the sentence.

1. I don't know if Vera **speaks** German.
2. I don't know if it's **German** that Vera is speaking. [I hear her speaking a foreign language, and it might just be German, but it might also be Dutch.]
3. I don't know if it's **Vera** who's speaking German now. [I hear someone speaking German, but I'm not sure if it's Vera or Anna.]
4. Was **Anton** in Petersburg last week? [Or was it Pavel?]
5. Was Anton in **Petersburg** last week? [Or was he in Omsk?]
6. Was it **last** week that Anton was in Petersburg? [Or was he there two weeks ago?]

Упражне́ние 18.5   Complete the following conditional and possible sentences, paying attention to tense and aspect.

1. Éсли сего́дня бу́дет идти́ дождь…
2. Éсли за́втра к нам зае́дут роди́тели…
3. Éсли профе́ссор за́втра не придёт на рабо́ту…
4. Éсли за́втра их не бу́дет, …
5. Éсли аэропо́рт бу́дет закры́т из-за нелётной пого́ды, …
6. Éсли слома́ется компью́тер, …

Упражне́ние 18.6   Translate the following sentences into Russian.

1. If Dima makes the cake, everyone will like it.
2. If Angela wants to go to the Hermitage after lunch, we can all go with her.
3. If they help us with this problem today, we'll write the report tomorrow.
4. If Tat'iana Borisovna can't come tonight, let's invite Aleksei Pavlovich.
5. If they can get (**доста́ть**) only four tickets to the concert, you can go without me.

Упражне́ние 18.7   Rewrite the sentences to make them contrary to fact.

1. Éсли Тама́ра прие́дет до семи́ часо́в, мы успе́ем на сеа́нс в во́семь.
2. Я приглашу́ их на ве́чер, е́сли они́ ещё бу́дут в Сама́ре на сле́дующей неде́ле.
3. Мы ку́пим молоко́, е́сли магази́н ещё бу́дет откры́т.
4. Мари́на Константи́новна напи́шет статью́, е́сли Па́вел ей даст ну́жную информа́цию.
5. Ефи́м Абра́мович пое́дет в Аме́рику, е́сли заболе́ет Са́ра Моисе́евна.
6. Лéна прода́ст свою́ кварти́ру, е́сли Ко́ля не найдёт но́вую рабо́ту.

Упражне́ние 18.8   Complete the following conditional and contrary-to-fact sentences. Taking into account the aspect of your completed Russian sentence, consider how you might translate the sentence into English.

1. Éсли бы слома́лся компью́тер, …
2. Éсли бы в суббо́ту был большо́й конце́рт, …
3. Éсли бы мне позвони́ла ба́бушка, …
4. Éсли бы на сле́дующей неде́ле был экза́мен, …
5. Éсли бы в воскресе́нье была́ хоро́шая пого́да, …

Упражнéние 18.9   Read the dialogue and then write a paragraph describing who said what, using the conventions of reported speech. This dialogue continues the situation developed in **Упражнéния 17.3–17.6.**

Яшимóто: Не понимáю, почемý вы не закóнчили вторýю часть рабóты.

Бáуэр: С немéцкой стороны́, могý сказáть, что мы бы́ли óчень недовóльны тéмпом вáшей рабóты ещё в прóшлом годý.

Рóджерс: Мы с коллéгами из Балтимóра надéемся, что вы спрáвитесь со всéми остáвшимися проблéмами.

Кузнецóв: Я вас уверя́ю: мы спрáвимся со всéми остáвшимися проблéмами. Мы бýдем рабóтать упóрно, несмотря́ на все трýдности.

 Упражнéние 18.10   Translate the following sentences into Russian. They reflect the situation described in **Упражнéние 18.9.**

1. I don't know if Rodgers speaks Russian.
2. If Bauer doesn't come to Moscow, Schultz will come.
3. If Yashimoto hadn't written this letter, I wouldn't have thought about this question.
4. I don't know if they will meet with us before they see the production schedule (**грáфик вы́пуска продýкции**).

 Упражнéние 18.11   Translate the following passage into Russian.

Liza told Kostia not to call her anymore and that she would call him when she was ready for that. She announced that she didn't love him. Kostia was disappointed. He admitted (**признáлся** + *dat.*) to Liza that he knew that he was often late when they met [up], and promised that he wouldn't be late anymore. Liza answered Kostia that she didn't believe him: she had already cancelled too many plans. She added (**добáвила**) that when she invites someone to dinner, she does not want to cancel the dinner at the last minute (**в послéднюю минýту**). She was angry at Kostia, although Kostia asked her not to be angry. Liza said she wouldn't be angry at Kostia if he stopped being late all the time.

Упражнéние 18.12.   The "play in four acts" from **Упражнéние 18з** in the textbook continues. Read acts II and III and complete IV by filling in the blanks with the correct form of the verb **любить/полюбить.**

II. Втóрник, 4:00

Пáша: Мáша, мне кáжется, что...

Мáша: Что тебé кáжется... Договáривай ужé, а то врéмя летит и мне скóро нáдо уходить...

Пáша: Я дýмаю, что...

Мáша: Не дýмай, а говори!

Пáша: Мáша, я тебя́ óчень люблю́!

Мáша: Что ты сказáл?!

Пáша: Я сказáл, что люблю́ тебя́.

Мáша: Ну ты даёшь! Интерéсно, ты чáсто объясня́ешься в любви рáзным дéвушкам?

Пáша: Ну, Мáша, почемý ты так жестóко поступáешь со мной? Я других дéвушек никогдá не любил. Я тóлько тебя́ люблю́ и бýду любить. Ты меня́ не лю́бишь?

Мáша: Нет, Пáша, я тебя́ не люблю́. Я тебя́ никогдá не любила. И я дýмаю, что я никогдá не полюблю́ тебя́. Ты мне прóсто не нрáвишься, и всё. До свидáния.

Пáша: О, жестóкая жéнщина!

III. Средá, 12:00

Мáша: Óля, Пáша в меня́ влюбился!

Óля: Неужéли? Он объяснился тебé в любви?

Máша: Да, сказáл, что лю́бит меня́. Дáже о́чень лю́бит, éсли я прáвильно по́мню. Он сказáл, что други́х дéвушек никогдá не люби́л, лю́бит то́лько меня́ и бу́дет люби́ть то́лько меня́.

Óля: Бéдный Пáша.

Máша: Почему́ «бéдный Пáша»? Почему́ ты не говори́шь «бéдная Máша»? Он же такóй зану́да! Он всё врéмя влюбля́ется во всех дéвушек и объясня́ется всéм в любви́. Почему́ ты его́ жалéешь?

Óля: Но он такóй одино́кий! Бéдный Пáша.

IV. Четвéрг, 6:00

Óля: Здрáвствуй, То́ля. Ну, ты был прав. Пáша влюби́лся в Máшу. Во вто́рник, он сказáл, что _____[1] Máшу.

То́ля: Да? И что онá ему́ отвéтила?

Óля: А ты как ду́маешь? Ты же знáешь Máшу! Онá спроси́ла его́, не _____[2] ли он мно́гих дéвушек.

То́ля: А он что сказáл?

Óля: Он спроси́л её, почему́ онá так жесто́ко поступáет с ним. Он сказáл, что он други́х дéвушек никогдá не _____,[3] что рáньше _____[4] то́лько её, и всегдá то́лько её _____ _____.[5] Пото́м он спроси́л её, не _____[6] ли онá его́.

То́ля: Да? И что онá отвéтила ему́?

Óля: Онá сказáла, что не _____[7] его́, рáньше никогдá не _____[8] его́, и никогдá не _____[9] его́.

То́ля: Э́то о́чень интерéсно.

Óля: Да, Máша мне всё рассказáла.

То́ля: Интерéсно, что сейчáс бу́дет дéлать Пáша?

Óля: Я ду́маю, что в пя́тницу он подойдёт к Áне и скáжет ей, что он её о́чень _____,[10] что рáньше _____[11] то́лько её, и что то́лько её _____ _____[12]!

То́ля: Да, ты навéрно правá, Óля. И Áня навéрно отвéтит ему́, что онá не _____[13] его́, что рáньше никогдá не _____[14] его́, и что никогдá не _____[15] его́.

Óля: Да. Бéдный Пáша. Ну, я пошлá. Покá, То́ля.

То́ля: Покá. Всего́ хоро́шего!

Зада́ние 18.2   Use one of the sentences you completed in **Упражне́ние 18.8** as the topic for an oral presentation or a brief composition, as assigned by your instructor.

 Зада́ние 18.3   Continue the story begun in **Упражне́ние 18.11** using only reported speech. Consider what Liza and Kostia's friends would do in their situation (**на его́/её ме́сте, я бы …**).

 Зада́ние 18.4   Write a continuation of the play in **Упражне́ние 18.12**.

Glossary

# боле́льщик	*fan*
# боле́ть (I) [за что? кого́]: боле́ю, боле́ешь, боле́ют	*to root for something or someone*
бы	*conditional particle [always used with the past tense]*
влюбля́ться (I) /влюби́ться (II) [в кого́?]: влюбля́юсь, влюбля́ешься, влюбля́ются; влюблю́сь, влю́бишься, влю́бятся	*to fall in love with someone*
встреча́ться (I) /встре́титься (II) [где? с кем?]: встреча́юсь, встреча́ешься, встреча́ются; встре́чусь, встре́тишься, встре́тятся	*to meet with someone somewhere*
# выи́грывать (I) /вы́играть (I): выи́грываю, выи́грываешь, выи́грывают; вы́играю, вы́играешь, вы́играют	*to win*
# де́лать (I) заря́дку: де́лаю, де́лаешь, де́лают	*to do calisthenics*
е́сли	*if (not whether)*
# занима́ться (I) спо́ртом, каки́м ви́дом спо́рта: занима́юсь, занима́ешься, занима́ются	*to engage in sports, in a kind or type of sport*
звони́ть/по– (II) [кому́? куда́?]: звоню́, звони́шь, звоня́т	*to call someone somewhere (on the phone)*
# игра́ть/по– (I) [во что?]: игра́ю, игра́ешь, игра́ют	*to play something (a game, sport)/to play for a while*
#игра́ть/сы́грать (I) [матч]	*to play a match, game, round*
ли	*whether (interrogative particle)*
люби́ть/по– (II) [кого́?]: люблю́, лю́бишь, лю́бят	*to love/to begin to love someone*

оказываться (I) /оказаться (I):
оказывается, что...; окажется, что...

to turn out to be

опаздывать (I) /опоздать (I) [на что?]:
опаздываю, опаздываешь, опаздывают;
опоздаю, опоздаешь, опоздают

to be running late/to be late for something

отменять(-ся) (I) /отменить(-ся) (II):
отменяю, отменяешь, отменяют; отменю, отменишь, отменят

to cancel (to be canceled)

приглашать (I) /пригласить (II) [кого? куда?]:
приглашаю, приглашаешь, приглашают; приглашу,
пригласишь, пригласят

to invite someone somewhere

проигрывать (I) /проиграть (I):
проигрываю, проигрываешь, проигрывают; проиграю,
проиграешь, проиграют

to lose

прощать (I) /простить (II) [кого? за что?]:
прощаю, прощаешь, прощают; прощу, простишь, простят

to forgive someone for something

разочарован/-а/-ы [в ком? в чём?]

disappointed in someone or something

сердиться/рас– (II) [на кого? за что?]:
сержусь, сердишься, сердятся

to be angry/to get angry at someone

UNIT 19

Lexicon: Art, Music, Literature and Film

Here is a chart showing various kinds of artists, the verbs used to convey the process of artistic creation, and the resulting art forms. The generic word for *artist* is **худо́жник**, which is generally reserved for someone working in the visual arts, excluding film. The word **арти́ст/-ка** is reserved for performing artists.

ARTIST	VERB	ART
живопи́сец, худо́жник (*painter*)	писа́ть/на–	жи́вопись: карти́на
модельёр (*fashion designer*)	модели́ровать, шить	модели́рование
ску́льптор (*sculptor*)	лепи́ть	ску́льптура
архите́ктор (*architect*)	проекти́ровать	архитекту́ра
музыка́нт, компози́тор, дирижёр (*musician, composer, conductor*)	игра́ть на музыка́льном инструме́нте, исполня́ть, сочиня́ть, дирижи́ровать орке́стром	му́зыка
певе́ц, певи́ца (*singer*)	петь, исполня́ть	вока́льная му́зыка:
писа́тель, поэ́т, драмату́рг (*writer, poet, playwright*)	писа́ть/на–	худо́жественная литерату́ра
режиссёр (кино– и́ли театра́льный) (*director*)	режисси́ровать, ста́вить	кино́, драматурги́я
фото́граф (*photographer*)	фотографи́ровать, снима́ть	фотогра́фия
актёр, актри́са (*actor*)	игра́ть (каку́ю роль)	игра́ (в пье́се, в фи́льме)
танцо́вщик, танцо́вщица, балери́на (*dancer*)	танцева́ть	та́нец, бале́т

Зада́ние 19.1   Choose one of the arts in the chart and find a recent article in a Russian newspaper or magazine about an artist, performer, or work of art that relates to that art. Read the article, create a vocabulary list of ten to fifteen lexical items important for this art form, and, using your vocabulary list, write a brief summary of the article.

Фо́то-зада́ние   Look at the photograph on the first page of this unit in the textbook. Write a paragraph or prepare a presentation, as assigned by your instructor, explaining why you like or don't like the painting shown in the photograph.

Listening Tasks

The listening text for this unit consists of a radio report about a famous writer who gave his personal art collection to his hometown.

PRE-LISTENING TASK

What sort of information do you expect to hear in the report?

LISTENING TASK

Listen to the text and then answer questions 1 through 11 in English and 12 through 15 in Russian.

1. What is the name of the writer discussed in this report? (His name and patronymic are mentioned in the first sentence, and his name and last name are mentioned in the second sentence.)
2. What is the name of the city in which he lived (also mentioned in the first sentence)?
3. What kind of literary works did this writer create?
4. Name some of his works.
5. To what institution did this writer bequeath his collection of paintings?
6. Approximately how many paintings were in the collection?
7. Where is the gallery located?
8. What do we know about the history of the institution in which the gallery is located?
9. What is the name of the gallery?
10. Where is this name derived from?
11. One painting intended for the gallery never got there. What is the name of the famous artist who created the painting and where did it wind up?
12. Find the Russian equivalent for the expression *feeling of gratitude*.
13. Find the Russian equivalent for the expression *this is connected first and foremost with the love and care*.
14. Find the Russian equivalent for the expression *more than ten years*.
15. Find the Russian equivalent for the expression *only one painting disappeared*.

DICTATION

Replay the tape and, as you listen, write out the text in full.

PERFORMANCE

Practice reciting the text.

POST-LISTENING TASK

Using the text as a model, prepare a brief report or presentation on civic donation to the arts.

CULTURAL PROBLEM

Why do you think the title of this text is «Культу́ра прови́нции»? What might that title imply?

Phonetics and Intonation

Voiced and Voiceless ж and ш

This unit reviews the pronunciation of voiced and voiceless ж and ш. Both consonants are pronounced with the tongue pointed into the hollow of the mouth near the point where the hard and soft palates meet.

Listen to the voiced and voiceless ж and ш on the tape and repeat.

1.	тажа	таж	таш
2.	пажа	паж	паш
3.	воже	вож	вош
4.	гоже	гож	гош
5.	дужу	дуж	душ
6.	ружу	руж	руш
7.	нэжи	нэж	нэш
8.	тежи	теж	теш
9.	тижа	тиж	тиш
10.	похо́жа	похо́ж	похо́ш
11.	В Воро́неже	Воро́неж	
12.	В Пари́же	Пари́ж	

▶ SELF-QUIZ

Write two spellings for each sound you hear.

1. _____ _____

2. _____ _____

3. _____ _____

4. _____ _____

5. _____ _____

6. _____ _____

7. _____ _____

8. _____ _____

Lexicon: Verbs of Memory and Perception

Verbs of Memory

Russian has several verbs to express the concept of memory.

По́мнить/вс– [кого́? что?]
   To remember or recall (this verb is never used with the verb мочь)

Я не пóмню, как спрягáется этот глагóл.
I don't (can't) remember how this verb is conjugated.

Подождúте, сейчáс я вспóмню: да, он был на лéкции.
Wait a second, let me remember: yes, he was at the lecture.

Запоминáть/запóмнить [когó? что?]
To commit to memory (a face or a fact)

Я легкó запоминáю телефóны.
I remember telephone numbers easily.

Я запóмню вас и никогдá не забýду то, что вы сдéлали.
I will remember you and never forget what you've done.

Узнавáть/узнáть [когó? что?]
To recognize someone or something

Я вас не узнáла: вы óчень изменúлись!
I didn't recognize you: you've changed so much!

Татья́на Владúмировна всегдá узнаёт своúх стáрых подрýг.
Tat'iana Vladimirovna always recognizes her old friends.

Вы узнáете егó по егó длúнным густы́м усáм.
You'll recognize him by his long thick mustache.

Учúть/вы́– (наизýсть) [что?]
To memorize

В Россúи ученикú чáсто ýчат стихú наизýсть.
In Russia schoolchildren often memorize poetry.

Олéг вы́учил свою́ роль в пьéсе.
Oleg memorized his role in the play.

Вспоминáть/вспóмнить [о ком? о чём?]
To recall (nostalgically), to reminisce

Я чáсто вспоминáю об университéтских друзья́х. ·
I often reminisce about my university friends.

Напоминáть/напóмнить [когó? что? комý? о чём?]
To resemble someone or something, to remind someone about something

Вы напоминáете мне моегó дрýга.
You remind me of my friend.

Напóмните мне, пожáлуйста, о Сáшиных кнúгах.
Please remind me about Sasha's books.

Упоминáть/упомянýть [когó? что?], поминáть [когó?] лúхом úли дóбрым слóвом
To remember by mentioning, to say bad or good things about someone

Вáше úмя упомянýли на собрáнии.
Your name was mentioned at the meeting.

Не поминáйте лúхом!
Don't say bad things [about me] (Don't remember [me] for the bad things).

Упражнéние 19.1   Fill in the blanks with the Russian equivalent of the English word or phrase in parentheses.

1. Милиционéр останови́л маши́ну и подошёл к води́телю, в котóром он (*recognized*)

   _____ своегó стáрого дрýга.

2. — Ми́ша! Это я, Антóн! Рáзве ты не (*remember*) _____ меня́?

3. — Антóша! Конéчно, ([*I*] *remember*) _____ . Я (*fixed in my*

   memory) _____ твоё лицó на всю жизнь!

4. И мы с женóй тóлько вчерá тебя́ (*remembered, mentioned*) _____,

   когдá рассмáтривали шкóльные фотогрáфии, (*reminisced*) _____

   шкóльных друзéй.

5. — Ми́ша, это óчень прия́тно. Извини́, но мне придётся тебé (*remind*)

   _____ о прáвилах движéния [*traffic rules*]: ты же превы́сил

   скóрость [*you were speeding*]!

6. — Извини́, Антóша! Бóльше не бýду, чéстное слóво. Я все э́ти прáвила знáю, ([*I*]

   memorized) _____ их, когдá получáл правá [*driver's license*].

Задáние 19.3   Continue the story begun in **Упражнéние 19.1**, using as many passive participles as you can.

Verbs of Perception

Russian has two pairs of verbs of perception that function in similar ways.

PASSIVE PERCEPTION	**ACTIVE PERCEPTION**
ви́деть/у– *to catch sight of*	смотрéть/по– *to watch*
слы́шать/у– *to happen to hear*	слýшать/про– *to listen*

Verbs that indicate a lack of active perception are used in those instances when people happen to see or hear without expending any effort or energy to do so. They are merely present as an action (or the report of an event) is unfolded for them.

> Игорь дýмал, что все ужé **слы́шали** об отъéзде Бори́совых.
> *Igor' thought that everyone had heard that the Borisovs had emigrated.*

> Вы случáйно не **ви́дели** Андрю́шу?
> *Did you happen to see Andriusha?*

These verbs are *never* used with the verb **мочь** except in reference to medical conditions of temporary or permanent blindness or deafness. Compare the following usage.

> Пóсле операции он дóлго не **мог** ни ви́деть, ни слы́шать.
> *After the operation he couldn't see or hear for a long time.*

> У нас бы́ли ужáсные местá на концéрте: мы ничегó **не ви́дели** и ничегó **не слы́шали**!
> *We had awful seats at the concert: we couldn't see a thing and we couldn't hear a thing!*

The words **ви́дно** and **слы́шно** are used to indicate whether things are visible or audible, respectively.

> Мне тут пло́хо **ви́дно**.
> *I can't see anything from here.*

> Всем бы́ло **слы́шно**, как де́ти ти́хо смея́лись в свое́й ко́мнате.
> *Everyone could hear how the children were laughing quietly in their room.*

The verbs **смотре́ть/по–** and **слу́шать/про–**, on the other hand, indicate the expenditure of energy or effort to perceive.

> Па́па! **Посмотри́**, как я бу́ду пры́гать!
> *Papa! Watch me hop!*

> Еле́на ча́сто **смо́трит** иностра́нные фи́льмы, но никогда́ не ви́дела ни одного́ фи́льма Ву́ди А́ллена.
> *Elena often watches foreign films, but she's never seen a single film by Woody Allen.*

> Бо́речка ре́дко **слу́шал** свои́х роди́телей, что приводи́ло их в отча́яние.
> *Borechka rarely listened to his parents, which brought them to despair.*

> Мы **прослу́шаем** всех, и пото́м реши́м кого́ пригласи́ть в хор.
> *We'll listen to how they sing and then decide whom to invite to join the chorus.*

Both pairs of verbs of perception may be used with the connectors **что** or **как**, depending on the meaning of the sentence in which they are used. Use **что** to focus attention on what is being perceived or the fact of perception, but use **как** to focus attention on the very act of perception.

> Мы ви́дели, что они́ игра́ли в «Монопо́лию».
> *We saw that they were playing Monopoly.*

> Мы ви́дели, как они́ игра́ли в «Монопо́лию».
> *We saw how they were playing Monopoly.*

> Психо́логи посмотре́ли на то, что нарисова́ли де́ти.
> *The psychologists were looking at what the children had drawn.*

> Психо́логи смотре́ли, как рисова́ли де́ти.
> *The psychologists were watching how the children were drawing. (The psychologists were watching as the children drew.)*

> Я слы́шала, что ты поёшь по–неме́цки.
> *I heard that you sing in German.*

> Я слы́шала, как ты пел по–неме́цки.
> *I heard you singing in German.*

> Роди́тели ре́дко слу́шают, что говоря́т учителя́.
> *Parents rarely listen to what the teachers say.*

> Мы слу́шаем, как поёт Пе́тя.
> *We're listening to Petia sing.*

Упражне́ние 19.2   Fill in the blanks with the correct verb of perception and, if necessary, connecting phrase.

1.   И́горь (*saw how*) _____, _____ игра́ли

    де́ти.

2.   Он (*heard that*) _____, _____ они́ бы́ли в

    восто́рге от но́вой игру́шки.

3. Катя (*saw that*) _____, _____ они говорили между собой.

4. Она думала о Ване: она не (*saw*) _____ его. Он, наверно, спрятался.

5. Его вообще не было ни (*visible*) _____, ни (*audible*) _____.

6. Вдруг она (*heard that*) _____, _____ он поёт детскую песню.

7. Она долго (*listened how*) _____, _____ он пел.

8. Игорь пришёл (*to listen how*) _____, _____ Ваня поёт.

Упражнение 19.3   Translate the following sentences into Russian.

1. We heard that Valia sings.
2. We listened to Valia singing.
3. We listened to Valia singing an American song.
4. We listened to the American song Valia was singing.
5. We heard that Valia sings American songs.

Упражнение 19.4   Translate the following passage into Russian, using verbs of memory and perception.

Sveta watched and listened as Misha talked with Kolia about Lena. She remembered Lena well: she used to hear her singing all morning. Lena had memorized all the songs that her parents used to sing. Sveta rarely listened to Lena sing, however: when Lena would sing, Sveta would turn on the radio and listen to the news. Misha and Kolia reminisced about Lena: they mentioned her mother, who was also a performer. Misha said that he had fixed in his memory Lena's father's face, and Kolia said that Lena's father reminded him of Brezhnev. Sveta asked Misha if he had seen Lena's father at the funeral. Misha said that he hadn't seen Lena's father because from where he was he couldn't see anything, but that he heard Lena's father talking about how Lena loved music.

Exercises and Activities

Упражнение 19.5   Translate the following sentences into English.

1. — Мясо уже приготовлено?
   — Нет ещё, мясо будет приготовлено только через час.
2. — Что ты читаешь?
   — Я читаю газету, забытую здесь Иваном Сергеевичем.
3. — Жаль, что тебя не было на лекции. Марине Леонтьевне были заданы очень интересные вопросы.
4. — Вчера мы нашли работу, начатую вами в апреле, но ещё не законченную.
   — Разве эта работа ещё не забыта?

Упражнéние 19.6   Create the past passive participle for each verb.

1. пройти́ _____

2. написа́ть _____

3. пригото́вить _____

4. купи́ть _____

5. потеря́ть _____

6. покры́ть _____

7. обману́ть _____

8. прода́ть _____

Упражнéние 19.7   Fill in the blanks with the correct participle of the verb in parentheses.

1. Мы пошли́ на вокза́л купи́ть биле́ты, но все биле́ты уже́ бы́ли (распрода́ть)

   _____.

2. Ру́сские бы́ли в у́жасе, когда́ узна́ли о всех (не/попра́вить)

   _____ оши́бках, (допусти́ть) _____

   коммуни́стами.

3. Э́та кни́га уже́ была́ давно́ (прочита́ть) _____ всей Москво́й.

4. В Жене́ве иду́т перегово́ры ме́жду Росси́ей и госуда́рствами Содру́жества (не/зависе́ть)

   _____ госуда́рств.

5. В э́том магази́не не продаётся (подержа́ть) _____ оде́жда.

6. Мы до́лго иска́ли, но всё равно́ не смогли́ найти́ (потеря́ть) _____

   материа́лы.

7. Вот спи́сок (рекомендова́ть) _____ книг.

8. У́тром пе́рвого декабря́ вся доро́га была́ (покры́ть) _____

   сне́гом.

9. В э́том до́ме, (постро́ить) _____ в 18–ом ве́ке, до сих пор

   сохраня́ются мно́гие элеме́нты архитекту́ры э́той эпо́хи.

10. Ва́ше поведе́ние про́сто (не/выноси́ть) _____!

 Упражнéние 19.8   Use each of the past passive participles you formed in **Упражнéние 19.6** to create sentences.

Зада́ние 19.4   Choose three sentences you wrote in **Упражнéние 19.8** and weave them together into a short story of two or more paragraphs. Try to include at least two present passive participles in your story.

Упражнéние 19.9 Fill in the blanks with the passive participle of the Russian verb in parentheses. Note that some sentences require present passive participles, while others require past passive participles. Some sentences require short forms, others require long forms.

1. Олéг потерял свою книгу о философии поколéния «Икс» [*Generation X*], но онá былá (*was found*: найти) _____ Ксéнией вчерá вéчером.

2. Ксéния нашлá книгу и срáзу обратила на неё внимáние, потому что не любит философию (*of the so-called*: так называть) _____ поколéния «Икс».

3. Онá чáсто пóльзуется материáлами, (*conveyed, given over*: передáть) _____ нáшим профéссором.

4. В книге о философии поколéния «Икс» говорится о (*irreparable*: не попрáвить) _____ ошибках, (*committed*: допустить) _____ стáршим поколéнием.

5. Напримéр, говорится о (*unforgettable*: не забывáть) _____ икóнах, котóрые были (*removed by vehicle*: вывезти) _____ из деревéнь в музéи.

6. Ксéния óчень любит поэзию 30-х годóв и поэтому подарила Олéгу три книжки своих (*favorite*: любить) _____ поэтов, котóрые были (*imprisoned*: заключить) _____ в эпóху стáлинского террóра.

7. Однá из этих книг былá (*published*: напечáтать) _____ в Петрозавóдске.

8. Мы все заинтересовáлись этими книгами, и Ксéния обещáла нам принести áдрес книжного магазина, (*written down, recorded*: записáть) _____ у неё в телефóнной книжке, (*left behind*: остáвить) _____ дóма.

Упражнéние 19.10 Translate the following sentences into Russian, using participles for underlined phrases.

1. Professor Mendovskii said that the material <u>had been covered</u> on Wednesday.
2. The <u>recommended</u> books <u>were purchased</u> by the students on Thursday.
3. All the stories (**истóрии**) about her <u>incomprehensible</u> behavior (**поведéние**) and <u>unbearable</u> character (**харáктер**) were <u>told</u>.
4. My <u>favorite</u> dinner was <u>prepared</u>.
5. We slowly drove along (**éхали по**) the road <u>covered</u> with snow.
6. We approached (**подъéхали к**) the <u>abandoned</u> building.
7. They avoided the <u>so-called</u> questions that <u>had been solved</u> by Alla.
8. They laughed at the photographs <u>taken by (made)</u> by Vasilii.
9. The vegetables for the salad must be <u>cleaned</u> before the soup is (will be) <u>made/prepared</u>.
10. It was <u>inexplicable</u>: among the <u>invited</u> guests were the Sergeevs.

Glossary

Only the names for artists, not art forms or artistic creations, are included here.

# актёр, актри́са	*actor, actress*
# арти́ст/-ка	*performing artist*
# архите́ктор	*architect*
бро́шен/-ный	*abandoned*
#ви́деть/у- (II) [кого́? что?]: ви́жу, ви́дишь, ви́дят	*to see*
#ви́дно	*visible*
# вспомина́ть (I) /вспо́мнить (II) [о чём? о ком?]: вспомина́ю, вспомина́ешь, вспомина́ют; вспо́мню, вспо́мнишь, вспо́мнят	*to recall, to remember* (*nostalgically*), *reminisce*
встре́чен/-ный	*met*
# дирижёр	*conductor (of an* *orchestra*)
# драмату́рг	*playwright*
# живопи́сец	*painter*
забы́т/-ый	*forgotten*
зако́нчен/-ный	*completed*
закры́т/-ый	*closed*
# запомина́ть (I) /запо́мнить (II) [кого́? что?]: запомина́ю, запомина́ешь, запомина́ют; запо́мню, запо́мнишь, запо́мнят, запо́мни(те)!	*to remember, to fix in* *one's memory*
заведён/-ный	*wound up (i.e., a watch or* *clock), started (i.e., an* *engine), or begun/set* *off*
за́дан/-ный	*assigned or posed*
за́перт/-ый	*closed, locked*
# компози́тор	*composer*
ко́нчен/-ный	*completed, finished*
ку́плен/-ный	*purchased*
ксерокопи́ровать (I) [что?]: ксерокопи́рую, ксерокопи́руешь, ксерокопи́руют	*to photocopy*
люби́м/-ый	*beloved, favorite*
# моделье́р	*fashion designer*
# музыка́нт	*musician*
надѐт/-ый	*put on (with respect to an* *item of clothing*)

напи́сан/-ный	written
# напомина́ть (I) /напо́мнить (II) [кого́? что? кому́? о чём?]: напомина́ю, напомина́ешь, напомина́ют; напо́мню, напо́мнишь, напо́мнят, напо́мни(те)!	to remind someone of or about someone or something
на́чат/-ый	begun
на́йден/-ный	found
невыноси́м/-ый	unbearable
незави́симый	independent
необъясни́м/-ый	inexplicable
неотврати́м/-ый	inevitable
непоправи́м/-ый	irreparable
непостижи́м/-ый	incomprehensible
объединённый	united
Организа́ция объединённых на́ций	United Nations
откры́т/-ый	open (opened)
отпра́влен/-ный	sent out
оши́бка	mistake
# певе́ц, певи́ца: бас, барито́н, те́нор, альт, сопра́но	singer: bass, baritone, tenor, alto, soprano
пе́редан/-ный	transferred, conveyed
#пе́сня	song
#петь/с- (I) [что?]: пою́, поёшь, пою́т	to sing
# писа́тель	writer
почи́щен/-ный	cleaned
покра́шен/-ный	painted
постро́ен/-ный	built
поведе́ние	behavior
# по́мнить/вс– (II) [кого́? что?]: по́мню, по́мнишь, по́мнят, по́мни(те)!	to remember, to recall
# поэ́т	poet
приглашён/-ный	invited
приго́товлен/-ный	prepared
принесён/-ный	brought
расска́зан/-ный	told
# режиссёр	director
рекоменду́ем/-ый	recommended
решён/-ный	decided

сбережён/-ный	saved
сделан/-ный	done, made
# скульптор	sculptor
слушать/про- (I) [кого? что? о ком? о чём?]: слушаю, слушаешь, слушают	to listen
слышать/у- (II) [кого? что? о ком? о чём?]: слышу, слышишь, слышат	to hear
#слышно	audible
#смотреть/по- (II) [кого? что?]: смотрю, смотришь, смотрят	sculptor
соединённый	united
Соединённые штаты Америки	United States of America
список	list
так называемый	so-called
# танцовщик, танцовщица	dancer
# учить/вы- (II) [что?]: учу, учишь, учат	to memorize

# упоминать (I) /упомянуть (I) [кого? что?]: 	
  упоминаю, упоминаешь, упоминают; упомяну, упомянешь,
  упомянут
	to remember, to mention

уважаемый [много–]	respected (*in salutation in a letter*)
# узнавать (I) /узнать (I) [кого? что?]: узнаю, узнаёшь, узнают; узнаю, узнаешь, узнают	to recognize someone or something
# фотограф	photographer
# художник	artist (*visual*)

UNIT 20

Lexicon: "Talking Politics"

Here is a list of some of the more commonly used terms in texts about politics.

Поли́тика/полити́ческие нау́ки... поли́тика... поли́тик
Politics, political science; policy; politician

> Тере́са о́чень интересу́ется поли́тикой и хо́чет стать поли́тиком.
> *Theresa is very interested in politics and wants to be a politician.*

Избира́ть(ся)/избра́ть(ся)
To run for office, to be elected

> Е́льцина избра́ли в президе́нты в 1992-ом году́.
> *Yeltsin was elected president in 1992.*

Голосова́ть/про- [за кого́? что? про́тив кого́? чего́?]
To vote for someone or something, against someone or something

> Мно́гие голосова́ли за Жирино́вского.
> *Many people voted for Zhirinovskii.*

Вы́боры, голосова́ние, избира́тельная кампа́ния
Elections, voting (process), election campaign

> Шла дли́тельная и дорога́я избира́тельная кампа́ния, и в день вы́боров голосова́ние
> проходи́ло ме́дленно в связи́ с техни́ческими пробле́мами.
> *It was a long and expensive election campaign and on election day the voting went slowly
> in connection with technical problems.*

За кого́? что? про́тив кого́? чего́?
For someone or something, against someone or something

> Э́ти депута́ты выступа́ют про́тив догово́ра с Япо́нией, но за но́вый зако́н по сниже́нию
> тари́фов.
> *These deputies [to Parliament] are speaking [out] against the treaty with Japan, but for the
> new law on the reduction of tariffs.*

Сторо́нник, проти́вник [кого́? чего́?]
Proponent or supporter, opponent of someone or something

> У Жирино́вского бы́ло мно́го сторо́нников, но и мно́го проти́вников.
> *Zhirinovskii had many supporters, but also many opponents.*

Подде́рживать/поддержа́ть [кого́? что?]
To support someone or something

> Мы подде́рживаем инициати́ву Черномы́рдина.
> *We support Chernomyrdin's initiative.*

Принима́ть/приня́ть реше́ние, зако́н
To make a decision or adopt a law

> Ду́ма приняла́ но́вый зако́н об эмигра́ции.
> *The Duma adopted a new law on emigration.*

Одобря́ть/одо́брить [кого́? что?]
To approve of someone or something

> Президе́нт вряд ли одо́брит после́днее предложе́ние Лужко́ва.
> *It is highly unlikely that the president will approve Luzhkov's latest proposal.*

Сходи́ться/сойти́сь во мне́нии
To agree, to have the same opinion

> Мы сошли́сь во мне́нии, что бо́льше так де́лать нельзя́.
> *We agreed that it can't be done that way anymore.*

Наста́ивать/настоя́ть [на чём?]
To insist on something

> Я ду́маю, что Екатери́на Ла́хова, ли́дер па́ртии «Же́нщины Росси́и», наста́ивает на
> необходи́мости реше́ния социа́льных пробле́м же́нщин в пе́рвую о́чередь.
> *Lakhova, the leader of the "Women of Russia" Party, insists on the urgency of solving
> women's social problems as top priority.*

Выступа́ть/вы́ступить с ре́чью
To give a speech

> Солжени́цын выступа́л с ре́чью вчера́ во Владивосто́ке.
> *Solzhenitsyn gave a speech yesterday in Vladivostok.*

Боро́ться [с кем?], борьба́ [с кем? чем?]
To fight with (against) someone, a fight or struggle against someone or something

> Росси́йское прави́тельство сейча́с бо́рется с но́вой ма́фией.
> *The government of the Russian Federation is struggling against the new mafia.*

Назнача́ть/назна́чить [кого́? на каку́ю до́лжность?]
To appoint someone to a position

> Интере́сно, кого́ назна́чит президе́нт на до́лжность мини́стра образова́ния?
> *I wonder whom the president will appoint to be Minister of Education?*

Снима́ть/снять [кого́? с како́й до́лжности?]
To dismiss someone from a position

> Президе́нт наве́рно сни́мет мини́стра оборо́ны в результа́те очередно́го сканда́ла.
> *The president will probably dismiss the Defense Minister as a result of the latest in a series
> of scandals.*

Ме́стные вла́сти, областны́е вла́сти, федера́льные вла́сти
Local authorities, regional authorities, federal authorities

> Ме́стные вла́сти противостоя́т федера́льным по э́тому вопро́су.
> *Local authorities are opposed to the federal authorities on this issue.*

Упражне́ние 20.1   Fill in the blanks in the text below.

1. Его́р Гайда́р проводи́л конфере́нцию (*supporters*) _____

    созда́ния па́ртии «Вы́бор Росси́и».

2. Он сказа́л, что пришёл моме́нт созда́ния полити́ческой структу́ры, спосо́бной отстоя́ть

свою́ програ́мму в (*struggle, conflict*) _____ с оппози́цией.

3. Большинство́ делега́тов (*supported*) _____ заявле́ние своего́

ли́дера.

4. Но мно́гие делега́ты не (*share this opinion*) _____

_____ с Гайда́ром

5. Поэ́тому, возмо́жно, что конфере́нция не (*approve*) _____

никаки́х но́вых реше́ний.

6. Гайда́р сказа́л, что е́сли так и произойдёт, мо́жет быть он (*will dismiss*)

_____ своего́ секретаря́ и (*will appoint*)

_____ но́вого.

Фо́то-зада́ние Look again at the photograph on the first page of this unit in the textbook. The young people in the photograph are part of a Komsomol Honor Guard in Arkhangel'sk, guarding the eternal flame in memory of those who fell during the American intervention immediately following the Russian Revolution of 1917. Write a paragraph or prepare a presentation, as assigned by your instructor, describing how one of these people might feel about the political changes in Russia since the collapse of the Soviet Union.

Listening Tasks

The listening text for this unit consists of a dialogue about politics.

PRE-LISTENING TASK

What do you know about Russian domestic politics? Name as many politicians, political parties, and government figures as you can.

LISTENING TASK

Listen to the text and then answer questions 1 through 6 in English and 7 and 8 in Russian.

1. According to the speakers in the dialogue, what does Zhirinovskii say must be done?
2. How do the speakers think people in the former Soviet republics will respond to this?
3. What does Zhirinovskii think about public opinion in these places, according to the speakers in the dialogue?
4. What did or did not happen in the Duma today?
5. What are the positive and negative aspects of this decision?
6. What do we find out about the appointment of a new Culture Minister?
7. Find the Russian equivalent of the expression *on the one hand, ... on the other hand.*
8. Find the Russian equivalent of the expression *well, that's not bad.*

DICTATION

Replay the text and, as you listen, write out the dialogue in full.

PERFORMANCE

Practice reciting the dialogue.

POST-LISTENING TASK

Using the dialogue in this section as a model, work with a classmate to create and perform your own dialogue in which you discuss Russian or American politics.

CULTURAL PROBLEM

What are some of the problems Russia faces in establishing democracy?

Phonetics and Intonation

Word Initial и

When word initial и is preceded by a hard consonant, it is pronounced like ы.

Listen to the words and phrases on the tape and repeat.

1.	Игорь	с Игорем	сигорем
2.	Иван	с Иваном	сиваном
3.	Италия	в Италию	Виталию
4.	Ира	к Ире	к Кире
5.	игра	с игрой	Сигройд
6.	известный	с известным	сизый
7.	имя	с именем	с Симоном
8.	Инна	к Инне	кинне
9.	интерес	с интересом	синтересом
10.	итог	в итоге	витоге

SELF-QUIZ

Circle the words, phrases or nonsense words that best represent the sounds you hear.

1.	с Игорем	сигорем
2.	сиваном	с Иваном
3.	Виталию	в Италию
4.	к Кире	к Ире
5.	витоке	в итоге
6.	с Игоря	сигоря
7.	сиваном	с Иваном
8.	Виталию	в Италию
9.	к Кире	к Ире
10.	витоге	в итоге

Lexicon: To Try

Three different Russian verbs are used to convey the English verb *to try*.

Стара́ться/по- де́лать/с- [что?]
  To make an attempt to do something

> Мы постара́емся прийти́ во́время.
> *We'll try to come on time.*

Пыта́ться/по- де́лать/с- [что?]
  To make an effort to do something that is difficult

> Мы попыта́емся вы́нести роя́ль из аудито́рии без по́мощи.
> *We'll try to move the piano out of the auditorium without help.*

Про́бовать/по- [что?]
  To try, sample, or test something

> Пиро́г о́чень вку́сный: попро́буй!
> *The pie is delicious: try (it)!*

Упражне́ние 20.2   Fill in the blanks with the Russian translation of the English word or phrase in parentheses.

1. Светла́на Андре́евна (*tried*) _____ познако́мить нас со все́ми

   специали́стами в Москве́!

2. Я (*will try*) _____ бо́льше занима́ться.

3. Ты (*tried*) _____ блины́ с икро́й? Они́ о́чень вку́сные!

4. Не на́до (*sample*) _____ во́ду из э́того коло́дца [*water from that

   well*].

5. Я понима́ю, что э́то о́чень тру́дно, но дава́йте всё равно́ (*try*)

   _____ э́то сде́лать.

Exercises and Activities

Упражне́ние 20.3   Fill in the blanks with the present active participle of the infinitive in parentheses. Make certain that the participle agrees in gender, case, and number with the noun it modifies or its antecedent.

1. Ра́ньше я о́чень о́чень боя́лся лета́ть, но пото́м прослу́шал курс для

   (страда́ть)_____ боя́знью лета́ть, и тепе́рь я лета́ю и не

   бою́сь!

2. Вы случа́йно не знако́мы с (идти́) _____ по ле́стнице

   де́вушками?

3. В ба́ре бы́ло мно́го наро́ду: я в жи́зни никогда́ ра́ньше не ви́дела сто́лько (пить)

   _____ и (кури́ть) _____ в одно́м

   ме́сте!

4. Ти́хо! Э́тот шум наве́рно разбу́дит ребёнка, (спать) _____ в

   сосе́дней ко́мнате.

5. Мы два часа́ говори́ли с инжене́рами, (возвраща́ться) _____

   из Волгогра́да.

6. Éсли ты действи́тельно бóлен, на́до приня́ть (соотве́тствовать) _____

   _____ лека́рства.

7. Тама́ра Евге́ньевна — (вести́) _____ экспе́рт по лёгким и

   се́рдцу в на́шей больни́це. Она́ — (блесте́ть) _____

   специали́ст.

Упражне́ние 20.4 Fill in the blanks with the present active participle of the infinitive in parentheses. Make certain that the participle agrees in gender, case, and number with the noun it modifies or its antecedent.

1. На э́том предприя́тии óчень нужны́ (говори́ть) _____ по-

   англи́йски.

2. В на́шей гру́ппе нé было (жела́ть) _____ пойти́ на экску́рскию в

   Мавзоле́й Ле́нина.

3. На студе́нческую конфере́нцию съезжа́ются (учи́ться) _____ из

   пяти́десяти стран.

4. Ма́ленькие де́ти, хорошó (ката́ться) _____ на лы́жах, иногда́

   меша́ют взро́слым, (начина́ть) _____ ката́ться.

5. Ты случа́йно не знако́ма с же́нщиной, (спра́шивать) _____

   сейча́с об экологи́ческих послéдствиях размеще́ния заво́да здесь?

6. Экскурсово́ды ненави́дят тури́стов, (жа́ловаться) _____ на

   гости́ницу.

7. Пассажи́ров, (приезжа́ть) _____ из Казахста́на, про́сят пройти́ в

   бюро́ обслу́живания.

8. Мы ча́сто говори́м с журнали́стом, (писа́ть) _____ статьи́ по

   э́тому вопро́су.

9. В э́том спорти́вном ко́мплексе трениру́ются спортсме́ны, (пыта́ться)

   _____ стать чле́ном олимпи́йской кома́нды.

10. Тут нельзя́ шуме́ть, а то мы бу́дем меша́ть студе́нтам, (гото́виться)

    _____ к экза́менам.

Упражне́ние 20.5 Whenever possible, rephrase the sentences in **Упражне́ния 20.3** and **20.4** so that they do not contain participial constructions.

   Образе́ц: Мы поговори́ли со студе́нтами, верну́вшимися из Пари́жа.
   Мы поговори́ли со студе́нтами, кото́рые верну́лись из Пари́жа.

Упражнéние 20.6 Fill in the blanks with the past active participle of the infinitive in parentheses. Make certain that the participle agrees in gender, case and number with the noun it modifies or its antecedent.

1. Мы поговорили с туристами, (спросить) _____ у нас дорóгу.

2. Фёдоровы, (уéхать) _____ на недéлю в Омск, попросили нас гулять с их собáкой.

3. На коврé, (лежáть) _____ на полу, бы́ли большие пя́тна.

4. Мы дóлго говорили со студéнтами, (учиться) _____ в России в прóшлом году.

5. Я не знáю жéнщину, (сказáть) _____, что онá говорит на трёх языкáх.

6. Лариса Васильевна продалá свою́ машину э́тому молодóму человéку, (говорить) _____ с Тóлей вчерá на вы́ставке.

7. Сегóдня мы собирáемся на лéкцию журналиста, (написáть) _____ _____ на прóшлой недéле интерéсную статью́ о проблéмах молодёжи.

8. Давáйте поговорим с москвичáми, (купить) _____ нóвые квартиры в прóшлом году.

9. Лю́ди, (сидéть) _____ в прóшлом году на молóчной диéте, не скáжут, что онá былá удáчной.

10. Пéтя получил письмó от своегó дрýга, (жить) _____ три гóда в Мýрманске.

11. Мы познакóмим Валéрию Ивáновну с (начáть) _____ изучáть эсперáнто, и они ей докáжут, что эсперáнто — нетрýдный язы́к.

12. Фрéд и Сéнди два часá говорили со студéнтами, (вернýться) _____ в Амéрику пóсле двухмéсячного пребывáния в России.

13. Представители завóда дéтских игрýшек хотя́т сообщить всем, (купить) _____ игрýшку «Тóмми», что в ней есть серьёзный дефéкт.

14. Я попросил сержáнта, (задержáть) _____ моегó дрýга, чтóбы он его отпустил.

15. Рáзве ты не видишь жéнщину, (читать) _____ свои стихи на вéчере в срéду? Онá стоит вон там!

Упражнéние 20.7 Whenever possible, rephrase the sentences in **Упражнéние 20.6** so that they do not require participial constructions.

Упражне́ние 20.8 Fill in the blanks with the present active or past active participle as required by context. Look for such clues as verb tense or time to determine whether to use the past or present.

1. Мы говори́ли о (заболе́ть) _____ студе́нте: его́ не́ было вчера́ на заня́тиях.

2. Вчера́ мы познако́мились с фи́зиком, (получи́ть) _____ Но́белевскую пре́мию.

3. Мы рабо́таем в ста́ром зда́нии, (находи́ться) _____ на углу́ Тверско́й у́лицы и Садо́вого кольца́.

4. Ко мне в го́сти прие́хала подру́га, (учи́ться) _____ в про́шлом году́ в Росси́и.

5. Вчера́ мы говори́ли о журнали́сте, ка́ждую неде́лю (писа́ть) _____ интере́сные статьи́ о Росси́и в журна́ле «Тайм».

6. Вчера́ мы встреча́лись с же́нщиной, (говори́ть) _____ на собра́нии на про́шлой неде́ле об экологи́ческих после́дствиях размеще́ния заво́да в э́том райо́не.

7. Ско́лько в ва́шей гру́ппе челове́к, (говори́ть) _____ по-япо́нски?

8. В го́роде эпиде́мия: я никогда́ не ви́дела сто́лько (чиха́ть) _____ и (ка́шлять) _____.

9. В самолёте мы ви́делись со студе́нтами, (возвраща́ться) _____ в Аме́рику по́сле трёхме́сячного пребыва́ния в Росси́и.

10. Мы обяза́тельно познако́мим вас со студе́нтами, (верну́ться) _____ в Аме́рику по́сле трёхме́сячного пребыва́ния в Росси́и.

11. Я жил в до́ме, (находи́ться) _____ на э́той у́лице ра́ньше, до того́, как его́ снесли́. На э́том ме́сте постро́или клуб для молодёжи.

12. Граждани́на, (отъезжа́ть) _____ в Аме́рику на постоя́нное жи́тельство, про́сим подойти́ к тре́тьему окну́.

13. Мы до́лго вспомина́ли о Гольдште́йнах, давно́ (уе́хать) _____ в Аме́рику.

14. Ко́ля Менто́вский хорошо́ знако́м с адвока́том, (соста́вить) _____ контра́кт для фи́рмы «МММ». Когда́ ло́пнула фи́рма, э́тот адвока́т оказа́лся без гроша́.

15. Сего́дня Ири́на Никола́евна поговори́т с ру́сской актри́сой, (снима́ться) _____ в но́вом италья́нском фи́льме.

Упражнёние 20.9 Whenever possible, rephrase the sentences in **Упражнёние 20.8** so that they do not require participial constructions.

Упражнёние 20.10 Translate the sentences into English and identify the present active and past active participles, using the summary chart in the textbook on p. 263 if necessary. Note that some sentences may have more than one participle!

1. Ско́лько бы́ло в ва́шей гру́ппе жела́ющих пойти́ в кино́?
2. Фёдоров о́чень изве́стный писа́тель: он оди́н из мои́х са́мых люби́мых писа́телей.
3. Я не зна́ю же́нщину, закры́вшую окно́, разби́тое вчера́ Са́шей.
4. Ру́сская грамма́тика соверше́нно невыноси́мая!
5. Но́вый уче́бник, напи́санный на́шим профе́ссором, не понра́вился студе́нтам, верну́вшимся из Росси́и.
6. Мы поговори́ли со студе́нткой, продаю́щей сло́манную маши́ну «Москви́ч».
7. Э́та маши́на была́ про́дана за де́сять ты́сяч до́лларов.
8. На двери́, открыва́емой сейча́с на́шей преподава́тельницей, виси́т плака́т, напи́санный одни́м из на́ших соку́рсников.
9. В кла́ссе мы нашли́ кни́гу, забы́тую дру́гом Па́ши.
10. Э́тот фильм соверше́нно незабыва́емый.
11. Мы пригласи́ли студе́нтов, учи́вшихся в про́шлом году́ в Росси́и, вы́ступить на на́шем собра́нии.
12. Я сове́тую всем, страда́ющим боя́знью лета́ть, прослу́шать специа́льный курс, предло́женный авиакомпа́нией «Аэрофло́т».
13. Все иду́щие по ле́стнице студе́нты изуча́ют ру́сский язы́к.
14. Вчера́ мы поговори́ли с же́нщиной, почини́вшей игру́шки, сло́манные детьми́.
15. Мы пришли́ поговори́ть с вы́шедшим покури́ть профе́ссором, мы её здесь подождём.

Упражнёние 20.11 Pick seven of the sentences in **Упражнёние 20.10** and rephrase them so that they do not contain participial constructions.

Зада́ние 20.1 Pick three sentences from **Упражнёние 20.11** and try to weave them into a story consisting of two or more paragraphs with as many participles as possible.

Упражнёние 20.12 Fill in the blanks with the correct form of the participle, checking for gender, case, and number, given the English cues in parentheses. This exercise assumes that you are ready to use all six cases, singular and plural, for both nouns and modifiers. The text is a letter from an American student to her former teacher at Moscow State University.

(Respected) _____ [1] Алекса́ндра Васи́льевна!

Здра́вствуйте! Я наде́юсь, что у Вас всё хорошо́. Наве́рно уже́ начался́ но́вый семе́стр.

Вам понра́вились студе́нты, (who arrived) _____ [2] из Аме́рики в э́том

году́? Мно́гие из нас говори́ли с ни́ми о на́ших (former) _____ [3]

преподава́телях и профессора́х в МГУ и расска́зывали, как мы познако́мились с други́ми

(students/ones who study) _____ [4] в МГУ. Коне́чно мы мно́го

говори́ли о на́шей (favorite) _____ [5] преподава́тельнице по фоне́тике

и о её (crazy) _____ [6] дома́шних зада́ниях!

Я ча́сто перепи́сываюсь с други́ми студе́нтами из на́шей гру́ппы. В на́шей гру́ппе мно́го (ones who want/desire) _____⁷ верну́ться в Росси́ю, в Москву́, в (so called) _____⁸ «Большу́ю карто́шку». (Это на́ше шу́точное назва́ние.) У всех нас там мно́го хоро́ших друзе́й и мно́го (favorite) _____⁹ мест.

Ка́жется, америка́нские профессора́ бы́ли о́чень дово́льны студе́нтами, (who returned) _____¹⁰ домо́й из Москвы́. Они́ говоря́т, что осо́бенно большо́й прогре́сс (beginning students) _____.¹¹ Оди́н профе́ссор наде́ется, что в (next) _____¹² гру́ппе бу́дет бо́льше студе́нтов из други́х шта́тов. Профе́ссор, (who told) _____¹³ мне об э́том, счита́ет, что так, наве́рно, бу́дет интере́снее для всех.

Я наде́юсь верну́ться в Москву́ в (next/future) _____¹⁴ году́, когда́ я зако́нчу университе́т. Я собира́юсь прие́хать в Москву́ в го́сти к одному́ из мои́х друзе́й, кото́рый меня́ приглаша́ет, и пото́м начну́ иска́ть себе́ рабо́ту в Москве́. Мой друг говори́т, что сейча́с в Москве́ о́чень нужны́ (speakers) _____¹⁵ по-англи́йски. Как Вы ду́маете, э́то пра́вда? Не смо́жете ли Вы мне рассказа́ть, что на́до де́лать америка́нцам, (ones who want/desire) _____¹⁶ жить и рабо́тать в Москве́? Не должна́ ли я написа́ть письмо́ в посо́льство [embassy] Росси́и в США? Я ду́мала, что Вы, наве́рно, мно́го зна́ете об э́том, так как рабо́таете с америка́нскими студе́нтами. Зара́нее благодарю́ Вас за информа́цию!

Жела́ю Вам всего́ до́брого!

С уваже́нием,

Сэ́лли Смит

 Упражне́ние 20.13   Choose three sentences without participial constructions in **Упражне́ние 20.12** and rephrase them so that they contain participial constructions.

 Упражне́ние 20.14   Here are some comments overheard in a teachers lounge at St. Petersburg State University. Translate them into Russian, using participles for underlined words or phrases.

1. I am very proud of the <u>beginners</u> <u>who arrived</u> last week. The students who <u>lived</u> in Russia for three months last year have not had as difficult a time as (**не так тру́дно, как**) the <u>beginners</u> who <u>are living</u> in Russia for the first time now. Many of the <u>beginners</u> who <u>wish</u> to speak only in Russian all the time are becoming acquainted with <u>students</u> (i.e., <u>those who study</u>) in the dining hall and cafe. Those who <u>are afraid</u> to speak Russian are speaking English more frequently, but even they are making progress.
2. Some of the students on the second level (**на второ́м у́ровне**) who <u>left</u> for Irkutsk yesterday for five days are complaining about the program, but the <u>complainers</u> do not understand that their teacher is one of the <u>outstanding</u> professors at our university.

Name _____ Date _____ Class _____

3. They say that they want to meet regularly with journalists <u>writing</u> about <u>so-called</u> political questions, so we will try to find some journalists for them.
4. Unfortunately, we had to send two students from this group who<u> became very ill</u> home to America.
5. The professors really like the students on the third level who <u>asked</u> to borrow copies of the articles <u>written</u> by Kuznetsova and Pavlov last year, their <u>favorite</u> specialists. These students are very hardworking. Liubov' Antonovna told me that she spoke with one student who <u>had called</u> her from America before the beginning of the semester to ask about <u>photocopied</u> materials. The American group is my favorite group this year.

Задание 20.2   Prepare a presentation or write a short story, as assigned by your instructor, about some exchange students in Russia who are not very hardworking. Use as many participles (active and passive) as you can.

Glossary

блестя́щий	*sparkling*
# боро́ться (I) [с кем? с чем?]: борю́сь, бо́решься, бо́рются	*to fight or struggle against someone or something*
# борьба́ [с кем? чем?]	*a fight or struggle*
бу́дущий	*future (adj.)*
бу́дущее [вре́мя]	*future (substantive)*
бы́вший	*former*
веду́щий	*leading*
верну́вшийся	*one who has returned*
# вла́сти: ме́стные, областны́е, федера́льные	*authorities: local, regional, federal*
# вы́боры, голосова́ние	*election, voting*
выдаю́щийся	*outstanding*
# выступа́ть (I) с ре́чью: выступа́ю, выступа́ешь, выступа́ют;	*to give a speech*
# голосова́ние	*voting*
# голосова́ть/про- (I) [за кого́? что? про́тив кого́? чего́?]: голосу́ю, голосу́ешь, голосу́ют	*to vote for or against someone or something*
говори́вший	*one who was talking, speaking*
говоря́щий	*one who talks or speaks*
греми́щий	*thundering, crashing*
жела́ющий	*one who wishes*
# за [кого́? что?]	*for someone or something*

# избира́тельная кампа́ния	*election campaign*
# избира́ть(-ся) (I): избира́ю(-сь), избира́ешь(-ся), избира́ют(-ся)[1]	*to run for office (reflexive), to elect someone (with accusative)*
куря́щий/некуря́щий	*smoker, nonsmoker*
могу́щий	*one capable of*
# назнача́ть (I) /назна́чить (I) [кого́? на что?]: назнача́ю, назнача́ешь, назнача́ют; назна́чу, назна́чишь, назна́чат	*to appoint someone to a position*
# наста́ивать (I) /настоя́ть (I) [на чём?]: наста́иваю, наста́иваешь, наста́ивают; настою́, настои́шь, настоя́т	*to insist on something*
находя́щийся	*located*
начина́ющий	*beginner*
ожида́ющий	*one who is expecting or waiting for something [used with the accusative or with an infinitive]*
# одобря́ть (I) /одо́брить (II) [кого́? что?]: одобря́ю, одобря́ешь, одобря́ют; одо́брю, одо́бришь, одо́брят	*to approve of someone or something*
отда́вший	*one who has given up something*
# подде́рживать (I) /поддержа́ть (II) [кого́? что?]: подде́рживаю, подде́рживаешь, подде́рживают; поддержу́, подде́ржишь, подде́ржат	*to support someone or something*
# поли́тик	*politician*
# поли́тика	*politics or policy*
#полити́ческие нау́ки	*political science*
потряса́ющий	*amazing*
прие́хавший	*one who arrived [by vehicle]*
# принима́ть (I) /приня́ть (I) реше́ние, зако́н: принима́ю, принима́ешь, принима́ют; приму́, при́мешь, при́мут, при́нял, приняла́, при́няли	*to make a decision or adopt a law*
приня́вший	*one who has taken something*
пришéдший	*one who has arrived [by foot]*

---

[1]For perfective, use бу́дет и́збран/а or бу́дут и́збраны.

про́бовать/по- (I) [что?]:
   про́бую, про́буешь, про́буют

про́тив [кого́? чего́?]

проти́вник [кого́? чего́?]

проше́дший

проше́дшее [вре́мя]

пыта́ться/по- (I) де́лать/с- [что?]:
   пыта́юсь, пыта́ешься, пыта́ются

пью́щий/непью́щий

сле́дующий

слу́жащий

снима́ть (I) /снять (I) [кого́? отку́да?]:
   снима́ю, снима́ешь, снима́ют; сниму́, сни́мешь, сни́мут,
   снял, сняла́, сня́ли

соотве́тствующий

стара́ться/по- (I) де́лать/с- [что?]:
   стара́юсь, стара́ешься, стара́ются

сторо́нник [кого́? чего́?]

сумасше́дший

сходи́ться (II) /сойти́сь (I) во мне́нии:
   схожу́сь, схо́дишься, схо́дятся; сойду́сь, сойдёшься,
   сойду́тся

тре́бующий

уе́хавший

уча́щийся

уше́дший

to try something [in the sense of testing or sampling]

against someone or something

opponent

past (adj.)

the past (substantive)

to try to do something difficult

drinker (of alcoholic beverages)/ teetotaler

next (in a sequence)

employee (white collar

to take someone from somewhere, to dismiss someone from a position

corresponding

to try to do something

supporter, proponent

insane

to agree in something, to share an opinion

one who demands

one who has left [by vehicle]

a student [one who is studying]

one who has left [by foot]

UNIT 21

Lexicon: Talking About Computers and Technology

Technical vocabulary used to talk about computers in Russian is largely cognate, i.e., it is borrowed from English and other languages.

Компью́тер, включа́ть/включи́ть и́ли выключа́ть/вы́ключить компью́тер
  Computer, to turn a computer on or off

  Мой ста́рый компью́тер слома́лся: я не могу́ его́ включи́ть.
  My old computer broke: I can't turn it on.

Ай-Би-Эм–совмести́мый компью́тер
  IBM-compatible computer

  Мне бо́льше нра́вятся Ай-Би-Эм–совмести́мые компью́теры, чем компью́теры
    «Макинто́ш».
  I prefer IBM-compatible computers.

Моде́м, электро́нная по́чта
  Modem, electronic mail (E-mail)

  Что́бы получа́ть и высыла́ть электро́нную по́чту, ну́жно име́ть до́ступ к моде́му.
  In order to receive and send E-mail, one has to have access to a modem.

Хране́ние и по́иск информа́ции
  Storage and retrieval of information

  Компью́теры о́чень облегча́ют хране́ние и по́иск информа́ции.
  Computers significantly simplify information storage and retrieval.

Открыва́ть/откры́ть электро́нный почто́вый я́щик
  To set up an E-mail account

  За́втра я пойду́ в компью́терный центр и откро́ю электро́нный почто́вый я́щик.
  Tomorrow I'll go to the computer center and set up an E-mail account.

При́нтер (ма́тричный, стру́йный, ла́зерный), руссифика́ция при́нтера и́ли уже́
руссифици́рованный при́нтер, монито́р, перифери́я, аксессуа́ры
  Printer (dot-matrix, jet, laser), Russification of a printer (allowing it to print in Russian),
  Russified printer, monitor, peripherals, accessories

  Вчера́ мы купи́ли но́вый ла́зерный при́нтер и сего́дня зака́жем руссифика́цию.
  Yesterday we bought a new laser printer and today we'll order its Russification.

  Вы бы лу́чше купи́ли уже́ руссифици́рованный при́нтер и монито́р!
  You should have bought a printer and a monitor that have already been Russified!

Скáнер, факс (факсимѝльный аппарáт), ксéрокс ѝли копировáльный аппарáт
Scanner, fax machine, photocopier

> У нас на рабóте нет скáнера, но есть факс и ксéрокс.
> *We don't have a scanner at the office, but we do have a fax machine and a photocopier.*

> Я вам отпрáвлю этот докумéнт фáксом к трём часáм.
> *I'll send you the document by fax by three o'clock.*

Изменéние конфигурáции компьютера
Reconfiguration of a computer

> Мы попросѝли, чтобы к нам заéхал специалѝст для изменéния конфигурáции компьютеров.
> *We asked for a specialist to come and reconfigure our computers.*

Сетевóе оборýдование, сéрвер
Network equipment, server

> Вчерá сломáлось сетевóе оборýдование и поэтому сегóдня мы не смóжем вам помóчь с этим.
> *Our network crashed yesterday and therefore we won't be able to help you today with this.*

Твёрдый диск, пáмять
Hard drive

> Придётся купѝть нóвый твёрдый диск для этого компьютера, потомý что нам нýжно бóльше пáмяти.
> *We'll have to buy a new hard drive for this computer because we need more memory.*

Дискéта, тóнер–кáртридж, мышь/мы́шка, кóврик для мы́ши/мы́шки, защѝтный экрáн
Diskette, toner cartridge, mouse, mouse pad, antiglare screen

> Мы вчерá купѝли нóвый компьютер. Сегóдня нáдо купѝть дискéты, тóнер–кáртриджи, мы́шку, кóврик для мы́шки и защѝтный экрáн.
> *We bought a new computer yesterday. Today we have to buy disks, toner cartridges, a mouse, a mouse pad, and an antiglare screen.*

Модернизáция, когдá устаревáет компьютер
Upgrading, when a computer becomes obsolete

> Наш компьютер устарéл. Нýжно заказáть модернизáцию.
> *Our computer has become obsolete. We need to order an upgrade.*

Упражнéние 21.1   Fill in the blanks with the Russian equivalent of the English word or phrase in parentheses.

1. Нýжно купѝть нóвый (*computer*) _____: стáрый ужé устарéл.

2. Для тогó, чтобы посылáть и получáть (*E-mail*) _____ дóма,

   придётся купѝть (*modem*) _____ и (*set up an E-mail account*)

   _____ .

3. Когдá вы бýдете в магазѝне тéхники, купѝте нóвые (*diskettes*) _____

   нóвый (*toner cartridge*) _____ для нáшего (*laser printer*)

   _____ .

4. Как вы дýмаете, какóй компьютер лýчше: «Макинтóш» и́ли (IBM-compatible)

_____ ?

5. Я бы хотéла купи́ть нéкоторые (accessories) _____: (a mouse)

_____, (a mouse pad) _____ ,

(anti glare screen) _____.

Фóто-задáние   Look at the photograph on the first page of this unit in the textbook. Write a paragraph or prepare a presentation, as assigned by your instructor, describing how the man in the photograph is using technology in his home.

Listening Tasks

The listening text for this unit is a dialogue about technology.

PRE-LISTENING TASK

Do you use E-mail? Have you ever sent a fax? What do you know about the "information superhighway"? What words and concepts do you associate with it?

LISTENING TASK

Listen to the text and then answer questions 1 through 3 in English and 4 through 6 in Russian.

1. What are the names of the two speakers in the dialogue?
2. What does the woman help the man with?
3. What are the costs the man will incur?
4. Find the Russian equivalent of the expression *I don't have such a possibility/opportunity.*
5. Find the Russian equivalent of the expression *it's free for students at our university.*
6. How do the two speakers end their conversation in agreement?

DICTATION

Replay the tape and, as you listen, write out the dialogue in full.

PERFORMANCE

Practice reciting the dialogue.

POST-LISTENING TASK

Using the dialogue as a model, work with a classmate to create and perform your own dialogue in which you discuss either setting up an E-mail account [at your school] or buying some computer equipment.

CULTURAL PROBLEM

How many English words were used in the dialogue? Why? How do you think Russians might feel about the abundance of English words in the realm of technology?

Phonetics and Intonation

Voiced and Voiceless б and п

This unit reviews the pronunciation of the voiced and voiceless б and **п**.

Listen to the voiced and voiceless б and **п** on the tape and repeat.

1.	та́ба	таб	тап
2.	шта́ба	штаб	штап
3.	во́бе	воб	воп
4.	го́бе	гоб	гоп
5.	ду́бу	дуб	дуп
6.	ру́бу	руб	руп
7.	нэ́би	нэб	нэп
8.	те́би	теб	теп
9.	ти́ба	тиб	тип
10.	сти́ба	стиб	стип

SELF-QUIZ

Write two spellings for each sound you hear on the tape.

1. _____ _____

2. _____ _____

3. _____ _____

4. _____ _____

5. _____ _____

6. _____ _____

7. _____ _____

8. _____ _____

Exercises and Activities

Упражне́ние 21.2   Rewrite the following sentences by replacing the boldfaced verbal adverb with **когда́** or **кото́рый** clause or a conjunction such as **а, но, и.**

> Образе́ц: Ма́ша писа́ла письмо́, **слу́шая** ра́дио.
> *Когда́ Ма́ша писа́ла письмо́, она́ слу́шала ра́дио.*

1. **Верну́вшись** домо́й, я сра́зу се́ла на дива́н и включи́ла телеви́зор, что́бы узна́ть после́дние но́вости.
2. **Уйдя́** с рабо́ты, Со́ня счита́ла, что она́ ско́ро найдёт но́вую рабо́ту, но она́ оши́блась.
3. **Уходя́** с рабо́ты, Лёня всегда́ выключа́ет свет.
4. Оконча́тельно **реши́в** э́тот вопро́с, мы ку́пим биле́ты и уе́дем в Оде́ссу в о́тпуск.
5. **Реша́я** таки́е вопро́сы, мы всегда́ се́рдимся друг на дру́га.
6. **Рассерди́вшись** на ма́льчика, учи́тельница, наве́рно, нака́жет его́.
7. **Покури́в**, они́ верну́лись в дом.
8. **Расска́зывая** о ней, он уви́дел, что она́ вошла́ в ко́мнату и се́ла напро́тив Зо́и.

Упражнéние 21.3   Fill in the blanks by forming a verbal adverb from the verb in parentheses.

1. (Доезжáть) _____ до Москвы́ мы всё врéмя говори́ли о ней.

2. (Вы́йти) _____ из кварти́ры, онá вспóмнила, что забы́ла дéньги.

3. (Научи́ться) _____ игрáть на гитáре, Тамáра захотéла вы́ступить на концéрте самодéятельности.

4. (Учи́ться) _____ говори́ть по-англи́йски, Бóря óчень боя́лся дéлать оши́бки.

5. (Запи́сывать) _____ телефóн Тóли, Вéра взгляну́ла на часы́ и понялá, что ужé опáздывает.

6. (Возвращáться) _____ домóй, он всегдá захóдит к дéдушке.

7. (Верну́ться) _____ домóй, онá ся́дет и напи́шет статью́.

8. Хорошó (познакóмиться) _____ с Áнной Пáвловной и её рабóтой, вы бу́дете считáть её óчень спосóбным архитéктором.

Упражнéние 21.4   Rewrite the following sentences by replacing the boldfaced verb with a verbal adverb. In some instances the verbal adverb must be formed from a verb synonymous in meaning with the boldfaced verb. Refer to the chart on page 272 of the main text.

1. Когдá он **пьёт**, он чáсто ругáет свои́х друзéй.
2. Когдá И́ра **смóтрит** на Кири́лла, онá вспоминáет своегó сóбственного сы́на.
3. Жóра не **хóчет** éхать в Челя́бинск и поэ́тому прóсит Вéру поéхать вмéсто негó.
4. Гали́на [**быть**] прекрáсный специали́ст: онá прекрáсно спрáвится с э́той задáчей.
5. Когдá он **поёт** э́ту пéсню, он чáсто дéлает оши́бки.

Задáние 21.1   Choose three sentences in **Упражнéния 21.2, 21.3,** and **21.4** and weave them together into a short story of two or more paragraphs.

Упражнéние 21.5   Translate the following sentences into Russian, using verbal adverbs for underlined expressions.

1. Boria was reading a letter <u>while listening</u> to the lecture.
2. <u>Having listened</u> to the lecture, the students asked some questions.
3. <u>Having told</u> the story (**истóрия**) of their trip to Estonia, they began to show their photographs.
4. <u>While telling</u> the story of their trip(**поéздка [кудá?]**) to Estonia, they mentioned your name several times.
5. <u>While answering</u> the students' questions, the teacher began to sneeze (**чихáть/чи́хнуть**).
6. <u>Having answered</u> the students' questions, the teacher dismissed (**отпусти́ть**) the students.
7. <u>While waiting</u> for Kolia, Irina called Maksim and told him about the lecture.
8. <u>Wishing</u> to go to (**поéхать**) to the Black Sea all his life (**всю жизнь**), Maksim was surprised when Irina called to talk about Estonia.
9. <u>Loudly singing</u> an Estonian song, Irina tried to convince (**уговори́ть**) Maksim to go to Estonia.
10. <u>Having sung</u> an Estonian song, Irina understood that Maksim still wanted to go to the Black Sea.

Glossary

This glossary does not include the technical vocabulary from the lexicon.

бу́дучи	*being*
верну́вшись	*having returned*
возвраща́ясь	*while returning*
вышива́я	*while drinking*
говоря́	*while speaking/talking*
де́лая	*while doing/making*
е́дучи	*while going by vehicle (archaic)*
жела́я	*while wishing*
запи́сывая	*while writing*
лёжа	*while lying down*
мо́лча	*while being silent*
научи́вшись	*having learned*
ожида́я	*while expecting*
посмотре́в	*having watched*
посыла́я	*while sending*
придя́	*having arrived by foot*
прочита́в	*having read*
распева́я	*while singing*
сде́лав	*having done or made*
си́дя	*while sitting*
сказа́в	*having said, told*
слу́шая	*while listening*
сто́я	*while standing*
уча́сь	*while studying, being enrolled*
уведя́	*having taken or led away*
чита́я	*while reading*

UNIT 22

Lexicon: Resting and Sleeping

Спать/по–
To sleep or nap

> Ребёнок поспа́л и почу́вствовал себя́ лу́чше.
> *My baby took a nap and felt better.*

Спа́ться/вы́–
To be able to sleep/to get enough sleep

> Она́ легла́ спать ра́но, но сказа́ла, что ей не спи́тся (не спало́сь).
> *She went to bed early, but she said that she isn't (wasn't) sleepy at all.*

> — Та́ня, как тебе́ спало́сь? — Спаси́бо, я вы́спалась.
> *Tanya, how did you sleep? Thanks, I got enough sleep (feel rested today).*

Ложи́ться/лечь спать
To go to bed

> Я обы́чно ложу́сь в оди́ннадцать часо́в, но вчера́ легла́ в час.
> *I usually go to bed at eleven, but last night I went to bed at one.*

Дрема́ть
To doze, to be between sleepfulness and wakefulness

> Посмотри́ на Па́шу: он дре́млет на заня́тиях!
> *Take a look at Pasha: he's dozing in class!*

Засыпа́ть/засну́ть
To fall asleep

> Зо́я засыпа́ет: она́ засну́ла вчера́ ве́чером то́лько к полу́ночи.
> *Zoia is falling asleep: she fell asleep last night only toward midnight.*

Баю́кать [кого́?]
To lull, to lullaby someone to sleep

> Оте́ц положи́л до́чку спать, а мать начала́ её баю́кать.
> *The father put his daughter to bed, and the mother started to sing her a lullaby.*

Сни́ться, ви́деть во сне
To dream (while sleeping)

> Вчера́ мне сни́лось, что я пришёл на заня́тия соверше́нно го́лым.
> *Yesterday I dreamed that I came to classes completely naked.*

> Вчера́ я ви́дела ба́бушку во сне́.
> *Last night I dreamed of my grandmother.*

Сон, бессóнница
Sleep/dream, insomnia

> Я ужé два дня без сна: у меня ужáсная бессóнница.
> *I've already gone two days without sleep: I have terrible insomnia.*

Просыпáться/проснýться
To wake up (to regain consciousness after sleep)

> Дéти проснýлись в шесть утрá: я совершéнно не вы́спался.
> *The kids got up at six A.M.: I didn't get enough sleep.*

Проспáть
To oversleep

> Он проспáл и опоздáл на самолёт.
> *He overslept and missed his plane.*

Вставáть/встать
To get up, to get out of bed

> Я всегдá встаю́ в семь, но зáвтра встáну тóлько в дéвять.
> *I always get up at seven, but tomorrow I plan to get up only at nine.*

Буд́ить/раз– [когó? когдá?]
To wake someone up

> Я обы́чно бужý мýжа, а меня бýдит буд́ильник.
> *I usually wake my husband, and I get up by the alarm clock.*

> Извин́ите, что так рáно звоню́. Надéюсь, что не разбуд́ила вас!
> *Sorry I'm calling so early. I hope I'm not waking you up.*

Уставáть/устáть
To get or become tired, to be tired (used in the past tense)

> Я óчень устаю́, когдá дóлго говорю́ тóлько по–рýсски.
> *I get very tired when I speak only in Russian for a long time.*

> Константин Валéрьевич помы́л посýду и óчень устáл.
> *Konstantin Valer'evich washed the dishes and was (became) very tired.*

Отдыхáть/отдохнýть
To rest, to relax, to vacation

> Я приготóвлю обéд, а ты покá отдохни́.
> *I'll make dinner, and you relax for a while.*

Расслáбить(-ся)
To relax or to relax something

> Мы совершéнно расслáбились в сáуне.
> *We completely relaxed in the sauna.*

> Я не могý расслáбить пáлец: у меня какóй–то спазм.
> *I can't relax my finger: I'm having some kind of spasm.*

Упражнéние 22.1   Fill in the blanks with the Russian equivalent of the English word or phrase in parentheses.

1. Обы́чно я (*go to bed*) _____ в полов́ине од́иннадцатого, но вчерá

    я (*went to bed*) _____ тóлько в два.

2. Я очень (*was very tired*) _____, но всё равно, (*couldn't sleep*)

_____.

3. Я обычно быстро и легко (*fall asleep*) _____, но вчера (*fell asleep*)

_____ только в три часа.

4. Всю ночь (*I was dreaming*) _____, что завтра будет какая-то

контрольная, но никто не говорил, именно какая.

5. Утром меня долго (*was trying to wake up*) _____ мама, но меня

(*woke*) _____ только звонок телефона, когда звонил Дима.

6. Я (*woke up*) _____, (*got up*) _____ и

подошёл к телефону. Дима сказал, что сегодня будет контрольная по физике. Мне

сразу захотелось (*go to bed*) _____!

Упражнение 22.2   Translate the following passage into Russian.

I usually go to sleep at eleven, but last night I went to bed at two in the morning. I had a hard time getting to sleep: I wasn't sleepy. Then I got up and drank some milk and went back to bed. I heard the alarm clock at six-thirty in the morning, but I couldn't get out of bed. I woke up, turned the alarm clock off, and went back to sleep. I finally woke up at ten and screamed in horror (**в ужасе**): I was more than an hour late for work!

Задание 22.1   Prepare a three-minute talk or write a composition, as assigned by your instructor, about your usual sleep patterns and how you had a particularly bad night in the last year or two.

Listening Tasks

The listening text for this unit consists of a dialogue about a bad night.

PRE-LISTENING TASK

When you haven't been able to get a good night's sleep, how do you feel? What words do you use to complain about this situation?

LISTENING TASK

Listen to the text and then answer questions 1 through 6 in English and 7 through 11 in Russian.

1. What's the name of the person who hasn't had a good night's sleep?
2. What happened while he was studying chemistry?
3. Why was that bad?
4. Why couldn't he sleep?
5. When did he fall asleep?
6. How was he woken from his sleep?
7. How does the man say that he couldn't get any sleep the night before?
8. How does the man say that he couldn't relax?
9. How does the man say that he's very nervous?

10. How does the man say that he almost slept through the biochemistry lecture?

11. What is the Russian equivalent for the expression *insomnia before a test*?

DICTATION

Replay the tape and, as you listen, write out the dialogue in full.

PERFORMANCE

Practice reciting the dialogue.

POST-LISTENING TASK

Using the dialogue as a model, work with a classmate to create and perform your own dialogue about a sleepless night before an exam.

CULTURAL PROBLEM

Many Russian families live in cramped quarters. A typical urban family, consisting of a husband, a wife, and a child, usually occupies what is called a **двухкомнатная квартира,** or in American terms a one-bedroom apartment. The parents sleep on a foldout couch in the living room, called the **гостиная** or simply **большая комната** and the child sleeps in the bedroom. How do you think this living arrangement affects sleep, health, and family life? Why aren't Russian families bigger?

Phonetics and Intonation

Voiced and Voiceless в and ф

This unit reviews the pronunciation of voiced and voiceless в and ф.

Listen to the voiced and voiceless в and ф on the tape and repeat.

1.	тáва	тав	таф
2.	штáва	штав	штаф
3.	вóве	вов	воф
4.	гóве	гов	гоф
5.	дýву	дув	дуф
6.	рýву	рув	руф
7.	нэ́ви	нэв	нэф
8.	тéви	тев	теф
9.	ти́ва	тив	тиф
10.	сти́ва	стив	стиф
11.	прáва	прав	праф
12.	прáвы	прав	праф
13.	в Ки́еве	Ки́ев	
14.	во Львóве	Львов	
15.	в Пскóве	Псков	
16.	в Крáкове	Крáков	
17.	в Бéлгород	в Петербýрг	
18.	в Донéцк	в Тýлу	
19.	в Женéву	в Швейцáрию	
20.	в ГУМ	в Ки́ев	

SELF-QUIZ

Write one or, if possible, two spellings for each sound you hear.

1. _____ _____
2. _____ _____
3. _____ _____
4. _____ _____
5. _____ _____
6. _____ _____
7. _____ _____
8. _____ _____
9. _____ _____
10. _____ _____
11. _____ _____
12. _____ _____
13. _____ _____
14. _____ _____
15. _____ _____
16. _____ _____

Exercises and Activities

Упражнéние 22.3 Fill in the blanks with the Russian equivalent of the English verb in parentheses, choosing from the verbs **висéть, сидéть/по–, стоя́ть/по–,** and **лежáть/по–.**

1. Сóня (*is standing*) _____ на углý Нéвского и ждёт меня́.

2. У нас в дóме (*are hanging*) _____ нóвые репродýкции Малéвича.

3. Тамáра ужé (*was standing*) _____ в óчереди 30 минýт, когдá

   откры́лся магази́н.

4. Они́ (*were sitting for a while*) _____, поговори́ли и потóм пошли́

   домóй.

5. Кóля (*was lying down for a while*) _____, потóм встал и ушёл.

6. Они́ ещё (*were sitting*) _____ за столóм, когдá мы ушли́.

7. Тáня (*is lying down*) _____ на дивáне: онá сказáла, что óчень

   устáла.

8. Мы (*were standing for a while*) _____, но потóм реши́ли уйти́.

Упражнéние 22.4 Fill in the blanks with the Russian equivalent of the English verb in parentheses, choosing from the verbs **вéшать/повéсить, класть/положи́ть, ста́вить/по–,** and **сажа́ть/посади́ть.**

1. Ва́ся вчера́ (*put*) _____ ви́ски в холоди́льник.

2. Э́лла (*is putting*) _____ духи́, кото́рые она́ то́лько что купи́ла, на
   сто́лик.

3. (*Put!*) _____ морко́вь в холоди́льник, пожа́луйста.

4. Куда́ их (*are they seating*) _____?

5. Пе́тя (*is hanging*) _____ пальто́ в шкаф.

6. Не (*put!*) _____ э́ту руба́шку в чемода́н: она́ ещё гря́зная.

7. Таки́х престу́пников обы́чно (*are imprisoned*) _____ на де́сять
   лет.

8. Его́ (*imprisoned*) _____ на пятна́дцать лет.

9. Я (*will put*) _____ э́тот журна́л сюда́, что́бы мы его́ не забы́ли.

10. Она́ наве́рно (*will seat*) _____ дете́й за э́тот сто́лик.

11. (*Don't put!*) _____ де́ньги на э́тот стол: он ещё мо́крый.

12. Не (*hang!*) _____ мо́крое полоте́нце туда́: э́тот крючо́к не
    вы́держит!

13. Мы всегда́ (*put*) _____ чесно́к в э́тот суп.

14. Они́ (*are putting*) _____ буты́лки туда́.

15. Мы уже́ (*put*) _____ всё докуме́нты ему́ на стол.

16. Мы (*will hang*) _____ твои́ ве́щи сюда́.

Упражнéние 22.5 Fill in the blanks with the Russian equivalent of the English verb in parentheses, choosing from the verbs **сади́ться/сесть, ложи́ться/лечь,** and **встава́ть/встать.**

1. Мы уже́ (*took seats*) _____ за стол и на́чали обе́дать, когда́
   пришла́ Ва́ря.

2. Он всегда́ (*get up*) _____ в шесть утра́.

3. Мы (*will take seats*) _____ туда́ и поговори́м с ни́ми.

4. Они́ (*got up*) _____, подошли́ к окну́ и посмотре́ли, кто идёт.

5. Он придёт домо́й с рабо́ты и сра́зу (*will lie down*) _____
   отдохну́ть.

6. Мы (*will get up*) _____ ра́но за́втра у́тром, потому́ что на́до
   пора́ньше прие́хать на рабо́ту.

7. Мы (*will go to bed*) _____ спать че́рез час.

8. Не (*get up!*) _____ пожа́луйста! Я не хочу́ вам меша́ть.

9. Он всегда́ (*lie down*) _____ на э́тот дива́н на не́сколько мину́т

    по́сле рабо́ты.

10. Ки́ра обы́чно (*takes a seat*) _____ ря́дом с Ми́шей.

Упражне́ние 22.6 Fill in the blanks with the Russian equivalent of the English verb in parentheses, choosing verbs of position or placement.

1. Таки́х престу́пников обы́чно (*are imprisoned*) _____ на 15 лет.

2. Зи́на (*put/ past*) _____ пусту́ю буты́лку за дверь.

3. Ве́ра (*put/ past*) _____ все свои́ ка́рты на стол.

4. Мы (*will hang*) _____ э́ту карти́ну туда́.

5. Во́дка давно́ (*is standing*) _____ на балко́не: она́ наве́рно уже́

    холо́дная.

6. Иро́чка (*was sitting*) _____ за э́тим столо́м, но тепе́рь её там нет.

7. (*Get up!*) _____, пожа́луйста, и посмотри́, кто стучи́т в на́шу дверь.

8. Не (*get up!*) _____ пожа́луйста! Ты ещё больна́!

9. Ка́тя всегда́ (*lie down*) _____ на пол, когда́ смо́трит телеви́зор.

10. Ви́тя обы́чно (*takes a seat*) _____ к Ире.

11. Эта официа́нтка ре́дко (*seats*) _____ меня́ за тако́й ма́ленький стол.

12. (*Don't put!*) _____ молоко́ в холоди́льник, пожа́луйста, оно́ мне

    ещё бу́дет ну́жно.

13. Де́ти (*will go to bed*) _____ спать че́рез час.

14. Не (*hang!*) _____ мо́крый зонт туда́!

15. Она́ (*was standing for a while*) _____ здесь и пото́м ушла́.

16. Они́ (*were sitting for a while*) _____, поговори́ли обо всём и пото́м

    пошли́ домо́й.

17. Лёва всегда́ (*get up*) _____ в 7 утра́.

18. Ба́бушка всегда́ (*used to put*) _____ свёклу в э́тот суп, но я (*am putting*)

    _____ морко́вь.

19. Я (*will get up*) _____ ра́но за́втра у́тром, потому́ что мой самолёт

    вылета́ет в 8 утра́.

20. (*Don't put!*) _____ э́ти помидо́ры в кастрю́лю: они́ уже́

    испо́ртились.

Упражнéние 22.7   Translate the following sentences into Russian.

1. We used to get up at seven, but tomorrow we'll get up at eight.
2. The children used to go to bed at eight, but tomorrow they'll go to bed at nine.
3. We usually take seats at this big table, but tomorrow we'll take seats at that small table.
4. We are usually seated at this big table, but tomorrow we'll be seated at that small table.
5. Elena Vladimirovna came (**пришлá**) home, sat down at the table, and began to tell us about her work.
6. Elena Vladimirovna will come (**придёт**) home, sit down at the table, and begin to tell us about her work.
7. Sergei Borisovich came home and went to bed; he got up in the morning and went to work.
8. Sergei Borisovich will come home and go to bed; he'll get up in the morning at eight as usual.
9. The bottles are under the table: I always put the bottles under the table.
10. The newspapers are on the table: I always put the newspapers on the table.
11. We always stand the books [vertically] on this shelf, but yesterday we put them [horizontally] under the table. They are under the table now.
12. The children usually put the empty bottles under the table, but yesterday they stood them behind the door. They are standing behind the door now.

Задáние 22.2   Choose three of the sentences from **Упражнéния 22.3, 22.4** and **22.5** and weave them together into a short story of two or more paragraphs.

Задáние 22.3   Find a picture in a magazine (perhaps an advertisement) depicting items on a table and write a description of the position of the items on the table and who might have put them there.

Задáние 22.4   Bring to class five small items from your home and work with a classmate to create a tableau of these items that could be the subject for a painting or photograph. Describe the positioning of the items in your tableau.

Задáние 22.5   Choose a famous person and prepare a three-minute talk or write a composition, as assigned by your instructor, describing that person's typical daily routine.

Задáние 22.6   Have you noticed particular seating patterns among students in your Russian class or in any other class you're currently taking? Prepare a three-minute talk or write a composition, as assigned by your instructor, describing these seating patterns.

Фóто-задáние   Look at the photograph on the first page of this unit in the textbook. Write a paragraph or prepare a presentation, as assigned by your instructor, explaining how each item was placed on the table.

Glossary

Sentences in parentheses following items are provided to indicate the usage of particular nouns with particular verbs of placement.

# баюкать (I) [когó?]: баюкаю, баюкаешь, баюкают	*to lull to sleep*
# будúть/раз– (II) [когó?]: бужý, бýдишь, бýдят	*to wake someone up*
бутылка (Кудá вы стáвите бутылку? Где стоúт бутылка?)	*bottle (Where are you putting the bottle? Where is the bottle?)*

вéшалка (Я повéшу кýртку на вéшалку в шкаф. Кýртка висúт на вéшалке в шкафý.)

hanger (I'll hang the coat on a hanger in the closet. The coat is hanging on a hanger in the closet.)

вéшать (I) /повéсить (II) [когó? что? кудá?]:
вéшаю, вéшаешь, вéшают; повéшу, повéсишь, повéсят

to hang something or someone somewhere

висéть (II) /по- (II) [где?]:
вишý, висúшь, вися́т

to be hanging[1]

внизý

below (loc. adverb)

впередú

in front (loc. adverb)

вставáть (I) /встать (I) [откýда?]:
встаю́, встаёшь, встаю́т, вставáй(те)!; встáну, встáнешь, встáнут

to get up from a seated position or from bed

дремáть (I):
дрéмлю, дрéмлешь, дрéмлют

to doze

засыпáть (I) /заснýть (I):
засыпáю, засыпáешь, засыпáют; заснý, заснёшь, заснýт

to fall asleep, to lose consciousness

картúна (Кудá вы вéшаете картúну? Где висúт картúна?)

painting (Where are you hanging the painting? Where is the painting hanging?)

класть (I) /положúть (II) [когó? что? кудá?]:
кладý, кладёшь, кладýт; положý, полóжишь, полóжат

to put or place something that has no "bottom surface," horizontally

кýртка (Кудá вы вéшаете кýртку? Где висúт кýртка?)

coat (Where are you hanging the coat? Where is the coat hanging?)

лежáть/по- (II) [где?]:
лежý, лежúшь, лежáт

to be lying down

ложúться (II) /лечь (I) [кудá?]:
ложýсь, ложúшься, ложáтся; ля́гу, ля́жешь, ля́гут, ля́г(те)!
лёг, леглá, леглú

to lie down (take up this position)

наверхý

above (loc. adverb)

óвощи (Кудá вы кладёте óвощи? Где лежáт óвощи?)

vegetables (Where are you putting the vegetables? Where are the vegetables)

отдыхáть (I) /отдохнýть (I):
отдыхáю, отдыхáешь, отдыхáют; отдохнý, отдохнёшь, отдохнýт

to rest, to relax

плакáт (Кудá вы вéшаете плакáт? Где висúт плакáт?)

poster (Where are you hanging the poster? Where is the poster hanging?)

---

[1]Note: except for idiomatic expressions, such as *I am hanging on the telephone all day,* this verb refers to inanimate objects or to hanging as an execution.

просыпа́ться (I) /просну́ться (I):
  просыпа́юсь, просыпа́ешься, просыпа́ются; просну́сь,
  проснёшься, просну́тся

to wake up, to regain consciousness from sleep

рассла́бить(-ся) (II):
  рассла́блюсь, рассла́бишься, рассла́бятся

to relax

сади́ться (II) /сесть (I) [куда́?]:
  сажу́сь, сади́шься, садя́тся; ся́ду, ся́дешь, ся́дут, сядь(те)!

to take a seat

сажа́ть (I) /посади́ть (II) [кого́? что? куда́?]:
  сажа́ю, сажа́ешь, сажа́ют; посажу́, поса́дишь, поса́дят

to seat someone , plant something, or imprison someone

салфе́тка (Куда́ вы кладёте салфе́тки? Где лежа́т салфе́тки?)

napkin (Where are you putting the napkins? Where are the napkins?)

сиде́ть/по– (II) [где?]:
  сижу́, сиди́шь, сидя́т

to be in a seated position

сза́ди

behind (loc. adverb)

сле́ва

on the left (loc. adverb)

сни́ться (II) , ви́деть (II) во сне:
  мне, тебе…сни́тся, сня́тся, сни́лся, сни́лась, сни́лось,
  сни́лись; я ви́дел/а во сне…

to dream

спать/по– (II):
  сплю, спишь, спят, спи́(те)!, спал, спала́, спа́ли

to sleep or nap

спа́ться (II):
  мне, тебе…не спи́тся, не спало́сь, пло́хо спало́сь

how one sleeps: I, you . . . can't sleep, couldn't sleep, slept poorly

спра́ва

on the right (loc. adverb)

ста́вить/по– (II) [что? куда́?]:
  ста́влю, ста́вишь, ста́вят

to stand something up somewhere (the object must have a bottom surface)

стака́н (Куда́ вы ста́вите стака́н? Где стоя́т стака́ны?)

drinking glass (Where are you putting the glass? Where are the glasses?)

стоя́ть/по– (II) [где?]:
  стою́, стои́шь, стоя́т, сто́й(те)!

to be in a standing position

таре́лка (Куда́ вы ста́вите таре́лку? Где стоя́т таре́лки?)

plate (Where are you putting the plate? Where are the plates?)

устава́ть (I) /уста́ть (I):
  устаю́, устаёшь, устаю́т, устава́й(те); уста́ну, уста́нешь,
  уста́нут

to get tired, to be tired

шкаф (Я пове́шу ку́ртку в шкаф. Ку́ртка виси́т в шкафу́.)

closet (I'll hang the coat in the closet. The coat is hanging in the closet.)

UNIT 23

Lexicon: Travel and Tourism

With the collapse of the iron curtain, citizens of the former Soviet Union are becoming world travelers. Many Russian newspapers feature a large number of advertisements from travel agencies offering tours to exotic places all around the world. Some travel packages include the cost of medical insurance to cover any medical emergencies that may arise.

Путешéствовать [по какóй странé?] путешéствие [кудá?]
To travel in a particular country or area, trip or journey [where?]

> Прóшлым лéтом мы путешéствовали по Зáпадной Еврóпе.
> *Last summer we traveled around western Europe.*

Éздить/éхать/поéхать [кудá?]
To go to a particular place

> В прóшлом годý они éздили во Фрáнцию.
> *Last year they went to France.*

Отдыхáть на мóре, на курóрте
To vacation at the sea or at a resort.

> Зинаúда Пáвловна кáждый год отдыхáет на э'том курóрте.
> *Zinaida Pavlovna vacations at this resort every year.*

Круúз
Cruise

> Кирúлл Анатóльевич хóчет отпрáвиться в круúз по Карúбскому мóрю!
> *Kirill Anatol'evich wants to go on a cruise in the Carribbean!*

Трёхзвёздочная гостúница, четырёхзвёздочный ресторáн
Three-star hotel, four-star restaurant

> Гостúница «Славя́нская» – четырёхзвёздочная гостúница в Москвé.
> *The "Slavianskaia" Hotel is a four-star hotel in Moscow.*

Стóимость на человéка в сýтки
Price per person per day

> Стóимость на чéловека в сýтки от 69 дóлларов США.
> *The price per person per day begins at $69 U.S.*

Туристúческое агéнтство, турагéнтство, агéнтство путешéствий
Travel agency

> Турагéнтство «Экспрéсс» предлагáет путешéствия в Лóндон, Парúж и Рим.
> *The Express Travel Agency offers trips to London, Paris, and Rome.*

Черноморское побережье, побережье Средиземного моря
The coast of the Black Sea, the coast of the Mediterranean Sea

> Русские любят отдыхать на черноморском побережье.
> *Russians like to vacation on the coast of the Black Sea.*

Льготные тарифы на авиабилеты, скидка/скидки
Discount rates on air tickets, discounts

> Это турагенство предлагает льготные тарифы на авиабилеты «Аэрофлота», «Дельты» и «Эр Франс» и скидки на билеты для детей, летящих в сопровождении взрослых.
> *This travel agency offers discount rates for tickets on Aeroflot, Delta, and Air France and discounts for tickets for children flying with adults.*

В стоимость включены…, в стоимость входят…
The price includes

> В стоимость включены авиабилеты, трансфер, проживание в гостинице, медицинская страховка и завтраки.
> *The price includes airplane tickets, transfers (to and from the airport abroad), hotel room, medical insurance, and breakfasts.*

Прямой рейс, прямые рейсы
direct flight(s)

> «Аэрофлот» предлагает прямые рейсы по маршрутам Москва—Лондон и Москва—Нью-Йорк.
> *Aeroflot has direct flights from Moscow to London and from Moscow to New York.*

Упражнение 23.1   Fill in the blanks with the Russian equivalent of the English word or phrase in parenthese to complete the advertisement.

(*Travel agency*) _____¹ «Отдых» предлагает (*trips*)

_____² на Майорку. (*Direct flights*) _____³

каждую субботу, апрель – октябрь. ([*In*] *the price*) _____⁴ (*per person*

per day) _____⁵ (*is included*) _____⁶

авиабилеты, трансфер, проживание в (*three-star hotel*) _____,⁷

завтраки.

Фото-задание   Look at the photograph on the first page of this unit in the textbook. Kizhi is a preserve of old Russian wooden architecture, located on an island in Lake Onega (**Онежское озеро**) near Petrozavodsk. Write a paragraph or prepare a presentation, as assigned by your instructor, explaining if you would like to go there and, if so, how you would get there. If you wouldn't like to go there, explain what your preferred destination would be, why, and how you would get there.

Listening Tasks

The listening text for this unit consists of a dialogue between two people asking each other about vacations.

PRE-LISTENING TASK

Make a list of four types of vacation trips, (e.g. relaxing on a beach, camping and so forth), noting not only destinations but also the activities offered at each destination.

LISTENING TASK

Listen to the text and then answer questions 1 through 7 in English and 8 through 13 in Russian.

1. How does the woman know that the man has gone away on vacation?
2. Where has the man gone on vacation?
3. Did he go alone or with someone else?
4. What do you know about his accommodations?
5. What kinds of complications does the woman ask about?
6. According to the man, in what ways are things more complicated than they were in the Soviet era? In what ways are they less complicated?
7. Where else did the man travel?
8. Find the Russian equivalent for the expression *on the very coast*.
9. Find the Russian equivalent for the expression *we had a view of the sea*. (Hint: the Russian expression uses the word *windows*, not the word *view*)
10. Find the Russian equivalent for the expression *to buy a tour package*.
11. Find the Russian equivalents for *service* and *conditions/accommodations*.
12. Find the Russian equivalent for *I/we didn't worry if I/we would be able to buy a ticket back to Petersburg*.
13. Find the Russian equivalent for *that's a big advantage*.

DICTATION

Replay the tape and, as you listen, write out the dialogue in full.

PERFORMANCE

Practice reciting the dialogue.

POST-LISTENING TASK

Using the dialogue as a model, work with a classmate to create and perform your own dialogue in which you plan a vacation or describe a previous one.

CULTURAL PROBLEM

Russians typically have a month of vacation per year, although in some instances that is changing. How might a month of vacation figure differently in vacation plans for Russians, as compared with a two-week vacation for the average American?

Phonetics and Intonation

Voiced and Voiceless **r** and **к**

This unit reviews the pronunciation of voiced and voiceless **r** and **к**.

Listen to voiced and voiceless **г** and **к** on the tape and repeat.

1.	тайга́	тайг	тайк
2.	шта́га	штаг	штак
3.	во́ге	вог	вок
4.	го́ге	гог	гок
5.	дугу́	дуг	дук
6.	ру́гу	руг	рук
7.	нэ́ги	нэг	нэк
8.	те́ги	тег	тек
9.	в Екатеринбу́рге	Екатеринбу́рг	
10.	в Петербу́рге	Петербу́рг	
11.	на ю́ге	юг	
12.	к Бо́ре	к Пе́те	
13.	к Зи́не	к Со́не	
14.	к Ди́ме	к Та́не	
15.	к Жо́ре	к Шу́ре	
16.	к Гео́ргию	к Ко́сте	

SELF-QUIZ

Write two spellings for each sound you hear.

1. _____ _____

2. _____ _____

3. _____ _____

4. _____ _____

5. _____ _____

6. _____ _____

7. _____ _____

8. _____ _____

Write one spelling for each sound you hear.

9. _____

10. _____

11. _____

12. _____

13. _____

14. _____

15. _____

16. _____

Exercises and Activities

Упражнéние 23.2   Answer the following questions using the verb **ходи́ть** or **éздить**.

Образéц: Где ты былá вчерá? (Антóн)

Вчерá я ходи́ла к Антóну.

1. Где был Сергéй в январé? (Амéрика)
2. Где былá Мари́я в прóшлом годý? (Украи́на)
3. Где был Макси́м вчерá вéчером? (я)
4. Где былá Тáня в суббóту вéчером? (балéт)
5. Где бы́ли Ири́на Васи́льевна и Лев Петрóвич вчерá? (Сýздаль)
6. Где он был на прóшлой недéле? (Челя́бинск)
7. Где они́ бы́ли в срéду? (Петрóвы)
8. Где онá былá в четвéрг вéчером? (вы́ставка)

Упражнéние 23.3   Review rules *a* through *f* in your textbook, pp. 289–290, and then determine which rule applies to the boldfaced verb in each sentence.

1. ____ В морскóм музéе мы ви́дели, как **плáвают** дельфи́ны.

2. ____ В бýдущем годý я **бýду** чáсто **éздить** в гóсти к своемý брáту в Москвý.

3. ____ Автóбусы регуля́рно **хóдят** по нáшей ýлице.

4. ____ Пти́цы чáсто **летáют** вокрýг нáшего дóма.

5. ____ Э́ти кóшки так бы́стро **бéгают** и пры́гают!

6. ____ Америкáнские маши́ны **éздят** быстрéе, чем **éздят** рýсские маши́ны.

7. ____ Я бою́сь **летáть** на мáленьких самолётах.

8. ____ Я чáсто **хожý** в э́ту библиотéку занимáться.

9. ____ Прóшлой веснóй мы **éздили** в Амéрику.

10. ____ Он не лю́бит **летáть** и поэ́тому тóлько **плáвает** в Япóнию.

Упражнéние 23.4   Fill in the blanks with the Russian equivalent of the English verb in parentheses, choosing from the verbs **ходи́ть, бéгать, éздить, летáть,** and **плáвать**.

1. Он чáсто (*fly*) _____на вертолёте отсю́да в аэропóрт.

2. Емý тóлько два гóда, но он ужé хорошó (*swims*) _____.

3. Наш óчень бли́зкий друг переéхал в Тýлу, и тепéрь мы чáсто (*will go*) _____ тудá.

4. Они́ рéдко (*go*) _____к Андрéевым в Москвý.

5. Вчерá мы (*went*) _____на балéт.

6. Пти́цы (*flew around*) _____над дéревом и потóм улетéли.

7. Ири́на Дми́триевна не лю́бит (*to fly*) _____ и поэ́тому в Амéрику

   онá (*sails*) _____.

8. Татья́на Влади́мировна (*went*) _____ в Каза́нь на про́шлой

неде́ле.

9. Ра́ньше он ходи́л на рабо́ту пешко́м, но тепе́рь он (*ride*) _____на

авто́бусе.

10. По суббо́там Ки́ра и Ви́тя (*go*) _____ в кино́.

Упражне́ние 23.5   Translate the following short dialogues into Russian.

1. — Where did you go last night?
   — We went to Anton Petrovich's.
2. — Where did you go last year?
   — Last year we went to Odessa.
3. — I often fly to Europe and America.
   — I'm afraid to fly: I go by boat to America.
4. — My son is only eight months old, and he already walks quite well.
   — My daughter is only eight months old, and she's already running!
5. — You swim quite well.
   — I run even better.

Упражне́ние 23.6   Review rules *a* through *f* in your textbook, pp. 295–296, and then determine which rule applies to the boldfaced verb in each sentence.

1. _____ Смотри́, дельфи́ны **плыву́т** к де́тям!

2. _____ Я **е́ду** в Москву́ в го́сти к своему́ бра́ту.

3. _____ Да, э́тот авто́бус **идёт** по Тверско́й у́лице.

4. _____ Щенки́ опя́ть **бегу́т** к ма́тери!

5. _____ Ты сли́шком бы́стро **е́дешь** — превыша́ешь ско́рость!

6. _____ Зсли ты **бу́дешь идти́** ми́мо магази́на, купи́ мне молоко́.

7. _____ Вчера́ То́ля **шёл** на рабо́ту пешко́м, но домо́й éхал на авто́бусе.

8. _____ Э́та канаре́йка **лети́т** к своему́ хозя́ину.

9. _____ Когда́ Ки́ра **éхала** в магази́н, она́ уви́дела своего́ му́жа.

10. _____ Когда́ они́ **шли́** на конце́рт, вдруг пошёл дождь.

Упражне́ние 23.7   Use the chart in your textbook, p. 294, to fill in the blanks with the Russian equivalent of the English verb in parentheses. Use only unidirectional verbs. Remember that the future tense of these verbs takes **бу́ду, бу́дешь, бу́дет,** and so on.

1. Он прочтёт все докуме́нты когда́ он (*will be flying*) _____ в

Москву́.

2. Когда́ ты (*will ride*) _____ ми́мо теа́тра, пожа́луйста, посмотри́,

како́й спекта́кль бу́дет идти́ в суббо́ту.

3. Смотри́! Вот (*runs*) _____ Па́ша. Па́ша, подожди́! Куда́ ты (*are*

running off to) _____?

4. Когда́ мы (*were going*) _____ на по́чту, вдруг пошёл дождь.

5. Мы (*were flying*) _____ в Омск, когда стюарде́сса объяви́ла, что
    бу́дет дополни́тельная поса́дка в Новосиби́рске.

6. Мы уви́дели Тама́ру Анто́новну, когда́ она́ (*was running*) _____ в
    лаборато́рию.

7. Е́сли ты (*will be walking*) _____ ми́мо магази́на, пожа́луйста,
    купи́ молоко́ и са́хар.

8. Он обы́чно (*walk*) _____ на рабо́ту, но е́дет домо́й на авто́бусе.

9. Э́тот самолёт (*is flying*) _____ в Алма́ты.

10. В Тверь мы (*will be riding*) _____ шесть часо́в, так что прие́дем
    туда́ то́лько к обе́ду.

Упражне́ние 23.8   Translate the following short dialogues into Russian.

1. — Where are you going now?
    — We're going to Anton Petrovich's. We often go to Anton Petrovich's.
2. — Where are you going? [on a train]
    — I'm going to Odessa. I often go to Odessa in the summer.
3. — I was flying to Moscow when I became acquainted with Vasilii Petrovich.
    — I always meet interesting people when I fly.
4. — Here comes my son now.
    — Your son is only a year old, but he walks quite well.
5. — Where's Anna Vladimirovna?
    — She's sailing to Yalta today; she'll return tomorrow. She loves to sail.

Упражне́ние 23.9   Review rules *a* through *r* in your textbook, pp. 291–292, and rules *a* and *b* on
p. 299. Determine which rule of each set applies to the boldfaced verb in each sentence.

1. ____ Я за́втра **пое́ду** в Москву́ в го́сти к своему́ бра́ту.

2. ____ Да, э́тот авто́бус **пойдёт** по Тверско́й у́лице.

3. ____ Щенки́ ско́ро **побегу́т** к ма́тери!

4. ____ Ты **пое́дешь** к Ивано́вым с на́ми?

5. ____ Когда́ ты **пойдёшь** в магази́н, купи́ мне молоко́.

6. ____ Когда́ О́ля **полети́т** в Аме́рику, мы бу́дем о́чень скуча́ть по ней.

7. ____ То́ля уже́ **пошёл** на рабо́ту.

8. ____ Когда́ Ки́ра **пое́хала** в магази́н, она́ ожида́ла уви́деть изоби́лие проду́ктов.

9. ____ Когда́ они́ **пошли́** на конце́рт, они́ забы́ли зонт.

10. ____ Све́та **побежа́ла** к нам, когда́ поняла́, что мы её и́щем.

Упражне́ние 23.10   Use the chart of perfective verbs in your textbook, p.298, to fill in the blanks
with the Russian equivalent of the English verb in parentheses. Use only perfective verbs of
motion.

1. Интéресно, кудá сейчáс (*will run off*) _____ Вúтя?

2. Мы (*flew*) _____ в Петербýрг, а потóм (*flew*) _____ во Владивостóк.

3. Мы (*will sail*) _____ в Хéльсинки на кораблé, потомý что э́то интерéсно.

4. Сначáла мы (*went*) _____ в Эрмитáж, а потóм мы вернýлись в гостúницу.

5. Сергéя сейчáс нет, он ужé (*left*) _____ на занятия.

6. Сначáла онá (*will fly*) _____ в Челябинск, а потóм в Хабáровск.

7. Э́лла сейчáс (*will swim*) _____ тудá.

8. Когдá вы (*will go*) _____ в Москвý, передáйте привéт Кузнецóвым.

9. Он не (*will go*) _____ с нáми в теáтр сегóдня вéчером?

10. В февралé Евгéния Степáновна (*will go*) _____ во Фрáнцию к своéй сестрé.

11. Зúна понялá, что опáздывает, и (*ran off*) _____ на рабóту.

12. Чéрез два часá Тáня (*will go*) _____ в магазúн за молокóм. Тебé чтó–нибудь нýжно?

Упражнéние 23.11   Translate the following short dialogues into Russian.

1. — Where are you going tomorrow?
   — We're going to Anton Petrovich's. We often go to Anton Petrovich's.
2. — Where are you going this summer?
   — I'm going to Odessa. I often go to Odessa in the summer.
3. — I flew to Moscow and became acquainted with Vasiliy Petrovich.
   — I always meet interesting people when I fly.
4. — Our daughter has already left for the store.
   — I'll run. Maybe I'll find her at the store.
5. — Where's Anna Vladimirovna?
   — She's sailing to Yalta tomorrow; she'll return next week. She loves to sail.

Упражнéние 23.12   Review the rules for selecting a verb for motion in your textbook, p.291–292, and fill in the blanks with the Russian equivalent of the English verb in parentheses, choosing from multidirectional, unidirectional, and perfective verbs of motion.

1. В прóшлом годý мы с Ивáном чáсто (*went*) _____ вмéсте в музéй.

2. Éсли вы (*will be going*) _____ мúмо кинотеáтра, купúте нам, пожáлуйста, два билéта на вóсемь часóв.

3 — Сáша! Кудá ты сейчáс (*going*) _____? — Я (*am going*) _____ в библиотéку.

4. Мы (*were going*) _____ на лéкцию профéссора Смирнóвой, когдá увúдели Сóню.

5. Врачú сказáли, что мне нельзя́ бýдет (*swim*) _____, потомý что у меня́ воспалéние срéднего ýха, поэтому на слéдующей недéле я (*will go running*) _____.

6. Зимóй онú с Марúей бýдут чáсто (*go*) _____ в похóды на лы́жах.

7. У нас кóнчился кóфе. Я (*will go*) _____ в магазúн.

8. Áлла óчень хорошó (*runs*) _____.

9. Гдé же Елéна Евгéньевна? Рáзве онá ужé (*left*) _____ в командирóвку в Амéрику?

10. На слéдующей недéле мы (*will go*) _____ в Москвý на две недéли.

Упражнéние 23.13   This report, written by a private investigator following a man who happens to be a friend of yours, has mistakenly fallen into your hands. You decide to rewrite it so that it sounds as though your friend is not doing anything suspicious but is simply following his daily routine.

Вóсемь часóв утрá: он идёт на останóвку автóбуса и éдет на шестóм автóбусе в инститýт кибернéтики. Три часá он нахóдится в инститýте. Одúннадцать часóв: он идёт в магазúн «Продýкты», покупáет мóрковь, свёклу, петрýшку, сыр и молокó, возвращáется в инститýт. Тринáдцать часóв: он идёт в столóвую, берёт бутербрóд с колбасóй, картóфельный салáт, пéпси-кóлу. Говорúт с неизвéстной жéнщиной пять минýт. Четы́рнадцать часóв: он идёт в кнúжный магазúн, покупáет Пýшкина. Пятнáдцать часóв: он идёт в инститýт кибернéтики. Он в инститýте три часá. Восемнáдцать часóв: он идёт на останóвку автóбуса и éдет в кафé «Мир». Там встречáется с неизвéстным мужчúной, пьёт кóфе. Вмéсте идýт в кинотеáтр «Россúя», где идёт документáльный фильм. Смóтрит фильм. Двáдцать одúн час: идёт на стáнцию метрó, éдет домóй.

Упражнéние 23.14   Rewrite the passage in **Упражнение 23.13** from the point of view of a fortune teller predicting the next day's events for this man.

Упражнéние 23.15   Now rewrite the passage from the point of view of a fortune-teller predicting the man's future for the next twenty years.

Glossary

Verbs with temporal prefixes are marked **по–** or **с–**. Multidirectional verbs are marked **M**, unidirectional verbs **U**, perfective verbs **P**.

# агéнство путешéствий	*travel agency*
бежáть (U–*) [кудá?]: бегý, бежúшь, бегýт	*to run in a particular direction, to be running somewhere*

бе́гать (M-I) [куда́?]: бе́гаю, бе́гаешь, бе́гают	*to run without a direction, to run as a sport, to run somewhere frequently*
# В сто́имость включены́...	*The price includes . . .*
# В сто́имость вхо́дят...	*The price includes . . .*
вниз	*below (dir. adverb)*
вперёд	*forward (dir. adverb)*
е́хать (U-I) [куда́?]: е́ду, е́дешь, е́дут, поезжа́й(те)!	*to go by vehicle in a particular direction, to be going by vehicle somewhere*
е́здить (M-II) [куда́?]: е́зжу, е́здишь, е́здят	*to go by vehicle without direction, to go by vehicle frequently*
идти́ (U-I) [куда́?]: иду́, идёшь, иду́т, шёл, шла, шли	*to go by foot in a particular direction, to be going somewhere by foot*
# круи́з	*cruise*
# льго́тные тари́фы	*discount rates*
лета́ть (M-I) [куда́?]: лета́ю, лета́ешь, лета́ют	*to fly somewhere without a direction, to be flying around without direction, to fly somewhere frequently*
лете́ть (U-II) [куда́?]: лечу́, лети́шь, летя́т	*to fly in a particular direction, to be flying somewhere*
наве́рх	*above (dir. adverb)*
наза́д	*back (dir. adverb)*
нале́во	*to the left (dir. adverb)*
напра́во	*to the right (dir. adverb)*
# отдыха́ть (I) на мо́ре, на куро́рте: отдыха́ю, отдыха́ешь, отдыха́ют	*to vacation at the sea or at a resort*
пла́вать (M-I) [куда́?]: пла́ваю, пла́ваешь, пла́вают	*to swim or sail without direction, to be swimming or sailing around, to swim or sail for sport*
плыть (U-I) [куда́?]: плыву́, плывёшь, плыву́т, плыл, плыла́, плы́ли	*to swim or sail somewhere, to be swimming or sailing somewhere, to swim or sail in a particular direction*
по [чему́?]	*around, about (with verbs of motion)*

побежа́ть (Р-*) [куда́?]: побегу́, побежи́шь, побегу́т	to run off somewhere
# побере́жье Чёрного мо́ря, Средизе́много мо́ря	the coast of the Black Sea or the Mediterranean Sea
побе́гать (по– I): побе́гаю, побе́гаешь, побе́гают	to be running around for a while
пое́хать (Р-I) [куда́?]: пое́ду, пое́дешь, пое́дут, поезжа́й(те)!	to go somewhere by vehicle (one particular trip)
пое́здить (по– II): пое́зжу, пое́здишь, пое́здят	to be traveling around by vehicle for a while
пойти́ (Р-I) [куда́?]: пойду́, пойдёшь, пойду́т, пошёл, пошла́, пошли́	to go somewhere on foot (one particular trip)
полета́ть (по– I): полета́ю, полета́ешь, полета́ют	to be flying around somewhere for a while
полете́ть (Р-II) [куда́?]: полечу́, полети́шь, полетя́т	to fly somewhere (one particular trip)
попла́вать (по– I): попла́ваю, попла́ваешь, попла́вают	to swim or sail around for a while
поплы́ть (Р-I) [куда́?]: поплыву́, поплывёшь, поплыву́т	to swim or sail somewhere (one particular trip)
походи́ть (по– II): похожу́, похо́дишь, похо́дят	to walk around somewhere for a while
# прямо́й рейс	direct flight(s)
# путеше́ствие [куда́?]	trip or journey to somewhere
# путеше́ствовать/по– [по како́й стране́?]: путеше́ствую, путеше́ствуешь, путеше́ствуют	to travel somewhere [in which country?]
сбе́гать (с– I) [куда́?]: сбе́гаю, сбе́гаешь, сбе́гают	to run somewhere and back [making a quick round-trip]
# ски́дка	discount
# сто́имость на челове́ка в су́тки	the price per person per day
сходи́ть (с– II) [куда́?]: схожу́, схо́дишь, схо́дят	to go somewhere and back [making a quick round-trip] on foot
съе́здить (с– II) [куда́?]: съе́зжу, съе́здишь, съе́здят	to go somewhere and back [making a quick round-trip] by vehicle
сюда́	here (dir. adverb)
# трёхзвёздочная гости́ница, четырёхзвёздочная гости́ница	three-star hotel, four-star hotel

туда   *there* (*dir. adverb*)

\# туристическое аге́нтство, тураге́нтство   *travel agency*

ходи́ть (М-II) [куда́?]:   *to walk without direction,*
   хожу́, хо́дишь, хо́дят   *to walk for sport, to go*
                                                 somewhere frequently

UNIT 24

Lexicon: Как дойти?

Prefixed verbs of motion and several other expressions are very important in the daily navigation of city streets. Russians do not measure distance in *blocks* as Americans do, but rather in buildings or street corners. In addition, most Russian residential areas in large cities are divided into complexes of buildings (дом/домá) with a single street number, subdivided into single buildings (кóрпус/корпусá), each of which has several entrances (подъéзд) serving different apartments. For example, your Russian friends might live at **Проспéкт Вернáдского, дом 125, кóрпус 2, квартíра 68**. In order to get to that apartment, it is helpful to know which подъéзд serves that apartment and which floor (**на какóм этажé?**) the apartment is on. Commuter trains are called электрíчка, while intercity trains are called пóезд/поездá. Both are served by central stations called вокзáл/-ы (**на вокзáле**), such as **Кíевский вокзáл** in Moscow (where trains depart to and arrive from Kiev and points south) and **Москóвский вокзáл** in St. Petersburg (where trains depart to and arrive from Moscow and points south).

Как мне дойти [до чегó?] Как мне попáсть [кудá?] Как мне пройти/проéхать [к чемý?]
  How can I get to . . .

> Извинíте, вы не подскáжете, как мне дойти до Большóго теáтра?
> *Excuse me, can you tell me how to get to the Bolshoy Theater?*

Поворáчивать/повернýть напрáво, налéво
  To turn right or left

> Когдá доéдете до Тверскóй ýлицы, повернíте напрáво, в стóрону Кремлá.
> *When you get to Tverskaya Street, turn right toward the Kremlin.*

Ходúть/идтú/пойтú прáмо
  To go straight

> Идíте прáмо по Нéвскому проспéкту, и кáссы Аэрофлóта бýдут спрáва.
> *Go straight on Nevsky Prospect and the Aeroflot ticket agency will be on your right.*

Пересекáть/пересéчь [что?], пересекáться/пересéчься
  To cross

> Садóвое кольцó пересекáется с Тверскóй ýлицей на Плóщади Маякóвского.
> *The Garden Ring crosses Tverskaia Street at Maiakovski Square.*

> Когдá пересечёшь Нéвский проспéкт, увúдишь слéва магазíн «Дом кнúги».
> *After you cross Nevskii Prospect, you'll see the store House of Books on your left.*

Окáзываться/оказáться [где?]
  To wind up, to turn out to be somewhere

> Когдá пересечёшь Дворцóвый мóст, окáжешься на Дворцóвой плóщади.
> *When you cross the Dvortsovyi (Palace) Bridge, you'll wind up on Palace Square.*

Спрáва/с прáвой стороны́, слéва/с лéвой стороны́ [от когó? чегó?]
  On the right, on the left [from whom?]

> Когдá стоúшь спинóй к Эрмитáжу, Нéвский проспéкт бýдет спрáва от тебя́.
> *When you stand with your back to the Hermitage, Nevskii Prospect will be on your right.*

Подъéзд
Driveway or one of several entrances to a residential building, each one of which features its own stairwell giving access to a number of apartments

Мы живём в пя́том подъéзде.
We live in the fifth entrance to the building.

Перехóд (подзéмный)
Underground pedestrian tunnel for busy streets

Тут нýжно перейти́ Нéвский проспéкт по перехóду.
Here we have to cross Nevskii Prospect in an underground pedestrian tunnel.

Брáть/взя́ть такси́, лови́ть/пойма́ть такси́
To take a taxi, to catch a taxi

Дава́йте возмьём такси́: здесь бýдет легкó егó пойма́ть.
Let's take a taxi: it will be easy to catch one here.

Стоя́нка такси́
Taxi stand

На террито́рии аэропóрта нахóдится стоя́нка такси́.
There's a taxi stand on the territory of the airport.

Стáнция — метрó; останóвка — автóбуса, троллéйбуса, трамвáя; вокзáл
Metro stop, bus stop (or trolley or tram stop), train station

Их кварти́ра в óчень удóбном мéсте: останóвка автóбуса — напрóтив, стáнция метрó «Ки́евская» и Ки́евский вокзáл в пяти́ минýтах ходьбы́.
Their apartment is in a very convenient location: the bus stop is across the street and the metro stop and Kiev Station are a five-minute walk away.

Стáнция/останóвка нахóдится напрóтив [чегó?] на углý [каки́х ýлиц?]
The stop is located across from what or on the corner of what streets

Стáнция «Охóтный ряд» нахóдится на углý Тверскóй ýлицы и Охóтного ря́да, напрóтив Манéжа.
The metro stop Okhotnyi riad is located on the corner of Tverskaia Street and Okhotnyi riad, across from the Manezh Exhibition Hall.

Покупáть/купи́ть жетóн/ы на метрó, талóны на автóбус, троллéйбус, трамвáй
To buy tokens for the metro (subway) or talons for the bus, trolley, or tram

Жетóны на метрó мóжно купи́ть в метрó, а талóны на автóбус мóжно купи́ть у води́теля автóбуса.
Tokens for the metro (subway) can be purchased in the metro, and tickets for the buses can be purchased from a bus driver.

Сади́ться/сесть в метрó, автóбус, троллéйбус, трамвáй
To get on/or take the metro, bus, trolley, or tram

Сади́тесь в метрó на стáнции «Ю́го–Зáпадная» и доезжáйте до стáнции «Тверскáя ýлица».
Get on the subway at the South-West Station and go to the Tverskaia Street Station.

Садиться/сесть не в ту сторону
To get on the metro, bus, trolley, or tram in the wrong direction

> Вы сéли не в ту сторону! Вам нужно выйти на следующей и сесть на поезд на другой
> стороне платформы.
> *You're going the wrong way! You need to get out at the next stop and take the train on the
> other side of the platform.*

Éздить/éхать на метро, автобусе, троллейбусе, трамвае
To travel by metro, bus, trolley, or tram

> На работу я éду на метро, но домой éду на трамвае: вечером хочется смотреть на город.
> *I go to work on the metro, but I go home on the tram: in the evenings I feel like looking at
> the city.*

Éздить/éхать сколько времени? Час пик
To travel for how long, rush hour

> На работу я éду 40 минут, но домой я éду почти целый час, потому что попадаю в
> пробки. Это ведь час пик.
> *It takes me forty minutes to get to work, but it takes me almost an hour to get home
> because I get into traffic jams. It's rush hour, after all.*

Проезжать/проехать сколько станций, остановок
To ride for how many stops (before exiting)

> Мы сéли в метро и проéхали три станции.
> *We got on the metro and rode for three stops.*

Выходить/выйти (*standard*), сходить/сойти (*colloquial*) на следующей станции/остановке,
через одну станцию/остановку, через две (три) станции/остановки
To get out (exit) on the next stop, on the stop after the next, in two or three stops

> Садитесь на шестой автобус, проезжайте две остановки и выйдите на остановке
>   «Школа».
> *Get on the number six bus, ride past two stops and get off at the School stop.*

> Пропустите, пожалуйста, мы выходим на следующей.
> *Please let us get by, we're getting off on the next stop.*

> Мы выходим через одну.
> *We're getting off on the stop after next.*

Пересаживаться/пересéсть, дéлать/с– пересáдку [на что?]
To make a transfer

> На станции «Белорусская» я пересаживаюсь на кольцевую линию.
> *At the Belarus station I transfer to the Circle Line [one of the subway lines in Moscow].*

Упражнéние 24.1   Fill in the blanks with the Russian equivalent of the English word or phrase in
parentheses.

1. Анатолий Кириллович каждый день (*goes*) _____ на работу на

   метро, (*makes a transfer*) _____ на седьмой троллейбус на

   Нéвском проспéкте.

2. Как (*can [Я] get to*) _____ до стадиона?

3. (*Take*) _____ девя́тый трамва́й и доезжа́йте до (*stop*)

_____ «Метро́», пото́м (*take*) _____ на

метро́ до (*stop*) _____ «Спорти́вная», и́ли, коне́чно, мо́жно (*take*)

_____ такси́.

4. В (*rush hour*) _____ (*it takes us*) _____ 50

мину́т с рабо́ты домо́й.

5. — Извини́те, я (*am getting off*) _____ (*at the stop after next*)

_____ .

— Ну и что, я (*am getting off*) _____ (*at the next stop*)

_____ !

6. Дойди́те до Проспе́кта Верна́дского и (*turn right*) _____ .

 Фо́то-зада́ние Look at the photograph on the first page of this unit in the textbook. Write a paragraph or prepare a presentation, as assigned by your instructor, describing the movement of people and vehicles as depicted.

Listening Tasks

The listening text for this unit consists of directions for a trip through downtown Moscow.

PRE-LISTENING TASK

Review the list of expressions on pp. 247–249 and look at the map on page 251 to familiarize yourself with the street names before you listen to the directions. You will need to know the name and the location of one of the most important streets in Moscow (**Садо́вое кольцо́**).

 LISTENING TASK

John and Erica are new American exchange students in Moscow. They like to explore downtown Moscow in their free time. They've been touring Red Square, and now they'd like to go to the U.S. embassy. They ask their Russian friend Volodia to show them on the map how to get from Red Square to the embassy.

Follow the route in Moscow described on the tape, **drawing the route on your map** as you listen. Then answer questions 1 and 2 in English and 3 through 5 in Russian.

1. There are two different ways to get to the embassy: which way does Volodia recommend and why?
2. What are the advantages, if any, of the other route?
3. What is the name of the street on which the embassy is located?
4. What is the previous name of this street?
5. What is the Russian equivalent for the expression *standing and facing the Mausoleum*?

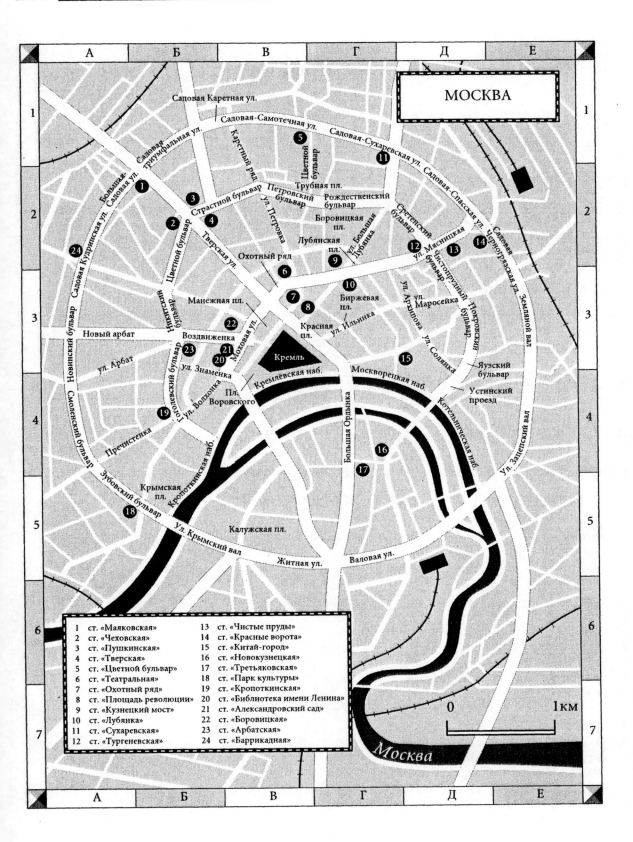

МОСКВА

Садовая Каретная ул.
Садовая-Самотечная ул.
Садовая-Сухаревская ул.
Садовая-Спасская ул.
Садовая Черногрязская ул.
Садовая
Садовая Триумфальная ул.
Большая Садовая ул.
Садовая Кудринская ул.
Каретный ряд
Цветной бульвар
Трубная пл.
Страстной бульвар
Петровский бульвар
Рождественский бульвар
Сретенский бульвар
ул. Петровка
Боровицкая пл.
Лубянская пл.
ул. Большая Лубянка
ул. Мясницкая
Чистопрудный бульвар
Покровский бульвар
Цветной бульвар
Тверская ул.
Охотный ряд
Манежная пл.
Биржевая пл.
ул. Маросейка
ул. Архипова
ул. Солянка
Никитский бульвар
Воздвиженка
Красная пл.
ул. Ильинка
Яузский бульвар
Новый арбат
Моховая ул.
Кремль
Москворецкая наб.
Устинский проезд
ул. Арбат
ул. Знаменка
Кремлёвская наб.
Котельническая наб.
Смоленский бульвар
Гоголевский бульвар
ул. Волхонка
Пл. Воровского
Большая Ордынка
ул. Зацепский вал
Пречистенка
Кропоткинская наб.
Крымская пл.
Зубовский бульвар
Калужская пл.
Крымский вал
ул. Крымский вал
Житная ул.
Валовая ул.
Москва

1 ст. «Маяковская»	13 ст. «Чистые пруды»
2 ст. «Чеховская»	14 ст. «Красные ворота»
3 ст. «Пушкинская»	15 ст. «Китай-город»
4 ст. «Тверская»	16 ст. «Новокузнецкая»
5 ст. «Цветной бульвар»	17 ст. «Третьяковская»
6 ст. «Театральная»	18 ст. «Парк культуры»
7 ст. «Охотный ряд»	19 ст. «Кропоткинская»
8 ст. «Площадь революции»	20 ст. «Библиотека имени Ленина»
9 ст. «Кузнецкий мост»	21 ст. «Александровский сад»
10 ст. «Лубянка»	22 ст. «Боровицкая»
11 ст. «Сухаревская»	23 ст. «Арбатская»
12 ст. «Тургеневская»	24 ст. «Баррикадная»

0   1 КМ

Москва́: Центр

DICTATION

Replay the tape and, as you listen, write out the directions in full.

PERFORMANCE

Practice reciting the directions.

POST-LISTENING TASKS

Using the directions as a model, work with a classmate to create and recite your own directions based on the Moscow map. Establish a clearly identified starting point and destination before you begin your directions. Recite your directions to another pair of classmates and see if they can follow on their map where you are sending them.

CULTURAL PROBLEM

In what ways are directions in Russian different from directions given in English by North Americans?

Phonetics and Intonation

Voiced and Voiceless д and т

This unit reviews the pronunciation of voiced and voiceless д and т.

Listen to the voiced and voiceless д and т on the tape and repeat.

1.	сáда	сад	сат
2.	грáда	град	грат
3.	вóду	вод	вот
4.	нýда	нуд	нут
5.	рóда	род	рот
6.	вúда	вид	вит
7.	сéда	сед	сет
8.	мёда	мёд	мёт
9.	пýда	пуд	пут
10.	в Самаркáнде	Самаркáнд	
11.	в Волгогрáде	Волгогрáд	
12.	в Нóвгороде	Нóвгород	
13.	от Бóри	от Пéти	
14.	от Зúны	от Сóни	
15.	от Дúмы	от Тáни	
16.	от Жóры	от Шýры	
17.	под бинóклем	под портфéлем	
18.	под зонтóм	под сýмкой	
19.	под двéрью	под тетрáдью	
20.	под газéтой	под Кúевом	

SELF-QUIZ

Write two spellings for each sound you hear.

1. _____ _____

2. _____ _____

3. _____ _____

4. _____ _____

5. _____ _____

6. _____ _____

7. _____ _____

8. _____ _____

9. _____ _____

10. _____ _____

Exercises and Activities

Упражнéние 24.2 Fill in the blanks with a prefix from the charts of prefixes in your textbook (pp. 311–314).

1. Онá сейчáс _____ойдёт к нам и спрóсит нас об э́том.

2. Ви́тя обы́чно _____хóдит домóй с рабóты в шесть часóв.

3. Маши́на «Феррáри» бы́стро _____ъéхала с дорóги.

4. Давáйте здесь _____плывём чéрез рéчку на другóй бéрег.

5. Самолёт _____летéл и улетéл из Москвы́.

6. Онá _____ъехáла на гóру и постáвила маши́ну тудá, чтóбы оттýда посмотрéть на

   гóрод.

7. _____ъéхались все делегáты на съезд.

8. Мéдленно _____ойди́ от злой собáки!

9. Мы _____йдём чéрез Крáсную плóщадь.

10. Мы _____ойдём все магази́ны, покá не найдём нóвое издáние Булгáкова.

11. Мы _____ъéхали грузови́к и поéхали дáльше.

12. Они́ _____ъéхали в гарáж и постáвили маши́ну.

13. Я дýмаю, что зáвтра мы наконéц _____éдем до Москвы́.

14. Сóлнце ужé давнó _____шлó, но ещё так светлó, что мóжно читáть!

15. Профéссор Смирнóва? Нет, онá тóлько что _____шла из лаборатóрии. Рáзве вы её не

    ви́дели в коридóре?

16. Тури́сты _____шли́ вокру́г па́мятника и пошли́ в музе́й.

17. Бели́нская уже́ _____е́хала в Читу́!

18. Мы _____плы́ли от при́стани и на́чали плыть быстре́е.

19. По́сле собра́ния все профессора́ _____ошли́сь по свои́м кабине́там.

20. Мы обяза́тельно _____йдём к вам, когда́ бу́дем в Москве́.

 Упражне́ние 24.3 Traffic jams are a part of life in any modern city, but these days Moscow seems to have more than its fare share of **про́бки** (*traffic bottlenecks*). A Russian newspaper published some maps showing how drivers can avoid some of the more predictable traffic hotspots in Moscow. Find the map that corresponds to the following description. You may want to refer to the key of abbreviations provided below.

пл.	пло́щадь (*ж.*)	р.	река́	М	ста́нция метро́
б–р	бульва́р	Б.	Больша́я	пер.	переу́лок
ул.	у́лица	пр.	проспе́кт	ш.	шоссе́
пр–д	прое́зд	наб.	на́бережная	М.	Ма́лая

Быва́ют больши́е про́бки на Китайгоро́дском проспе́кте на пересече́нии с Москворе́цкой на́бережной. Вме́сто того́, чтобы повора́чивать на пра́во на Лубя́нский прое́зд, лу́чше пое́хать да́льше по Маросе́йке и дое́хать до Покро́вского бульва́ра. Там поверни́те напра́во и вы смо́жете споко́йно перее́хать ре́ку.

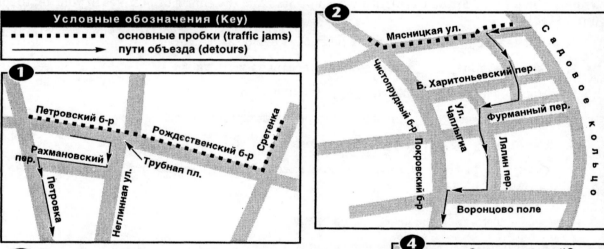

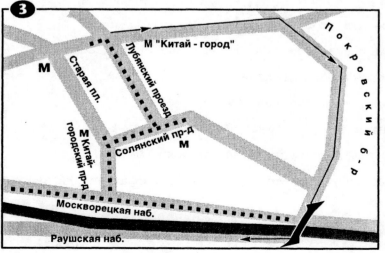

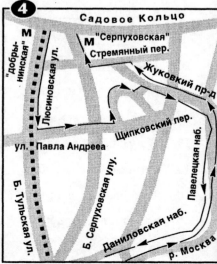

Упражнéние 24.4 Now choose two of the other maps and write out directions to a friend, explaining how to avoid the traffic jam in that spot. You may want to refer to the list of abbreviations provided in **Упражнéние 24.3**.

Задáние 24.1 Describe two typical traffic jams on your campus or in your hometown and how best to avoid them. You may want to use the expression **там иногдá бывáет больш́ое движéние** (*there is a lot of traffic there sometimes*).

Задáние 24.2 Describe how a student gets from his or her dormitory to class as if you were watching the trip.

Задáние 24.3 Recast the narrative you told in the **Задáние 24.2** to describe the student's trip as a habitual one, made every day last semester.

Задáние 24.4 You have a friend who wants to find the same student from **Задáние 24.2** and **24.3** sometime during the day tomorrow. Since you know that student's itinerary quite well, describe to your friend what that student will do tomorrow.

Упражнéние 24.5 Translate the following passage into Russian.

> Inna picked up her things and walked out of the office. She calmly walked down the corridor to the elevator, saying good-bye to all the colleagues she saw. She summoned (**вы́звать**) the elevator and waited for it to arrive (approach) silently. When the doors opened, she saw that Nikolai Petrovich was standing in the elevator. She looked at him and entered the elevator. Silently, they rode down to the first floor. Inna thought that when the doors opened, she would run out, but when the doors did open, she walked out and calmly crossed the lobby (**фойé**) of the building, approached the cloakroom (**гардерóб**), and got her coat and umbrella. It was still raining. She got as far as the doors when she heard someone call her name. She thought for a moment and walked to the door. She exited from the building and caught a taxi. She wanted to ride as far as the metro, and from there she would take the metro home. The taxi drove quickly: she imagined that she was in an airplane, flying along the city streets . . .

Задáние 24.6 Continue the story begun in **Упражнéние 24.5**. Be sure to justify the suspense or intrigue of the story.

Glossary

The conjugation patterns of verbs of motion with and without prefixes presented in Units 23 and 24 are not included (see the appropriate tables in those units in the textbook).

# брать (I) /взять (I) такси́: беру́, берёшь, беру́т, брал, брала́, бра́ли; возьму́, возьмёшь, возьму́т, взял, взяла́, взя́ли	*to take a cab*
вбегáть (I) /вбежáть (*) [кудá? во что? откýда?]	*to run into an enclosed space*
влетáть (I) /влетéть (II) [кудá? во что? откýда?]	*to fly into an enclosed space*
# вокзáл	*train station*

вплыва́ть (I) /вплыть (I) [куда́? во что? отку́да?]	*to swim or sail into an enclosed space*
входи́ть (II) /войти́ (I) [куда́? во что? отку́да?]	*to walk into an enclosed space*
входи́ть (II) /войти́ (I) в си́лу, в де́йствие, в систе́му	*to go into effect*
выбега́ть (I) /вы́бежать (*) [отку́да? куда́?]	*to run out of an enclosed space*
выезжа́ть (I) /вы́ехать (I) [отку́да? куда́?]	*to ride or drive out of an enclosed space*
вылета́ть (I) /вы́лететь (II) [отку́да? куда́?]	*to fly out of an enclosed space*
выплыва́ть (I) /вы́плыть (I) [отку́да? куда́?]	*to swim or sail out of an enclosed space*
выходи́ть (II) /вы́йти (I) [отку́да? куда́?]	*to walk out of an enclosed space*
# выходи́ть (II) /вы́йти (I) на сле́дующей, че́рез одну́, че́рез две (ста́нции, остано́вки)	*to get off (exit) at the next stop, at the stop after next, or in two stops*
выходи́ть (II) /вы́йти (I) за́муж [за кого́?]	*to get married (said of a woman only)*
въезжа́ть (I) /въе́хать (I) [куда́? во что? отку́да?]	*to ride or drive into an enclosed space*
добега́ть (I) /добежа́ть (*) [до чего́?]	*to run up to or as far as something*
доезжа́ть (I) /дое́хать (I) [до чего́?]	*to ride up to or as far as something*
долета́ть (I) /долете́ть (II) [до чего́?]	*to fly up to or as far as something*
доплыва́ть (I) /доплы́ть (I) [до чего́?]	*to swim or sail up to or as far as something*
доходи́ть (II) /дойти́ (I) [до чего́?]	*to walk up to or as far as something*
доходи́ть (II) /дойти́ (I) до того́, что	*to get to the point when*
# е́здить (II) /е́хать (I) ско́лько вре́мени?	*it takes ____ how long to get to . . .*
# жето́н	*token (for the metro or telephone)*
забега́ть (I) /забежа́ть (*) [куда́?]	*to run into or behind something*
заезжа́ть (I) /зае́хать (I) [куда́?]	*to ride or drive into or behind something*
залета́ть (I) /залете́ть (II) [куда́?]	*to fly into or behind something*

заплыва́ть (I) /заплы́ть (I) [куда́?]	*to swim or sail into or behind something*
заходи́ть (II) /зайти́ (I) [куда́?]	*to walk into or behind something*
# как мне дойти́ (II) [до чего́?]	*how can I get to . . .*
# как мне пройти́ (I) /прое́хать (I) [к чему́?]	*how can I get to . . .*
# как попа́сть (I) [куда́?]	*how can I get to . . .*
# ко́рпус	*individual building in a complex of buildings*
# кварти́ра	*apartment*
# лови́ть (II) /пойма́ть (I) такси́: ловлю́, ло́вишь, ло́вят; пойма́ю, пойма́ешь, пойма́ют	*to catch a taxi*
оббега́ть (I) /оббежа́ть (*) [что? вокру́г чего́?]	*to pass or run around*
облета́ть (I) /облете́ть (II) [что? вокру́г чего́?]	*to pass or fly around*
обплыва́ть (I) /обплы́ть (I) [что? вокру́г чего́?]	*to pass or swim or sail around*
обходи́ть (II) /обойти́ (I) [что? вокру́г чего́?]	*to pass or walk around*
обходи́ться (II) /обойти́сь (I) [без чего́?]	*to get by (without something)*
объезжа́ть (I) /объе́хать (I) [что? вокру́г чего́?]	*to drive around or pass*
# ока́зываться (II) /оказа́ться (I) [где?]: ока́зываюсь, ока́зываешься, ока́зываются; окажу́сь, ока́жешься, ока́жутся	*to turn out to be somewhere, to wind up somewhere (as a result of movement, either figurative or literal)*
# остано́вка авто́буса, тролле́йбуса, трамва́я	*bus stop, trolley stop, tram stop*
отбега́ть (I) /отбежа́ть (*) [от чего́?]	*to run away from something*
отлета́ть (I) /отлете́ть (*) [от чего́?]	*to fly away from something*
отплыва́ть (I) /отплы́ть (I) [от чего́?]	*to swim or sail away from something*
отходи́ть (II) /отойти́ (I) [от чего́?]	*to walk away from something*
отъезжа́ть (I) /отъе́хать (I) [от чего́?]	*to ride or drive away from something*
перебега́ть (I) /перебежа́ть (*) [куда́? че́рез что?]	*to run across something*
переезжа́ть (I) /перее́хать (I) [куда́? че́рез что?]	*to ride or drive across something*
переезжа́ть (I) /перее́хать (I) [куда́? отку́да?]	*to move (from one home to another)*
перелета́ть (I) /перелете́ть (II) [куда́? че́рез что?]	*to fly across something*

переплыва́ть (I) /переплы́ть (I) [куда́? че́рез что?]	to swim or sail across something
# переса́живаться (I) /пересе́сть (I), де́лать/с– (I) переса́дку, [на что? где? на како́й ста́нции и́ли остано́вке?]: переса́живаюсь, переса́живаешься, переса́живаются; переся́ду, переся́дешь, переся́дут	to make a transfer (onto what? at what station?)
# пересека́ть (I) /пересе́чь (I) [что?]: пересека́ю, пересека́ешь, пересека́ют; пересеку́, пересечёшь, пересеку́т, пересёк, пересекла́, пересекли́	to cross something
# пересека́ться (I) /пересе́чься (I): пересека́ется, пересека́ются; пересечётся, пересеку́тся	to cross each other (usually only 3rd person forms)
переходи́ть (II) /перейти́ (I) все преде́лы	to cross all boundaries
переходи́ть (II) /перейти́ (I) [куда́? че́рез что?]	to walk across something
# перехо́д	pedestrian crossing (usually underground)
# повора́чивать (I) /поверну́ть (I) [напра́во, нале́во, куда́?] повора́чиваю, повора́чиваешь, повора́чивают; поверну́, повернёшь, поверну́т	to turn right or left where (on to what street?)
подбега́ть (I) /подбежа́ть (*) [к чему́?]	to run up to something, to approach something
подлета́ть (I) /подлете́ть (II) [к чему́?]	to fly up to something, to approach something
подплыва́ть (I) /подплы́ть (I) [к чему́?]	to swim or sail up to something, to approach something
подходи́ть (II) /подойти́ (I) [к чему́?]	to walk up to something, to approach something
# подъе́зд	driveway or entrance to a building
подъезжа́ть (I) /подъе́хать (I) [к чему́?]	to drive up to something, to approach something
прибега́ть (I) /прибежа́ть (I) [куда́? отку́да?]	to run somewhere
прибега́ть (I) /прибе́гнуть (I) [к чему́?]	to resort to something
приезжа́ть (I) /прие́хать (I) [куда́? отку́да?]	to ride or drive somewhere
прилета́ть (I) /прилете́ть (II) [куда́? отку́да?]	to fly somewhere
приплыва́ть (I) /приплы́ть (I) [куда́? отку́да?]	to swim or sail somewhere
приходи́ть (II) /прийти́ (I) в го́лову (кому́?)	to come to mind to someone
приходи́ть (II) /прийти́ (I) [куда́? отку́да?]	to walk somewhere
приходи́ть (II) /прийти́ (I) в себя́	to come to oneself
пробега́ть (I) /пробежа́ть (*) [куда́? че́рез что?]	to run through something

пробега́ть (I) /пробежа́ть (*) [па́льцами по кла́вишам, глаза́ми по страни́це]	to run one's fingers over the keyboard, one's eyes over the page
# проезжа́ть (I) /прое́хать (I) ско́лько ста́нций, остано́вок?	to ride how many stops (before getting off)?
проезжа́ть (I) /прое́хать (I) [куда́? че́рез что?]	to ride or drive through something, to miss one's stop on a bus or train
пролета́ть (I) /пролете́ть (I) [куда́? че́рез что?]	to fly through something
проплыва́ть (I) /проплы́ть (I) [куда́? че́рез что?]	to swim or sail through something
прохо́дит/пройдёт вре́мя	some time goes (will go) by
проходи́ть (II) /пройти́ (I) [куда́? че́рез что?]	to walk through something
проходи́ть (II) /пройти́ (I) [что?] (материа́л)	to cover something (to cover some material) or go through something (endure something)
# пря́мо	straight
разбега́ться (I) /разбежа́ться (*) [отку́да? куда́? по каки́м места́м?]	to run off in separate directions
# развора́чиваться (I) /разверну́ться (I) [куда́?]: развора́чиваюсь, развора́чиваешься, развора́чиваются; разверну́сь, развернёшься, разверну́тся	to make a U-turn (while driving or riding)
разъезжа́ться (I) /разъе́хаться (I) [отку́да? куда́? по каки́м места́м?]	to go separate ways (by vehicle)
расходи́ться (II) /разойти́сь (I) [отку́да? куда́? по каки́м места́м?]	to go separate ways (on foot)
сбега́ть (I) /сбежа́ть (*) [с чего́? куда́?]	to run down off something
# сади́ться (II) /сесть (I) в метро́, авто́бус: сажу́сь, сади́шься, садя́тся; ся́ду, ся́дешь, ся́дут	to get on or take the subway or a bus
# сади́ться (II) /се́сть (I) не в ту сто́рону: сажу́сь, сади́шься, садя́тся; ся́ду, ся́дешь, ся́дут	to get on a bus or train going in the wrong direction
слета́ть (I) /слете́ть (II) [с чего́? куда́?]	to fly down off something
# сле́ва, с ле́вой стороны́	on the left
сплыва́ть (I) /сплы́ть (I) [с чего́? куда́?]	to swim or sail down off something (usually metaphoric)
# спра́ва, с пра́вой стороны́	on the right
# ста́нция метро́	metro stop
# стоя́нка такси́ (на)	taxi stand
сходи́ть (II) /сойти́ (I) [с чего́? куда́?]	to walk down off something

сходи́ть (II) /сойти́ (I) с ума́	*to go crazy*
сходи́ться (II) /сойти́сь (I) [куда́? из каки́х мест?]	*to come together (by foot)*
съезжа́ть (I) /съе́хать (I) [с чего́? куда́?]	*to ride or drive down off something*
съезжа́ться (I) /съе́хаться (I) [куда́? из каки́х мест?]	*to come together (by vehicle)*
# тало́н	*talon (a kind of ticket)*
убега́ть (I) /убежа́ть (*) [отку́да? куда́?]	*to run away somewhere*
уезжа́ть (I) /уе́хать (I) [отку́да? куда́?]	*to ride or drive away somewhere*
улета́ть (I) /улете́ть (II) [отку́да? куда́?]	*to fly away somewhere*
уплыва́ть (I) /уплы́ть (I) [отку́да? куда́?]	*to swim or sail away somewhere*
уходи́ть (II) /уйти́ (I) [отку́да? куда́?]	*to walk away somewhere*
# час пик	*rush hour*
# электри́чка	*commuter train*
# эта́ж, на како́м этаже́	*floor, on what floor*

UNIT 25

Listening Tasks

Note: Listening tasks in this unit are based on the vocabulary and grammar of the textbook, not the lexicon.

The listening text for this unit consists of directions for a sightseeing trip through historic landmarks in St. Petersburg.

PRE-LISTENING TASK

Review the list of expressions on pp. 247–249 and look at the following map to familiarize yourself with the street names and historic sites before you listen to the directions.

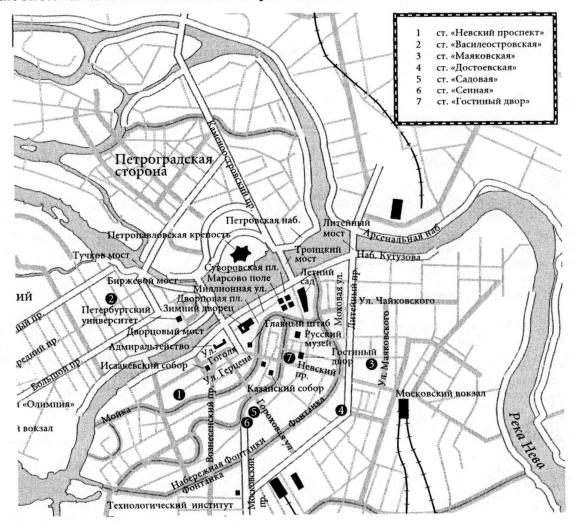

1	ст. «Невский проспект»
2	ст. «Василеостровская»
3	ст. «Маяковская»
4	ст. «Достоевская»
5	ст. «Садовая»
6	ст. «Сенная»
7	ст. «Гостиный двор»

Карта 25.1 Санкт–Петербург: Центр

LISTENING TASK

A group of American tourists went on a bus tour of St. Petersburg on their first day in town. After a three-hour drive around the city they felt overwhelmed by the number of sites and everything seemed like a blur. On the next morning, their bus driver, Arkadii, showed them on the map where he had taken them on the previous day.

Listen to Arkadii's story on the tape and **draw the group's itinerary on the map.** (The tour started at the Olimpia Hotel on Vasil'evskii Island.) Then answer questions 1 and 2 in English and 3 through 6 in Russian.

1. To what does Arkadii attribute the tourists' fatigue?
2. Arkadii makes a reference to **Исаáкий**. What do you think this name refers to, given the rest of the day's itinerary?
3. What is the "filler word" that Arkadii uses to begin his description?
4. What was the last place the tourists saw before Arkadii brought them back to the hotel?
5. What is the name of the place that they didn't get to see because they were tired?
6. When did Arkadii pick the tourists up and when did he drop them off at the end of the tour?

DICTATION

Replay the tape and, as you listen, write out the directions in full.

PERFORMANCE

Practice reciting the directions.

POST-LISTENING TASK

Pretend that you are the supervisor of a Russian travel agency and have just hired a new guide to lead American tourists on a tour of downtown St. Petersburg (by bus). Using the directions as a model, work with a classmate to create and recite your own directions based on the map in order to tell your new guide exactly how and where to lead the tourists. Establish a clearly identified starting point and destination before you begin your directions. Recite your directions to another pair of classmates and see if they can follow on their map where you are sending them.

CULTURAL PROBLEM

Arkadii, the bus driver, makes a statement concerning why the American tourists were so tired. What do you think about this stereotypical remark? What other stereotypes might Russians hold of Americans? Why do you think these tourists might have been tired? What might be some of the causes of "foreigner fatigue" in any culture?

Phonetics and Intonation

Soft Sign ь and Hard Sign ъ

This unit explains how the soft sign and the hard sign affect the pronunciation of preceding consonants and the vowels that follow them.

Listen to how the soft sign affects pronunciation and repeat.

1.	ест	есть	
2.	ел	ель	
3.	тен	тень	
4.	надёт	надёть	
5.	колóт	колóть	
6.	ла	ля	лья
7.	ты	ти	тьи
8.	ду	дю	дью
9.	но	нё	ньё
10.	сэ	се	сье

SELF-QUIZ #1

Circle the letters that best represent the sounds you hear.

1.	ест	есть	
2.	ел	ель	
3.	тен	тень	
4.	надёт	надёть	
5.	колóт	колóть	
6.	ла	ля	лья
7.	ты	ти	тьи
8.	ду	дю	дью
9.	но	нё	ньё
10.	сэ	се	сье

Listen to how the hard sign affects pronunciation and repeat.

1.	сесть	съесть		6.	сезд	съезд
2.	зех	зъех		7.	зех	зъех
3.	дез	дъез		8.	дез	дъез
4.	бех	бъех		9.	бех	бъех
5.	сех	съех		10.	сех	съех

SELF-QUIZ #2

Circle the letters that best represent the sounds you hear.

1.	сесть	съесть		6.	сезд	съезд
2.	зех	зъех		7.	зех	зъех
3.	дез	дъез		8.	дез	дъез
4.	бех	бъех		9.	бех	бъех
5.	сех	съех		10.	сех	съех

Lexicon: В мúре бúзнеса

After nearly seventy-five years of Communist rule, Russians are now discovering the marketplace. This discovery is accompanied by a great deal of change in the Russian language. During the same seventy-five years in which Russian was expanded (or distorted) by such Communist inventions as **колхóз** (*collective farm*) or **жэк** (*housing department*: **жилúщно–эксплуатациóнная контóра**), languages of the West expanded to accommodate such phenomena of twentieth-century capitalism as *securities analyst* and *telemarketing*. In some cases, the Russian language has recovered some words and expressions from its pre-Communist past, such as **биржа,** (*stock market*), but in other cases, Russian is now struggling with a flood of foreign words, borrowed to express suddenly changing economic conditions. It is unclear how many of these foreign words will ultimately remain part of the language, and how many of them will be replaced by more Russian equivalents. In the meantime, all those interested in business in Russia use many of the following terms to express themselves

Бизнесме́н, бизнесме́нка
Businessman, businesswoman

В Росси́и в после́днее вре́мя стано́вится всё бо́льше и бо́льше бизнесме́нов.
There are more and more businessmen in Russia these days.

Де́нежный ры́нок, биржево́й валю́тный ры́нок; курс (росси́йского рубля́, америка́нского до́ллара, англи́йского фу́нта сте́рлингов, неме́цкой ма́рки, япо́нской ие́ны); валю́та
Currency market; rate (of exchange) of the ruble, dollar, pound, mark, yen; currency

На валю́тном ры́нке наблюда́ется подъём неме́цкой ма́рки по отноше́нию к росси́йскому рублю́ и америка́нскому до́ллару.
In the currency market the German mark has risen against the Russian ruble and the American dollar.

Прода́жа; поку́пка; торг
Sale; purchase; trade (in currency or securities)

В январе́ 1995-го го́да на Моско́вской валю́тной би́рже предлага́ли за до́ллар четы́ре ты́сячи рубле́й при прода́же и четы́ре ты́сячи пятьсо́т рубле́й при поку́пке.
In January 1995 at the Moscow Currency Market one could buy a dollar for four thousand rubles and sell one for four thousand five hundred rubles.

Начали́сь то́рги по росси́йскому рублю́ наконе́ц на фи́нских валю́тных би́ржах.
Finally trade in the Russian ruble began to take place in Finnish currency markets.

Повыша́ться/повы́ситься; повыше́ние; понижа́ться/пони́зиться; паде́ние/сниже́ние; колеба́ться
To increase or rise; an increase; to decrease or fall; a decline or decrease; to fluctuate

Курс кана́дского до́ллара не́которое вре́мя колеба́лся, пото́м повы́сился в отноше́нии к росси́йскому рублю́ и пони́зился в отноше́нии к америка́нскому до́ллару.
The Canadian dollar fluctuated for a while, then increased in value against the Russian ruble and decreased in value against the American dollar.

Това́рный ры́нок
Market for goods

Вы́сшие руководи́тели Росси́и удиви́ли това́рный ры́нок, заяви́в, что в э́том году́ Росси́я мо́жет обойти́сь без заку́пок зерна́ за рубежо́м.
The highest leaders of Russia surprised the goods market by announcing that Russia can get by without buying grain from abroad this year.

Опто́вая цена́/прода́жа, ро́зничная цена́/прода́жа
Wholesale price (for sale by wholesale), retail price (for sale by retail)

Компа́ния ТиМ предлага́ет опто́вые па́ртии а́удио-ви́део те́хники; ро́зничную торго́влю осуществля́ет магази́н «Пионе́р» на Тверско́й.
T and M Company offers audio-video components; retail trade [in these items] is available through Pioneer on Tverskaia Street.

Торго́вля; э́кспорт; и́мпорт; э́кспортные/и́мпортные това́ры
Trade (in goods); exports; imports; exported/imported goods

> Идёт бу́рная торго́вля ме́жду Росси́ей и Финля́ндией.
> *There is active trade between Russia and Finland.*

Приватиза́ция
Privatization

> В Росси́и идёт акти́вная приватиза́ция госуда́рственных предприя́тий.
> *There is an active process of privatization of government enterprises in Russia.*

Спрос и предло́жение
Supply and demand (demand and supply)

> Вот табли́ца соотноше́ния спро́са и предложе́ния на приватизи́руемое иму́щество.
> *Here is a table depicting the correlation of supply and demand for privatized property.*

Нало́г/-и; облага́ются нало́гами [на что?]; регули́рование [чего́?]
Tax/taxes; taxes are levied on what; regulation of what

> В Росси́и предлага́ется повы́сить максима́льную ста́вку нало́га на при́быль до 38%.
> *In Russia it is proposed to raise the maximum rate of taxation on profits to 38%.*

Фина́нсы; банк; кредито́р/дебито́р; ссу́да (заём, креди́т); ба́нковский проце́нт по креди́ту; ба́нковский проце́нт по депози́ту; ба́нковские счета́; банкро́тство; чек
Finances; bank; creditor/debtor; loan; interest on loans; interest on deposits; bank accounts; bankruptcy; check

> Они́ поговори́ли с экспе́ртами по фина́нсам, и их фи́рме предложи́ли обрати́ться в ба́нк за ссу́дой со сни́женными проце́нтами, без кото́рой фи́рме грози́т банкро́тство.
> *They spoke with some finance experts and their firm was recommended to ask a bank for a low-interest loan, without which it will face bankruptcy.*

Рекла́ма; рекла́мный аге́нт; сре́дство рекла́мы; па́блик риле́йшн; и́мидж
Advertising; advertising agent; means of advertisement (medium of advertisement); public relations; image

> Больши́е америка́нские компа́нии в Росси́и серьёзно занима́ются свои́м и́миджем и проводя́т большие рекла́мные кампа́нии.
> *Large American companies in Russia are seriously interested in their image and are ordering big advertising campaigns.*

Увели́чиваться; подъём; уменьша́ться; паде́ние
To be increasing; increase or rise; to be falling or shrinking; fall or decline

> Ре́зко увели́чивается коли́чество ча́стных предприя́тий в э́том райо́не, и, есте́ственно, уменьша́ется коли́чество госуда́рственных.
> *There is a sharp increase in the number of private enterprises in this region and, naturally, the number of state enterprises is decreasing.*

Упражне́ние 25.1   Fill in the blanks with the Russian equivalent of the English word or phrase in parentheses.

Произошли́ о́чень интере́сные собы́тия на (*currency markets*) _____

_____[1] бы́вшего СССР, когда́ начало́сь проведе́ние регуля́рных (*trading*)

_____[2] по белору́сскому рублю́ на Моско́вской межба́нковской валю́тной би́рже. Во вто́рник курс белору́сской де́нежной едини́цы (*fell*)

_____³ с 9,62 до 10,93 белору́сских рубле́й за оди́н росси́йский.

На (*goods market*) _____⁴ реаги́ровали на (*fall*)

_____⁵ белору́сского рубля́ (*increase, rise [instrumental]*)

_____⁶ цен на росси́йское зерно́. Белору́сские (*businesspeople*)

_____⁷ обеща́ли, что белору́сский рубль ещё (*will increase, rise*)

_____.⁸ Они́ сказа́ли, что ско́ро начнётся больша́я (*advertising*

campaign) _____⁹ белору́сских това́ров в кру́пных

ру́сских города́х.

Росси́йские ли́деры сказа́ли, что в Белору́ссии ещё должна́ быть зако́нчена

(*privatization*) _____,¹⁰ что́бы уви́деть како́й-либо прогре́сс в

торго́вых отноше́ниях. Без э́того, сказа́ли ру́сские, не бу́дет (*demand*)

_____¹¹ на белору́сские това́ры среди́ населе́ния в Росси́и.

В да́нный моме́нт не́которые белору́сские экспе́рты по (*finances*)

_____¹² прие́хали в Москву́, что́бы доби́ться (*a big loan [genitive]*)

_____¹³ для белору́сской промы́шленности. Они́ боя́тся, что

моско́вские ба́нки бу́дут тре́бовать больши́х (*interest*) _____.¹⁴

Зада́ние 25.1 Find an article about business in any Russian newspaper or magazine and paraphrase (in English) the main ideas of the article.

Зада́ние 25.2 Find an article about business in an American newspaper or magazine. Summarize the article in three of four sentences in English and then paraphrase in Russian.

Фо́то-зада́ние Look at the photograph on the first page of this unit in the textbook. Imagine that you are opening up a new branch of this business in another city in Russia. Write a paragraph or prepare a presentation, as assigned by your instructor, describing your concerns about reaching Russian customers and describe an advertising campaign.

Exercises and Activities

Упражне́ние 25.2 Fill in the blanks with the Russian equivalent of the English verb in parentheses, choosing from the verb **носи́ть, вози́ть,** and **води́ть.**

1. Э́тот авто́бус (*takes*) _____ тури́стов в Эрмита́ж.

2. И́нна Вита́льевна ча́сто (*took*) _____ америка́нских стажёров по места́м Достое́вского.

3. Э́тот почтальо́н ка́ждый день (*will take/carry*) _____ пи́сьма по всему́ райо́ну.

4. Та́ня всегда́ (*wears*) _____ плато́к, когда́ хо́дит за поку́пками.

5. Мы (*used to take*) _____ собáку на урóки по дрессирóвке три

рáза в недéлю.

6. Америкáнские мáльчики и дéвочки (*take/carry*) _____ газéты,

чтóбы зарабáтывать дéньги.

7. Они (*will take*) _____ бáбушку на процедýры два рáза в нéделю.

8. Дима иногдá (*used to take*) _____ дипломáтов по стáрым

особнякáм Петербýрга.

9. Сенáтор Пол Сáймон всё врéмя (*wears*) _____ бáбочку: э́то егó

«торгóвый знак».

10. На э́тих грузовикáх ([*they*] *take*) _____ солдáт на бáзу.

Упражнéние 25.3   Define the use of each of the verbs of motion in **Упражнéние 25.2**, using the list of uses of these verbs in your textbook (pp.326–328).

Упражнéние 25.4   Fill in the blanks with the Russian equivalent of the English verb in parentheses. Use only the verbs **нести, вести,** and **везти.** Future-tense forms of these verbs require **бýду, бýдешь, бýдет,** and so on.

1. Когдá ты (*will be walking*) _____ Пáвлика мимо книжного

магазина, пожáлуйста, купи мне нóвый англо–рýсский словáрь.

2. Смотри! Вот Áня (*is taking*) _____ своегó млáдшего брáта в

поликлинику. Онá сказáла, что он бóлен гриппом. Хорошó, что поликлиника

нахóдится совсéм рядом.

3. Извините, ребя́та, но я óчень опáздываю — я (*am taking*) _____

брáта к специалисту на другóй конéц гóрода! Мне нáдо поймáть такси.

4. Тáня всё врéмя спешит. Кудá онá сейчáс (*is carrying*) _____

такýю кýчу бумáг?

5. Мы увидели Антóна, когдá он (*was driving*) _____ бáбушку в

аптéку за лекáрствами.

6. Сломáлся автóбус для инострáнных студéнтов и поэ́тому преподавáтели (*are taking*)

_____ их в Кремль на метрó; пóсле экскýрсии по Кремлю́,

студéнты сáми доберýтся обрáтно, как смóгут.

7. Когдá они (*were taking*) _____ нас на вокзáл, их остановила

милиция за превышéние скóрости.

8. Вадим сейчáс (*take*) _____ дочь в шкóлу.

9. Вот Жáнна (*is carrying*) _____ подáрок: навéрно, для Тóли!

10. Поликлиника нахóдится далекó. Пешкóм мы (*will be carrying*) _____

_____ ребёнка 40 минýт. Давáй лýчше поéдем на автóбусе.

Упражнéние 25.5 Referring to rules *a* through *f* in your textbook (pp. 329–330), identify the use of unidirectional verbs in **Упражнéние 25.4**.

Упражнéние 25.6 Using the chart of perfective transitive verbs of motion in your textbook (p.331), fill in the blanks with the Russian equivalent of the verb in parentheses.

1. Где Борúс Николáевич? Он (*left to take*) _____ пýстые бутылки в магазúн.

2. Где же Ира? Онá ужé (*left to take*) _____ дирéктора на собрáние.

3. Когдá вы (*will take*) _____ Кáтю в Тýлу, купúте нам, пожáлуйста, самовáр.

4. Тóли сейчáс нет — он ужé (*left to take*) _____ печéнье сосéдям.

5. Надéжда Денúсовна (*will take*) _____ отцá с собóй в Читý.

6. Олéг (*took*) _____ подрýгу на останóвку автóбуса.

7. Ты не (*will take*) _____ с собóй газéту? В поликлúнике чáсто прихóдится дóлго ждать.

8. Сначáла нас (*took*) _____ в Мавзолéй Лéнина, а потóм мы пошлú в Исторúческий музéй.

9. Кудá сейчáс Дúна (*will take*) _____ своегó сына?

10. Чéрез час Вúка (*will take*) _____ Сáшеньку в шкóлу.

Упражнéние 25.7 Reread the sentences in **Упражнéние 25.6** and assign to each the letter *a* or *b* corresponding to the two uses of perfective verbs of motion as described in your textbook (p. 332).

Упражнéние 25.8 The story begun in **Упражнéние 25з** in your textbook (p.336) continues. Fill in the blanks with the correct form of one of the following verbs of motion: **ходúть, идтú, пойтú, выходúть, выйти, сходúть, сойтú, относúть, отнестú, уходúть, уйтú, уезжáть, уéхать, переезжáть, переéхать, переносúть, перенестú, переводúть, перевестú, проводúть** and **провестú**.

Я _____¹ с пятого этажá на пéрвый и _____ ²

на ýлицу. Светúло сóлнце: — В пáрке бýдет хорошó, — подýмал я, и отпрáвился в продуктóвый магазúн.

По дорóге тудá я увúдел свою приятельницу с млáдшим брáтом.

— Эй! Ларúса! Привéт! Кудá ты _____³ так быстро? Ты кудá-нибудь _____⁴ Мúшку?

— Я _____ ⁵ Мишку к дедушке, а сама

_____ ⁶ в спортивный комплекс. Я _____ ⁷

туда три раза в неделю. У нас там _____ ⁸ занятия по каратэ.

— Ты — молодец!

— Ты не хочешь _____ ⁹ вместе со мной?

— Спасибо, Лариса. Но не могу. Я договорился с подругой встретиться сегодня. Может

быть, в другой раз. Слушай, Лариса, ты не знаешь, где сейчас работает Катя?

— Она _____ ¹⁰ со старой работы и

_____ ¹¹ в Петербург, где нашла хорошую работу по специальности.

— А что будет с её мужем, Борей?

— Говорят, что и его (*will transfer*) _____ ¹² в Петербург.

— Интересно. Ну ладно. Пока. Пока, Мишка.

— Счастливо.

Упражнение 25.9 The story continues. Fill in the blanks with the correct form of one of the following verbs of motion: **ходить, идти, пойти, выходить, выйти, приходить, прийти, выносить, вынести, входить, войти, уходить, уйти, переходить, перейти, подвозить, подвезти, проходить, пройти, приносить, принести, сносить, снести, подъезжать, подъехать, ездить, ехать, поехать, относить** and **отнести.**

Я быстро _____ ¹ в магазин и _____ ² в него. К

сожалению, не было российского сыра, и мне пришлось купить швейцарский. Я

_____ ³ из магазина, _____ ⁴ через улицу,

повернул направо, _____ ⁵ двести метров и

_____ ⁶ в мастерскую, куда я хотел _____ ⁷

сапоги бабушки. Я вытащил сапоги из своей сумки и сдал их мастеру. Когда я

_____ ⁸ из мастерской, _____ ⁹ парень,

который хотел _____ ¹⁰ очень большой ящик старой обуви из

магазина. Он попросил меня помочь ему _____ ¹¹ ящик из магазина

и поставить его в грузовик, который должен был вот-вот _____.¹²

Мы с ним _____ ¹³ ящик и потом болтали пару минут, пока не

_____ ¹⁴ грузовик. Мы поставили ящик в грузовик и парень с

шофёром предложили _____ ¹⁵ меня на станцию метро. Я охотно

согласился и мы все вместе _____.¹⁶

Упражне́ние 25.10 The story continues. Fill in the blanks with the correct form of one of the following verbs of motion: ходи́ть, идти́, пойти́, приезжа́ть, прие́хать, подходи́ть, подойти́, выходи́ть, вы́йти, сходи́ть, сойти́, выноси́ть, вы́нести, входи́ть, войти́, уходи́ть, уйти́, переходи́ть, перейти́, проходи́ть, пройти́, приноси́ть, принести́, доезжа́ть, дое́хать, приходи́ть, прийти́, подъезжа́ть, подъе́хать, е́здить, е́хать, пое́хать, расходи́ться, and разойти́сь.

Мы _____¹ на ста́нцию метро́, я _____² с

грузовика́ и спусти́лся по ле́стнице на ста́нцию. Опусти́л жето́н и

_____³ че́рез контро́ль; как раз в э́то вре́мя

_____⁴ по́езд. Две́ри откры́лись и я _____.⁵

Ко мне́ в ваго́не _____⁶ пожила́я же́нщина и спроси́ла: «Не зна́ете

ли вы, как мне _____⁷ до Ки́евского вокза́ла?» Я ей объясни́л, что ей

на́до бу́дет _____⁸ на сле́дующей ста́нции и сде́лать переса́дку.

Мы вско́ре _____⁹ на ста́нцию «Изма́йловская». Там моя́

подру́га Зо́я уже́ ждала́ меня́. Мы _____¹⁰ из метро́ и

_____¹¹ в парк. Мы гуля́ли в па́рке пять часо́в:

_____¹² по тропи́нкам, (ran around) _____¹³

по поля́м и да́же _____¹⁴ на реке́. Нам бы́ло о́чень прия́тно, о́чень

ве́село. Но вре́мя _____,¹⁵ и вдруг я заме́тил, что

_____¹⁶ шесто́й час.

«Зо́я! Мне на́до _____!¹⁷ До́ма меня́ давно́ ждут!»

«Ну, тогда́, _____¹⁸ домо́й.»

Мы собра́ли свои́ ве́щи и верну́лись на ста́нцию метро́. Там мы стоя́ли и

разгова́ривали ещё не́сколько мину́т и договори́лись _____¹⁹ на

конце́рт на сле́дующей неде́ле.

Мы _____,²⁰ и я верну́лся домо́й о́чень дово́льным свое́й

прогу́лкой.

Упражне́ние 25.11 Fill in the blanks with the Russian equivalent of the English word or phrase in parentheses, choosing from the idiomatic expressions explained in Unit 25 in your textbook.

1. Мы пло́хо (relate) _____ к э́той иде́е.

2. Я э́то (will translate) _____ сего́дня ве́чером.

3. Когда́ ([they] imported) _____ э́ти буты́лки вина́ из Фра́нции?

4. Макси́м всё вре́мя (disappoints) _____ нас.

5. Из Росси́и ([they] export) _____ во́дку по всему́ ми́ру.

6. Я хочу́ (pronounce) _____ тост: за ва́ше здоро́вье!

7. Ты меня́ (drive) _____ до того́, что я сам/а́ не зна́ю, что я де́лаю!

8. Вы меня́ (will drive) _____ с ума́!

9. Дéти чáсто (drive) _____ родителей с умá.

10. ([They] have torn down) _____ всю ýлицу, чтóбы пострóить тут

торгóвый центр с гостúницей.

Упражнéние 25.12   Translate the following sentences into Russian.

1. They are tearing down this building.
2. This company imports vodka from Russia to America.
3. This company exports cars from America to Russia.
4. You have deceived me!
5. I'll give you a lift to the university.
6. I'll translate this from Russian into English tonight.
7. We translated this from English into Russian yesterday.
8. They relate well to us.
9. This question is related to that problem.
10. How is this word pronounced?
11. These children are behaving themselves very well, because I told them to behave themselves.
12. He is driving us crazy!

Glossary

Verbs of motion without spatial prefixes are marked M for multidirectional, U for unidirectional, and P for perfective (as in Units 23 and 24). For verbs with different definitions but identical conjugations, conjugations are provided only in the first listing. Vocabulary items from the lexicon are *not* included here.

ввозúть (II) /ввезтú (I) [что? кудá?]:
ввожý, ввóзишь, ввóзят; ввезý, ввезёшь, ввезýт, ввёз, ввезлá, ввезлú
to import something somewhere

вестú (U-I) [когó? что? кудá?]:
ведý, ведёшь, ведýт, вёл, велá, велú
to lead someone somewhere

вестú (U-I) дневнúк, обсуждéние, лéкцию
to conduct or keep a diary, to conduct a conversation/discussion or a lecture

вестú (U-I) себя хорошó úли плóхо
to behave oneself well or poorly

везтú (U-I) [когó? что? кудá?]:
везý, везёшь, везýт, вёз, везлá, везлú
to transport someone or something somewhere

везтú (U-I) /повезтú (I) [комý?]:
мне, тебé...везёт; мне, тебé...повезёт, повезлó
to be lucky
I'm lucky (in luck), You're lucky (in luck) I (You) will be in luck, were in luck

водúть (M-II) [когó? что? кудá?]:
вожý, вóдишь, вóдят
to lead someone somewhere

возить (М–II) [кого? что? куда?]: вожу́, во́зишь, во́зят	*to transport someone or something somewhere*
вывози́ть (II) /вы́везти (I) [что? куда? откуда?] вывожу́, вывóзишь, вывóзят; вы́везу, вы́везешь, вы́везут, вы́вез, вы́везла, вы́везли	*to export something somewhere from somewhere*
доводи́ть (II) /довести́ (I) [кого́–нибудь до чего́, до отча́яния]: довожу́, довóдишь, довóдят; доведу́, доведёшь, доведу́т, довёл, довела́, довели́	*to bring someone to some point (e.g., to the point of despair)*
доноси́ть (I) /донести́ (I) [что? до чего́?]: донощу́, донóсишь, донóсят; донесу́, донесёшь, донесу́т, донёс, донесла́, донесли́	*to take something somewhere*
доноси́ть (II) /донести́ (I) [на кого́? кому́?]	*to inform on someone to someone*
нести́ (U–I) [кого́? что? куда́?]: несу́, несёшь, несу́т, нёс, несла́, несли́	*to carry someone or something somewhere*
носи́ть (М–II) [кого́? что? куда́?]: ношу́, нóсишь, нóсят	*to carry someone or something somewhere*
отводи́ть (II) /отвести́ (I) [кого́? что? куда́?] отвожу́, отвóдишь, отвóдят; отведу́, отведёшь, отведу́т, отвёл, отвела́, отвели́	*to take someone or something somewhere and drop it (them) off there*
отвози́ть (II) /отвезти́ (I) [кого́? что? куда́?] отвожу́, отвóзишь, отвóзят; отвезу́, отвезёшь, отвезу́т, отвёз, отвезла́, отвезли́	*to take someone or something somewhere and drop it (them) off there*
относи́ть (II) /отнести́ (I) [что? к чему́?]: отнощу́, отнóсишь, отнóсят; отнесу́, отнесёшь, отнесу́т, отнёс, отнесла́, отнесли́	*to relate something to something else*
относи́ться (II) /отнести́сь (I) [к чему́?]: отнощу́сь, отнóсишься, отнóсятся; отнесу́сь, отнесёшься, отнесу́тся, отнёсся, отнесла́сь, отнесли́сь	*to have an attitude toward something or to be related to something*
отноше́ние [к чему́?]	*attitude toward something (for relationship to something or someone, use the plural form only)*
переводи́ть (II) /перевести́ (I) [с какóго языка́ на какóй язы́к?]: перевожу́, перевóдишь, перевóдят; переведу́, переведёшь, переведу́т, перевёл, перевела́, перевели́	*to translate something from one language to another*
подводи́ть (II) /подвести́ (I) [кого́? что? куда́?]: подвожу́, подвóдишь, подвóдят; подведу́, подведёшь, подведу́т, подвёл, подвела́, подвели́	*to take someone or something somewhere*
подводи́ть (II) /подвести́ (I) когó–нибудь	*to disappoint someone, to let someone down*
подвози́ть (II) /подвезти́ (I) [кого́? что? куда́?]: подвожу́, подвóзишь, подвóзят; подвезу́, подвезёшь, подвезу́т, подвёз, подвезла́, подвезли́	*to take someone or something somewhere in a vehicle*

повезти (P-I) [кого? что? куда?]:
  повезу, повезёшь, повезут, повёз, повезла, повезли

to take someone or something somewhere

повести (P-I) [кого? что? куда?]:
  поведу, поведёшь, поведут, повёл, повела, повели

to take someone or something somewhere

подносить (II) /поднести (I) [кого? что? куда?]:
  подношу, подносишь, подносят; поднесу, поднесёшь, поднесут, поднёс, поднесла, поднесли

to carry something or someone someplace

понести (P-I) [кого? что? куда?]:
  понесу, понесёшь, понесут, понёс, понесла, понесли

to carry someone or something somewhere

приводить (II) /привести (I) [кого? что? куда?]
  привожу, приводишь, приводят; приведу, приведёшь, приведут, привёл, привела, привели

to bring someone or something somewhere or to cite something

приводить (II) /привести (I) [кого в себя]

to bring someone to oneself

привозить (II) /привезти (I) [кого? что? куда?]:
  привожу, привозишь, привозят; привезу, привезёшь, привезут, привёз, привезла, привезли

to transport someone or something somewhere

приносить (II) /принести (I) [кого? что? куда?]:
  приношу, приносишь, приносят; принесу, принесёшь, принесут, принёс, принесла, принесли

to carry someone or something somewhere

произносить (II) /произнести (I) [что?]:
  произношу, произносишь, произносят; произнесу, произнесёшь, произнесут, произнёс, произнесла, произнесли

to pronounce something

сводить (II) /свести (I) [кого с ума]:
  свожу, сводишь, сводят; сведу, сведёшь, сведут, свёл, свела, свели

to drive someone crazy

сносить (II) /снести (I) [что?]:
  сношу, сносишь, сносят снесу, снесёшь, снесут, снёс, снесла, снесли

to tear something down